Jessie Cromwell

SESAME AND LILIES

AND

THE KING OF THE GOLDEN RIVER

Macmillan's Pocket American and English Classics

A Series of English Texts, edited for use in Elementary and
Secondary Schools, with Critical Introductions, Notes, etc.

16mo   Cloth   25 cents each

Addison's Sir Roger de Coverley.
Andersen's Fairy Tales.
Arabian Nights' Entertainments.
Arnold's Sohrab and Rustum.
Bacon's Essays.
Bible (Memorable Passages from).
Blackmore's Lorna Doone.
Browning's Shorter Poems.
Browning, Mrs., Poems (Selected).
Bryant's Thanatopsis, etc.
Bunyan's The Pilgrim's Progress.
Burke's Speech on Conciliation.
Burns' Poems (Selections from).
Byron's Childe Harold's Pilgrimage.
Byron's Shorter Poems.
Carlyle's Essay on Burns.
Carlyle's Heroes and Hero Worship.
Carroll's Alice's Adventures in Wonderland (Illustrated).
Chaucer's Prologue and Knight's Tale.
Church's The Story of the Iliad.
Church's The Story of the Odyssey.
Coleridge's The Ancient Mariner.
Cooper's The Deerslayer.
Cooper's The Last of the Mohicans.
Defoe's Robinson Crusoe.
De Quincey's Confessions of an English Opium-Eater.
De Quincey's Joan of Arc, and The English Mail-Coach.

Dickens' A Christmas Carol, and The Cricket on the Hearth.
Dickens' A Tale of Two Cities.
Dryden's Palamon and Arcite.
Early American Orations, 1760-1824.
Edwards' (Jonathan) Sermons.
Eliot's Silas Marner.
Emerson's Essays.
Emerson's Representative Men.
Epoch-making Papers in U. S. History.
Franklin's Autobiography.
Gaskell's Cranford.
Goldsmith's The Deserted Village.
Goldsmith's The Vicar of Wakefield.
Grimm's Fairy Tales.
Hawthorne's Grandfather's Chair.
Hawthorne's Tanglewood Tales.
Hawthorne's The House of the Seven Gables.
Hawthorne's Twice-told Tales (Selections from).
Hawthorne's Wonder-Book.
Holmes' Poems.
Homer's Iliad (Translated).
Homer's Odyssey (Translated).
Irving's Life of Goldsmith.
Irving's The Alhambra.
Irving's Sketch Book.
Keary's Heroes of Asgard.

Macmillan's Pocket American and English Classics

A SERIES OF ENGLISH TEXTS, EDITED FOR USE IN ELEMENTARY AND SECONDARY SCHOOLS, WITH CRITICAL INTRODUCTIONS, NOTES, ETC.

16mo   Cloth   25 cents each

Kingsley's The Heroes.
Lamb's The Essays of Elia.
Longfellow's Evangeline.
Longfellow's Hiawatha.
Longfellow's Miles Standish.
Longfellow's Tales of a Wayside Inn.
Lowell's The Vision of Sir Launfal.
Macaulay's Essay on Addison.
Macaulay's Essay on Hastings.
Macaulay's Essay on Lord Clive.
Macaulay's Essay on Milton.
Macaulay's Lays of Ancient Rome.
Macaulay's Life of Samuel Johnson.
Milton's Comus and Other Poems.
Milton's Paradise Lost, Books I. and II.
Old English Ballads.
Out of the Northland.
Palgrave's Golden Treasury.
Plutarch's Lives (Cæsar, Brutus, and Mark Antony).
Poe's Poems.
Poe's Prose Tales (Selections from).
Pope's Homer's Iliad.
Pope's The Rape of the Lock.
Ruskin's Sesame and Lilies.
Scott's Ivanhoe.
Scott's Kenilworth.
Scott's Lady of the Lake.

Scott's Lay of the Last Minstrel.
Scott's Marmion.
Scott's Quentin Durward.
Scott's The Talisman.
Shakespeare's As You Like It.
Shakespeare's Hamlet.
Shakespeare's Henry V.
Shakespeare's Julius Cæsar.
Shakespeare's King Lear.
Shakespeare's Macbeth.
Shakespeare's Merchant of Venice.
Shakespeare's The Tempest.
Shakespeare's Twelfth Night.
Shelley and Keats: Poems.
Sheridan's Rivals and School for Scandal.
Southern Poets: Selections.
Spenser's Faerie Queene, Book I.
Stevenson's Treasure Island.
Swift's Gulliver's Travels.
Tennyson's Idylls of the King.
Tennyson's The Princess.
Tennyson's Shorter Poems.
Thackeray's Henry Esmond.
Washington's Farewell Address, and Webster's First Bunker Hill Oration.
Woolman's Journal.
Wordsworth's Shorter Poems.

J Ruskin.

SESAME AND LILIES

AND

THE KING OF THE GOLDEN RIVER

BY

JOHN RUSKIN

Edited with Notes and an Introduction

BY

HERBERT BATES

*Head Teacher of English in the Manual Training
High School of Brooklyn, N.Y.*

New York

THE MACMILLAN COMPANY

LONDON: MACMILLAN & CO., Ltd.

1908

PREFATORY NOTE

THE text of this edition is based upon that of the English editions published by George Allen, Orpington, though there have been occasional returns, in minor details of punctuation, etc., to editions preceding. The editor would acknowledge the aid received in the preparation of these notes from P. W. T. Warren's excellent *Reader's Companion to Sesame and Lilies*.

The preparation of this volume for use in schools has been the pleasanter task from the conviction, inevitably growing upon one as he studies these lectures, that they are, more than any book in our school courses, fitted to counteract the satisfied materialism and sordid commercialism of our cities. No work makes a stronger appeal to the best that is in every boy and girl. Few books are more ennobling, few so helpful in the shaping high ideals of life.

Ruskin has his faults of style, of thought, of character. No one can study his work continuously without realizing these. But no one, thus studying his work, can fail to feel, little by little, that these defects, numerous as they are, sink into insignificance before the kindly, tender, wrong-hating, right-seeking man whose character shines from every page and paragraph. We go to him, not to learn mere facts, but to feel the stimulus of his genius and the inspiration of his generous idealism.

H. B.

▼

CONTENTS

INTRODUCTION

◆

RUSKIN THE MAN

In mere events Ruskin's life offers little that is memorable. The main outline may be given very briefly. John Ruskin was born in London, on the 8th of February, 1819. His father was well off and of steadily increasing prosperity, a prosperity which became, in later years, really notable wealth. The boy's surroundings were such as to encourage taste for literature and the arts. His father, though in business a wine-merchant, felt no little interest both in books and in pictures, and the boy Ruskin had no lack of opportunity to form his taste. His early home education in one respect had a great influence upon his later style. His mother, who was deeply religious — reminding us in this respect of the influence of Carlyle's mother — required him not only to read the Bible aloud, every word, from Genesis to Revelation, but required also that he should memorize long passages. This early familiarity with the noble English of the King James version, coupled with an acquaintance with the grand words of the liturgy of the Church of England, had no little effect, as we shall see later, upon Ruskin's own manner of expression.

Ruskin's childhood was spent only partially in London. Even in his first years, the summers were spent out of town, and, in his fourth year, his parents removed to Dulwich, on Herne Hill, a district built up now, but then open undulating country with a noble outlook. It was here that Ruskin spent all his childhood and early youth, and here that he formed

the intimacy with nature which marks his work — here, and in
the little tours taken in company with his father and mother.

   For personal recollections of this period, read Ruskin's *Prœte-
rita*, a book of charming reminiscense, written in his old age,
looking back with a not uncheerful regret to these days of childhood.   We find that not only was he observing and enjoying, but
that he had also begun to record his thoughts in rather primitive
form.   He made rhymes early (most writers of prose begin by
writing verse) and began, at the advanced age of seven, a book.
It was in three volumes, *Harry and Lucy, or Early Lessons*,
obviously under the influence of the writings of Maria Edge-
worth.   There was to be a fourth volume, but the writer's per-
sistence gave out, or his attention was distracted elsewhere,
before it was accomplished.   In themselves these books were
not of much importance; but in several points they are significant.   They were, for one thing, printed letter by letter, by
hand, with scrupulous industry — a typical feature in Ruskin's
work in all branches.   They were to be illustrated by copper-
plates by himself, a feature showing his early interest in art
and illustration, and typical of his earlier views in criticism,
regarding art as illustration rather than as an end in itself.

   The tours, mentioned above, had an important influence.
Every year Mr. and Mrs. Ruskin would set off on long journeys
by carriage, in various parts of England and Scotland.   These
trips Mr. Ruskin took for business reasons, his wife going with
him to watch over his health, and the boy John naturally
accompanying them.   Mr. Ruskin was a man of too refined
tastes to give his whole attention to the customers of his house.
He arranged the itinerary so that they should pass through the
most picturesque country and the places of the greatest historical
interest.   And everything that they did see, they studied carefully, recording their impressions, the father in his mature fashion,
the boy in his *Harry and Lucy*, and similar boyish "books,"
illustrating his own work to the best of his boyish ability.

In tours of this kind, the family visited the greater part of England, including the lake country, Scotland, and, extending the limits beyond seas, France, Germany, and at last (1833), when, at the age of fourteen, John Ruskin had given over *Harry and Lucy*, to Switzerland, a country that was to have momentous influence on his writing and character. In *Præterita* he writes with the deepest feeling of his first sight of the Alps, and of their effect upon his imagination. In all these tours, early or late, the written records were continued, and with these, sketches and study of drawing, especially of the work of Turner as shown in his illustrations to Roger's *Italy*, a book that the young Ruskin began to long to imitate, perhaps to surpass, both in text and pictures.

All this time he had continued the writing of verse, and had gained strength in it. Not that his verse was the verse of a real poet. Ruskin had something of the gift of the poet, but not in measured song. His verses had melody, a charm of phrase, and imaginative beauty of thought, but they lacked as a rule any certainty of poetic inspiration. It was his later realization of this that made him give over attempts in verse. What does concern us in these first poetic writings is this: first that Ruskin had the spirit of the poet, a spirit developed in the attempt to sing for himself; second, that he had something of the gift of the poet, not enough to wing his verses, but enough to lift his prose into lyric regions. If the poetic pinions of his Pegasus could not lift him off the earth, they could at least aid the swiftness and grace of his course upon it.

Ruskin's education had been received at home, under a private tutor, Dr. Andrews. At the age of fifteen, as he was to go to college, it became necessary that he should have preparation of another sort. He was therefore sent to a day-school in London, where he remained about two years, till an attack of pleurisy interrupted his studies. At this point in his life, then, the age of seventeen, he had received a decidedly desultory education, at home and from private teachers. He had, in addition, taken lessons in drawing, from a Mr. Runciman, and had learned a great deal about the art himself by practice and the study of masterpieces. (It is interesting to conjecture as to the effect of a public school — Eton, Harrow, or Rugby — upon a boy of his tastes and disposition.)

In 1836, Ruskin had reached the age of seventeen. Few young men get far past this age without at least the fancy that they are in love. It happened in Ruskin's case that a partner of his father, a Mr. Demecq, came over from Paris, bringing his four younger daughters, who all became guests at the Ruskin house. Ruskin was especially charmed with the eldest, Adèle, whom he admired with shy reverence — which her Parisian nature did not exactly comprehend. He remained devoted to her — without any obvious return to his devotion and various literary offerings — for several years, when he heard of her approaching marriage to a young French nobleman. It is unlikely that the disappointment left any deep trace on his nature. It probably did have an immediate influence on his health, doing something to bring about the general breakdown that followed, in 1840.

In the meantime, Ruskin had done some little studying in water-color, and had become more and more interested in the paintings of Turner. (See page 190.) This interest went so far that he wrote and sent to Turner, for his approval, a defence of one of that artist's paintings of Venice. It was injudiciously superlative, and perhaps Turner did well in restraining his young admirer from rushing into print with it. In it, however, we can see clearly the beginnings of the *Modern Painters*, that grand eulogy of Turner, which is in itself greater than the work of the master it champions.

In Ruskin's college life, at Christ's College, Oxford, he continued his interest in questions of art, writing a series of magazine papers on questions in architecture or painting, papers in which he seems, at the early age of nineteen, to have won not a little respectful attention. At Oxford, too, Ruskin began to form acquaintances. His father's ambition had thrown him into a set (the gentlemen commoners) with whom, in England, under ordinary circumstances, the son of a prosperous wine-merchant might have not had the chance to associate. Here he became acquainted at once with men of the very highest refinement, and with scholars of masterly attainments and inspiring originality. He gained far more from such association than from his regular studies, in which his interest seems to have been merely moderate. He won a prize, it is true, for a poem, — but that lay rather outside the regular curriculum. These years of college were, in short, while amounting to little in formal learning, years important in stimulus and in beginnings of activity — years of awakening and initiation of effort.

In 1840, perhaps partly owing to the romance mentioned above, perhaps owing to over-application to books, Ruskin's health suddenly failed, and he was ordered abroad for the winter. He travelled rather despondently through France, into Italy, always under the cloud of threatened consumption, undergoing, besides, an attack of Roman fever, until at last there came a change, and strength and confidence began to return. He threw off the disease and gradually overcame its effects. It was on his return from abroad, in Scotland, in the latter period of his convalescence, that he wrote — at the invitation of a charming Scotch maiden, who was to some extent taking in his affections the place of the lost Adèle — the story, *The King of the Golden River*, included in this volume.

In 1841, Ruskin had so far recovered that he could return to Oxford and "go up for a pass," honors being, on account of his lost year, quite out of reach. He received his degree of B.A., and returned to Herne Hill, where he diligently set to work upon the book that first brought him public attention, *Modern Painters*. His admiration for Turner had continued,

and study of his works had led to the perception that the
secret of art lay in the endeavor to attain, not conventionalized,
artificial beauty, but the beauty of truth, beauty attained by
sincere, laboriously wrought representation of what the eye sees.
This thought is summed up in a sentence in his *Two Paths :*
"Whenever people don't look at nature, they always think
they can improve her." He saw that the art of his day — and
of many ages preceding — had been attempting to improve
upon nature, not to search out humbly and worshipfully the
beauty that is in her. It was to the preaching of this new
gospel, — sincere, watchful study of the beauty of the visible
world, that he resolved to devote himself. In this preaching
he selected, as his text, the paintings of Turner.

At Herne House, he began and completed Part I. of the
work which was to develop these ideas — to apply to art the
gospel of sincerity that Carlyle had begun to announce in his
tempestuous writings. And here his previous interest in mineralogy and other forms of natural science served him in good
stead. His studies of mountain form, of forms of foliage, of
the lines of wave and cloud, gave his work a definiteness that
demanded attention. He painted, with the pen of the artist in
words, what he was urging artists to paint with the brush.
The book appeared in April, 1843. Ruskin withheld his name,
issuing the work simply as "By a Graduate of Oxford." It was
a book which could not be overlooked ; but the attention it
received was, on the whole, hostile. It depreciated, perhaps
unduly, the established masters and models in the art ; it exalted, altogether unduly, the paintings of Turner. Its teaching
was true and needed ; but, like many new and true teachings,
was uttered in superlatives. The theory, as a whole, was too
firmly rooted in truth to be overthrown by attack. But details
afforded unlimited opportunities for assault, and these opportunities were not neglected. Ruskin awoke to find himself
famous — or infamous, according to the views of his reader

His book became, among artists and critics, a centre of heated discussion.

The next few years he spent studying art in Italy, and mountain form in the Alps — becoming newly and deeply interested in works of early Christian art. It was at this time that he wrote the *Seven Lamps of Architecture*, pointing out the spirit that must underlie all great achievement in that art; following it, a few years later, by the *Stones of Venice*, a more detailed and definite study of the connection of art with national and religious life.

In 1848 he was married to the young Scotch girl for whom he had written *The King of the Golden River*. This marriage — for reasons for which Ruskin cannot well be blamed — turned out most unhappily. Six years later his wife left him. Ruskin bore this trial with the most dignified and unselfish silence. There is little doubt, however, that it affected his later life and character. One may bear it in mind in reading in the third lecture what he has to say of disappointment.

In 1851 came the beginnings of the great Pre-Raphaelite movement, a movement in which Ruskin took deep interest, and which associates his name with those of Rossetti, Morris, Swinburne, Holman Hunt, and Edward Burne-Jones. It was a movement marked by imitation of some peculiarities of early Christian and mediæval art. Detail was rendered with peculiar fidelity; symbolism lay in everything represented; the works of the Pre-Raphaelites, in short, were marked by oddity and novel beauty — and puzzled the public. In defending this work, as in his advocacy of Turner, Ruskin came into opposition to popular opinion, yet in the end prevailed, bringing the public to his way of thinking. The paintings of Burne-Jones and Rossetti are to-day highly prized, and the indirect influence of the teachings of the "Pre-Raphaelite Brotherhood," as applied by Morris to household decorations and painting, is seen on every hand.

About this time, Ruskin began to take an interest in political economy, the science dealing with distribution of wealth and the condition of society. This interest came naturally from his interest in art; there was a connection, — a vital connection, which maturity made him see with increasing clearness. In his earlier writings, the chief end was art, the faithful depiction of beauty. Then came the perception that such depiction was possible only as a result of right living and right thinking, and, following on this, came clearer and clearer a realization that the life and thought of this world are far, very far indeed, from what they should be.

The more Ruskin reflected on the life of the average laboring man, a life of ugliness and mechanical drudgery, devoid of beauty or aspiration — the more he looked at our cities, full of smoke and iron and ugliness — the more clearly he perceived that our ideals are at fault. It was owing to this perception, a perception which with every year sank deeper into his nature, that he left questions purely of art, neglecting the mere symptoms of the evil, and attacking what he felt to be the root, — the greed and commercialism of modern life. Nothing, he tells us, can be done in art unless men are right in life — and our whole theory of life is evil, selfish, mean, degrading. In *Unto this Last* he denounces the premises of modern political economy, which takes it for granted that one man is always trying to "get ahead" of every other; he insists that value should denote not worth, or value in exchange, but usefulness to man. In *Sesame and Lilies*, his teaching lies before us. In later works, *Fors Clavigera* and others, the same lessons are reiterated, reiterated because not learned, — nor have they been learned yet! It was to preach these that Ruskin forsook, not entirely but in part, his art criticism, and it is for this new preaching that, at the time, and even since his death, admirers of his earlier writings on art have condemned him. The question of the wisdom of his action is too large to consider here.

For a somewhat more extended treatment, see page xxxiv. Here it is important merely to record the change in his interests.

Additional parts of *Modern Painters* came out, at intervals. Obviously in a work covering so many years, there were very significant changes both in style and thought. Ruskin, in his old age, attached comparatively little value to the earlier volumes. The world, however, is hardly of his opinion, regarding many of the descriptive passages found in them as among the finest in our literature.

A list of Ruskin's principal writings is given, with comments, on the last page of this Introduction. The most notable have been mentioned. These, and some others, will be further discussed in the consideration of Ruskin as a writer.

Of other elements in Ruskin's life, space permits but a brief summary. His interest in the progress of the workingman led to more than words. He himself taught, in university extension classes, and lectured frequently on subjects related to art and culture. The lectures included in this volume illustrate the latter form of his work. He was, besides, for many years, connected with university work as regular lecturer at Oxford.

In the latter part of his life we find the breakdown almost to be expected after a life of such overstrenuous activity. His mind showed the strain first. Attacks of melancholia, temporary cloudings of the intellect, made further work impossible, and from 1889 to the end of his life, 1900, he lived quietly at Brantwood, in the lake country, abandoning all attempts at work, beyond the revision of his earlier works, and the writing of such scattered biographical notes as are found in *Præterita*. It was not that he suffered continually from derangement. The cloud that ended his work passed away; but the impulse for active work and active championship of his beliefs was over. His work was ended. He must rest, must watch, from afar off, the success or failure of his past endeavor.

Of Ruskin's person in 1853 we get the following picture : " A thin gentleman with light hair, a stiff white cravat, dark overcoat with velvet collar, walking, too, with a slight stoop. . . . ' Dark hair, pale face, and massive marble brow — that is my ideal of Mr. Ruskin,' said a young lady near us. . . . This proved to be quite a fancy portrait. Mr. Ruskin has light, sand-colored hair ; his face is more red than pale ; the mouth well cut, with a great deal of decision in its curve, though somewhat wanting in sustained dignity and strength ; an aquiline nose ; his forehead by no means broad or massive, but the brows full and well bound together." Of his manner the same writer says : "There were two styles essentially distinct, and not well blended, — a speaking and a writing style ; the former colloquial and spoken offhand ; the latter rhetorical and carefully read in quite a different voice, — we had almost said intoned. . . . His elocution is peculiar ; he has a difficulty in sounding the letter ' r,' and there is a peculiar tone in the rising and falling of his voice at measured intervals, in a way scarcely ever heard, except in the public lection of the services appointed to be read in churches. You expect, in one so independent, a manner free from conventional restraint, and an utterance, whatever may be the power of voice, at least expressive of a strong individuality ; and you find instead a Christ Church man of ten years' standing, who has not yet taken orders ; his dress and manners derived from his college tutor, and his elocution from the chapel reader."

This is not altogether a kindly description, but it sounds as if true. As for the "two styles," they may be easily detected without hearing the voice of the reader. We can distinguish them in the Lectures before us. In Lecture I., for example, Section 5 is in the offhand tone of conversation ; Section 42, on the other hand, is in the written manner, and, if one read aloud, one will, especially if familiar with the cadences of the English Church or Episcopal ritual, find one's self slipping into the "intoning" of which the Edinburgh critic speaks.

In 1870 we find a description differing from the first not more than we should expect, after an interval of almost twenty years. "A face young-looking and beardless; made for expression, and sensitive to every change of emotion." His hair, we learn, had darkened into deep brown, without a trace of grey. His forehead was not "of the heroic type," but "as if the sculptor had heaped his clay in handfuls over the eyebrows, and then heaped more." The size of the nose and of the large "thoroughbred" nostrils is mentioned, as well as the general firmness of the whole face, to which the twenty years seem to have given intensity. The portrait of 1871 affords some interesting points of comparison with that of Carlyle. Both faces are typically Scotch, and there is between them a resemblance, hard to reduce to particulars, but according well with the intellectual kinship in the writings of the two men.

Ruskin was not only charitable, but singularly well placed in life to put his kindly feelings to active exercise. It has been mentioned that Ruskin's father was rich. At his death Ruskin fell heir to a very considerable fortune, — some $600,000, with other property. Yet when he died, in 1900, this property was found, by numerous acts of philanthropy, to have diminished to a very moderate amount. We find him, 1854, taking charge of drawing classes at the workingmen's college, giving work, not money, and work of a singularly exhausting sort. His giving, we observe, was generally of a public sort. Philanthropy, rather than charity, in fact, describes Ruskin's spirit. He cared less for giving than for aiding. His tendencies were broadly humanitarian. He desires, he says, rather to give where his money "will be fruitful than where it will be merely helpful. I would rather lecture for a school than I would *not* for a distressed author. . . . I like to prop the falling more than to feed the fallen." In accordance with this statement, as an examination of his life shows, he carried on a multitude of such fruitful charities. Rossetti received important assistance. Letters, published (without authority) in the *New Review*, March, 1892, show the extent and true helpfulness of the assistance extended in other directions. In many workingmen he took a personal interest, and some of the letters he wrote to them have been collected and published in his works.

We find him trying to improve the condition of the lower-class dwellings of London, experimenting with property of his own. Later, in 1877, and the years following, we find him establishing an organization, St. George's Guild, to put into practice the very moderate form of socialism that he advocated. Each member must do some work for his living, practise certain general precepts of religion and morality, obey the authority of the guild, and contribute to the common fund. The guild was to acquire land, and to cultivate it, preferring manual labor to machinery. It was to purchase or construct mills and factories, preferring water-power to steam, and making the lives of the employees as healthful and happy as possible. It was, besides, to establish places of recreation and of elementary instruction in literature, science, and art. These plans were, to some extent, carried out in reality. A museum was organized at Sheffield, land was farmed, though with no great success, by a community, and mills, under the auspices of the guild, began to put into practice principles of coöperation. The museum, installed in a new and adequate building, remains, and the industries begun by the guild are still, many of them, flourishing, though severed from its direct oversight.

By means of gifts to such objects, and by other gifts of which the public has been permitted to know nothing, a great part of the wealth inherited from the elder Ruskin had disappeared, as has been said, before John Ruskin's death. And its disappearance, if not creditable to Ruskin's economy, is certainly creditable to the sincerity of his sympathy. It is true that he did refuse to give, often from reasons apparently eccentric, but these refusals were never founded in unkindness or in the lack of charity. He did feel the desirability of self-help, and he did his best, by advice, by endowments, by gift of his own time and thought and skill, to better the condition of the workingmen of England. And the workingmen of England and of America have not failed to recognize his endeavor.

A trait which is very significant in the study of his character is Ruskin's love of children. All children recognized in him at once a sincere friend. There was in him, as in Lowell, the eternal childhood of the true poet, a childhood that children at once recognized. He had no "dignity" with them. He romped with them, like a child himself, and wrote nonsense letters and verses that cast a very pleasant light upon his character. No man with such tenderness can be a cynic. Read his recollections of child friends in *Præterita*, — a book that casts much light on this part of his nature, — and see if you can regard him as a "scold," or as a man embittered with the world. In his relations with all who were striving to accomplish good, he appears ever the same — kindly, helpful, a true friend, tender in sympathy. If to such as antagonized, or seemed to him to antagonize, the cause of beauty and truth, he was stern, even fierce, in his resentment, this resentment sprang from his very love for the beautiful and gentle right that they seemed to him opposing. There was, through all minor errors of his life, the one great endeavor that he urges in others, — "the effort to be chaste, knightly, faithful, holy in thought, lovely in word and deed." No life, certainly no life of genius, devoted to this effort, can fail to make the world better.

RUSKIN THE WRITER

PEOPLE read Ruskin's works for several reasons — some for his teaching regarding man's ideals and duties to his fellowman; some for his teachings on art; some for his portrayal of the wonders of nature and his helpful guidance to those that would see these; some for the wonderful magic of his style, the "prose-poetry" of his utterance, the ability, as he calls it, of setting "his words prettily together"; some for all these combined. Yet the last, which Ruskin holds least, the mere knack of setting words prettily together, is an art not to be esteemed lightly.

Ruskin's style has several clearly marked characteristics. In some of these it reminds us of the writings of Blackmore, in others of Carlyle, in others of the English Bible, in others of Hooker and the great prose Elizabethans, in others, and in the whole accumulated impression, it resembles nothing but itself — and the writing of those that imitate it. Let us note a few of these peculiarities: —

First, the effect is remarkably connected. The impression is uniformly liquid. There are no breaks, no abrupt leaps required of the reader, as in Carlyle. So far from being annoyed by irregularity, we are lulled even to inattention by a blandness of fluency and are carried uncomprehendingly, as in the verse of Swinburne, on a stream of gliding words. The connection, in short, amounts almost to diffuseness. There is the copiousness of offhand speech, rather than the compressed restraint of deliberated writing.

To some extent this characteristic is traceable to his early study of the English Bible, in which fluent clearness and paralleled reiteration are so apparent. It marks, too, Hooker and the early Elizabethan writers whom he admired. Still more does it spring from the didactic nature of Ruskin's own mind, from his desire to explain as to a child. He is always talking or writing " down," not from a conceited notion that he is much wiser than his audience, but from a wish — originating in his great earnestness — to be " understood." He is not only telling you a fact; he is teaching you that fact, explaining, reiterating, and illustrating. And sometimes indeed, so extensive are his explanations, so intricate his comments, that his very desire to be understood results in difficulty in comprehending his meaning.

This difficulty in following his thought springs also, in part, from a peculiarity of his mind. His work, while excelling in connection, — in, that is, what the text-books of rhetoric call "Coherence," — is singularly deficient in real connection of thought, in oneness of main idea, or, technically, in "Unity." One subject suggests another, and he lacks resolution to resist the enticing suggestion. "Ruskin," says Mr. Robertson, "is simply an irregular series of lightning zig-zags." Perhaps he might as justly be compared to the child that follows the butterfly and loses his way. Ruskin is always pursuing butterflies. He usually captures them, but he often incidentally leads his reader far afield, and sometimes leaves him there. This peculiarity results from the intense alertness of his mind, combined with a certain irresolution in intention. No matter what he sets out to do, he is likely, on the way, to catch sight of something more enticing. It is, one must own, often something far better than what he set out in search of. He finds gold while looking for coal, and one is not inclined to censure the substitution. Still, this characteristic lends to his writing at once a peculiar charm, and a peculiar sense of defect. One feels at once a delightful surprise at finding treasures where one expected only merchandise, and a sense of perplexity that one is not where one expected to be, a bewildered impression " of having forgotten something." In this, Ruskin differs from De Quincey. De Quincey too is inclined to ramble, but with this difference : When De Quincey leaves the path, he always puts in a peg to mark the place, and comes back to that peg. Ruskin, while always leading us along softly and pleasantly, apparently does not know when he leaves the path, seldom returns to it where he left it, and sometimes fails to get back to the original path at all. De Quincey has a mind that pursues a straight road, with endless little "stop-over" excursions to interesting points on this side and that. Ruskin "wanders at his own sweet will," in a course that is the mere resultant of his passing impressions, but a course so charming that the reader follows him without question.

A distinguishing mark of Ruskin's prose style is its rhythm, the regularity and harmonious distribution of the accent. Toward this, his early writing of verse and familiarity with the Bible and the English Prayer Book (especially the versions of the Psalms) undoubtedly had great influence. Usually this is a merit. Sometimes, where he oversteps the demarcation between prose and verse, and indulges in regular metrical form, it becomes a defect. Observe, for example, such passages as, "That the fabric of it was fragile as a dream, and the endurance of it as transient as the dew," or, "There is fire stronger than the lightning, and a grace more precious than the rain." In these the rhythm seems too pronounced for prose. Compare with these the following : "Far among the moorlands and the rocks, — far in the darkness of the terrible streets, — these feeble florets are lying, with all their fresh leaves torn, and their stems broken — will you never go down to them, nor set in order their little fragrant beds, nor fence them in, in their trembling, from the fierce wind ?" Here the rhythm is more irregular, not lapsing into the beat of verse ; yet perceptible, avoiding the uninspired irregularity of familiar prose. In both there is a related element, the harmony and smooth conjunction of sound, sometimes in obvious alliteration, as in *fabric, fragile, feeble, florets, fence,* and *fierce;* in other cases felt but not recognized as such, in concealed alliteration, as *among the moorlands ; endurance, dew ; beds, fence, trembling.* Note other instances of this, for it is a marked beauty of Ruskin's style.

In Ruskin's writing two distinct manners have been noted, — one conversational, offhand ; the other a "written style," delivered in rhythmical intonation. Such passages as those quoted above were certainly delivered in the latter manner ; they cannot, in fact, be rightly delivered without some enforcement of their lyric, poetic character. Ruskin's conversational style — in which he shows a tendency to "write down" to his readers — is very different. Compare the opening part of Lecture I. with the more lyric passages toward the end and note the differences. In the first case, Ruskin is talking ; in the second, preaching, or chanting in the cadences of the poet. The two styles are not, as has been said, well mingled. There is no fusion. Points of junction show plainly. Yet, after all, the contrast stimulates, and the whole effect, like that of a building of rough freestone and shining marble, gains in richness by the contrast in texture.

Rhetorically considered, Ruskin's sentences incline to be loose, rather than periodic. Their grammatical structure, that is, is complete long before the last word. Generally, they have what might be called a continued construction, clause added to clause, phrase to phrase, the continuation frequently indicated by the dash, as in the sentence last but one in Lecture II ; see also examples in *Queen of the Air*, — as the celebrated description of the Serpent, Section 68, or of the Bird, Sections 65, 66.

With regard to his use of words, Ruskin is, again, individual. What he advised the reader to do (Lecture I., Section 15) he has done himself ; he has mastered the history and character of words, and uses them with a fine regard to all their meanings, "masked" and apparent. The notes call attention to some such cases of fitness. The number of words from which he chooses seems, besides, unusually large. He employs at least, words which the ordinary reader finds unfamiliar — a habit that is in some respects a disadvantage.

Another peculiarity is the odd exuberance of Ruskin's fancy — his liking for doing rather simple things in fashions deliberately eccentric — a grotesque playfulness, related, perhaps, to his admiration for the quaint elaboration of Gothic ornament. One finds examples in plenty in these lectures, in the mention, for example, of the screen "folded in two, instead of four," and in the playing upon the name Maud, in Sections 94–95 of *Queens' Gardens*. The same fantastic tendency shows in his choice of titles. Note the titles of his books and compare these with the descriptions that follow. *Ariadne Florentina, Deucalion, Ethics of the Dust*, and *Notes on the Construction of Sheepfolds* cast little light on the nature of the subject-matter. Each is appropriate, but its appropriateness is ingeniously remote. The fancy is of the same sort that made Ruskin, in writing to children, describe himself by such extraordinary titles as "Little Pigs," and play tricks of fancy that would do credit to the author of *Alice's Adventures*. This oddity, while it entertains the reader, certainly does not assist him.

Related to this peculiarity, — no less noticeable, and, to the average reader, no less objectionable, is his inclination to reference and allusion. Of wide reading himself — reading largely in unusual directions — he seems to presuppose in the reader an equal familiarity with all that he himself happens to recall. His reader is presumed not only to have read, like himself, the Bible from end to end, word by word, to have studied Dante and Shakespeare with no less patient accuracy, but also to have mastered and trodden all the picturesque byways of early Italian art and modern science. Nor is this limited to book experience. He presupposes also actual travel, — travel in England, France, Belgium, Switzerland, Italy, — till the stay-at-home reader despairs of comprehension. Lowell tells us that familiarity with the common sources of allusion and reference is justly to be expected of all readers. But Ruskin goes far beyond common sources, and complacently takes it for granted that books and places of which Ruskin may himself have been for years quite ignorant are matters of course to every reader. That this habit of reference and allusion was carried too far, Ruskin himself later recognized. Yet, in its way, it is not unstimulating. For it is an active reminder of what one is supposed to have read and seen, an index of what one should resolve to read and see. And, if the actual wonderland of Switzerland and Italy is inaccessible, there remains the accessible wonderland of Dante, Milton, and Shakespeare, treasures from which Ruskin has exhibited the enticement of stray gems and strewn gold dust.

To return, in conclusion, to Ruskin's writings as a whole, not only does he wander, but he repeats. In each new book, he goes over the ground he has trodden in his previous works, or, — perhaps a truer figure, — on whatever ground he wanders, he reiterates the same lessons. Take any one subject, the evil, for example, of ugly factories, and you will find it emerging, in a hundred vivid forms in a hundred different chapters. Each new book amends the teaching of its predecessor, and with each new book, Ruskin, like the child who recopies an exercise, casts the earlier draft away dissatisfied. It would be interesting to compile a table of cross-references that would enable one to compare these varied forms of each teaching. In some places in the notes such references have been indicated, but the whole task is too great to undertake in this volume. The pupil in his reading (if he owns his copy, as he should) should pencil in the margin any additional parallelisms.

As for Ruskin's literary style in general, all critics agree as to its beauty. He is master of a medium between prose and verse, a cadenced utterance of his own, so musical that, were it meaningless, the ear would still find pleasure in its harmonies.

RUSKIN'S TEACHING AND INFLUENCE

No study of Ruskin's life is complete without consideration of his teaching and his influence. This topic can be treated here but slightly. The literature of the subject is considerable, however, and the student will find that opinions by no means coincide. There are several distinctly defined positions, in relation to which the opinions of critics may be classified. There are, first, those that think that Ruskin, fallacious in his philosophy of human life, his views of art, and his theories of economics, holds a high place as a writer, a position due to his power of expression, presenting pictures that, "to the inner eye," surpass sights really seen. To them his greatest writing lies in the descriptive passages of *Modern Painters*, and in similar passages in his other writings. To some, his philosophy of life, as expressed in the lectures before us, is an additional excellence. They cannot approve of his economy, and distrust his opinions on art, but feel that he did have a perception — a perception he was singularly able to convey to others, of the nobility of life, and the dignity of work, and the beauty of spiritual charity. Others yet will indorse his teachings in art, holding that much of the progress of the English art of the nineteenth century is owing to his influence. Others — and these are a minority — will defend his utterances upon political economy and social philosophy, holding that he pointed out vital truths that economists prior to his day neglected — that he has even, so one writer has declared, revolutionized the theory of the economists. All, to sum up, recognize Ruskin as a writer of genius ; almost all admit him to be an inspiring preacher of spirituality ; many admit him to have been an epoch-making critic of art ; a certain number assert that he taught the world new lessons about Work and Wealth.

What was Ruskin's teaching and what his influence upon the

world? A close reading of the three lectures before us will show certain dominant lessons; and a reading of his other works will show the same teaching the common factor in all his utterances. Let us see what this is.

The eighteenth century was a century of materialism. Not that there was little religion, in the conventional sense. There was little interest in what lay above the real, the practical, the human. Romance had been tabooed. The novel studied not emotion, but man, "the proper study of mankind." Writing had become an attempt to attain technical rhetorical perfection. Poetry had become mere polished verse; life, mere polished existence. To possess money, to be "respected,"—that, in the eighteenth century, was the ultimate of the English ideal. And these characteristics, or a considerable part of them, did not cease with the eighteenth century, but continued into the nineteenth, and are with us still in the twentieth, and will be with us, in some measure, till the Millennium. The eighteenth century differed from others only in the universality of this mood, in the comparative absence of higher ideals, and the absence of prophets to arouse it from its sluggishness.

With the nineteenth century, these prophets came. Following on the casual songs of Burns, the stray lyrics of Blake, came the great poetic utterances of Coleridge and Wordsworth, followed by the lyric power and beauty of Byron, Keats, and Shelley. And upon these, like supporting artillery, followed the writings of Carlyle and Ruskin, to awake the public to the meaning of the age in which they lived.

A prophet does not necessarily foretell. He may merely denounce evil and arouse to good. All great prophets, philosophers, and teachers have been of this type. All have striven in the attempt to make people stop in their selfish haste after food and animal comfort, to make them stop and question and consider, — to make them feel a divine discontent with the brute in man, the aspiration of the god that within us struggles with the brute

At this aimed Carlyle's *Sartor Resartus*, or "Clothes Philosophy." It stripped man and his life of the artificial trappings of custom and convention, and showed us Man, the being, the mystery, alone, bewildered, here upon the earth, and asked, "How came he here? Where is he going?" It forced people to do what so many regard as ridiculous — to take life seriously, to ask the great question, "What is worth while?" — and to search nature, heaven, earth, the stars, and their souls, for an answer. It was with such a message that Carlyle jarred the world awake with Saxon-clashing sentences. It was with such a message — in far other terms, — that the Wesleys roused the conscience of the lethargic English. It was with such a message that Newman and his circle stirred Catholic and Episcopal England to the core. It was with such a message that Ruskin came before the world, already stirring in its sleep — a message tenderer than Carlyle's, yet with a loving scorn of all that hindered the good that he sought to bring about.

Ruskin's teaching is, first of all, the lesson of self-development. It is not what a man has that is to be considered, or what a man is thought to be, but what *is* he. Is he a "self-made man," not in exterior circumstances, but in wealth of character? One must, at the very outset, realize the mystery and wonder of life, discard the placid superiority to enthusiasm that is the mark of the artificial man, cultivate the openness of perception, the retention of the childish sense of wonder that marks the true man, the man who, his eyes admiringly wide to the world about him, is worthy of the power that placed him in it.

For such development, one must have suitable inspiration. One must learn from the noble fellowship of great writers, whose companionship is gained in books (Kings' Treasuries), from the noble surroundings of nature, from the noble inspiration of noble women, and from the reflex impulse of noble activity in well doing. If we disfigure nature with smoke, ugly buildings, vulgar advertising, — if we close our eyes to beauty, and are too "superior" to notice the wonderful changes of star and cloud, — if we close our hearts to compassion and cultivate indifference to the welfare of our fellow-man, — if we withhold our hands from work, and make it our ideal to exist in aristocratic idleness and empty pleasure, — if we do all these, we may estimate ourselves highly according to the artificial standard of "society" — but we shall fall far short of the true stature of spiritual manhood.

To be willing to see the beauty that is, — to show helpful sympathy for men about us, to be willing to and glad to work for the joy of doing our work well, and, above all, to keep clear our sight of the real mystery and nobility of life, — that, in short, is the burden of Ruskin's teaching. And it is a teaching that the world still needs, for the lesson is by no means learned.

In matters of art, there has been an inclination to depreciate Ruskin's influence. This seems unwarranted. True, Ruskin was not himself an artist of genius. Yet no one studying his work can deny that he was a skilful craftsman, and that he had an eye gifted to catch the essence of what he drew. As for his teaching, one should, before disparaging, read through the five volumes of *Modern Painters* thoughtfully and without prejudice, and should, while reading, bear in mind what traditions governed English painting when these volumes were written. The book may have been unnecessary, yet where English painters formerly painted what they wished to see, they now try to paint what they do see, to render character in tree and cloud and wave and mountain as Ruskin counselled. Take the best-drawn illustrations of our magazines. Compare them with the average illustrations of Ruskin's day. Compare them with such illustration as Ruskin praised, and see if his advice has not produced its effect. Artists study nature as they did not, and respect the truth of nature as they had no notion of doing until the time of *Modern Painters*. True, the change of taste may have been independent of the book; yet when one considers how widely *Modern Painters* has been read, and how widely it has been admired, it does not seem unreasonable to presume a connection.

However the change came about, present-day art is largely in accord with the teachings of Ruskin, and is criticised in accordance with the principles put before us in his volume — the main principles, for the details are naturally often at fault. *Modern Painters* was the work of his youth, and in it there grow literary tares among the true sesame. Yet the vital principles stand out permanent above minor errors of observation or judgment, — permanent because founded on the very nature of man and art.

The aim of *Modern Painters* was chiefly this: to enunciate a theory of art, to show, that is, the proper aims and methods of landscape painting, discussing selection of material, truth in tone, color, outline, light, and shade, and then, in detail, truth in representation of sky, of earth, of water, of vegetation. All these are discussed chiefly in regard to the works of Turner, a painter who, in the eyes of Ruskin, excelled in truth to nature all contemporary English artists.[1] Ruskin pointed out in Turner's work attempted fidelity to nature, and indicated no less definitely where others went astray. He was often extreme, even injudicious. His enthusiasm led him to see Turner's merits magnified, to overlook equal merits in others, and to overlook, moreover, Turner's own defects. So far as his statements apply merely to Turner, they are open to dispute. So far as they apply to painting in general or to nature in general, most of them are now accepted as a matter of course. In Turner's famous Slaveship — perhaps owing to the fading of the pigment — we can no longer see what Ruskin saw there. Yet that description gave new ideals as to what a picture might be

---

[1] See note on Turner and his work, on page 190 of this edition.

Ruskin's teaching has led the world beyond Turner. At the time, Turner revealed new truth. The same truth has since found revelation more adequate. Ruskin's theories have found her exponents. Yet it seems more than likely that the present disparagement may be merely a fashion — partly a miscomprehension, that time will again overcome. It is only just, in any event, to trace the present art spirit to its origin. The words of *Modern Painters*, the advice and influence which directed the efforts of admiring Pre-Raphaelites, the host of books and lectures addressed to all art lovers of England, have done more to shape English and American taste in art than any other single influence traceable in history. It is easy, now, to point out errors in the manner. It was not easy for one man, though armed with energy and eloquence, to convince a world that cared nothing.

Many who admit the value of Ruskin's teachings in art, speak slightingly of his doctrines in political economy. Here we find a bewildering difference in opinion. If you would study the question more thoroughly, read *Unto this Last*, comparing with it some standard text-book, and reading besides articles that discuss Ruskin's views. You will find between Ruskin's ideas and the accepted views notable differences. A chief distinction lies in his definition of Value as "the power of any thing to support life." Wheat can sustain the substance of the body, pure air can sustain its warmth, and a "cluster of flowers of given beauty" has "a fixed power of enlivening or animating the senses and heart." The whole attention of the orthodox economists has been given to purchasing power, value in exchange. To Ruskin, viewing man as a being of emotions, sentiments, and sympathies, any view which did not call these into account seemed inadequate. Profit is not the only motive of human action. If, as he puts it, there is but one piece of bread for a starving family, — mother and several little children, — the mother, as strongest, would, according to orthodox theory, get that piece. That she does not, shows that power does not always imply possession. Happiness in life must, besides, be measured by other things than money. People, to be ideal men and women, not only must have food, clothes, and a place to sleep, but must have also beautiful and ennobling surroundings. Pleasure should be an estimable asset. In its ugly cities, its dishonestly made clothing, its prevailing shams and meannesses, the present time offends against the ideals of life. William Morris, affected by these teachings, preached an ideal social commonwealth, without smoke or machinery, without competition or envy. Ruskin saw little good in the extreme socialistic ideal, nor did he wish entirely to dispose of machinery; he did feel that the ugliness should be done away with, and that working people should not be relegated, as a penalty for leading industrious lives, to filth and degradation. And the economist's idea that progress depends on competition, the unceasing and merciless battle of each man against his neighbor, he denounced as infamous.

It was sympathy with man, especially with the workingman of England, which led him to take up these questions. Was it necessary that things should be as they were? Was ugliness irremediable, vulgarity a part of the eternal scheme of creation? He preferred to look for a remedy. Apparently he failed. His writings were not well received. He was told that an art critic should not meddle with such matters, and what he said was regarded, coming from the writer of *Modern Painters*, as the dreaming of a man who knew nothing of his subject. Yet, looking back to-day, we see that he did not fail. His lessons have had their effect, and time has justified, at least in part, his social philosophy.

In taking up the study of political economy, Ruskin was not changing his interests. There is a common factor between his writings upon art and upon political economy. In both he advocated higher ideals. In both his end was the improvement of man's condition in the world and the development of the spiritual in man. As to his knowledge of his subject, John Ruskin was not a man to write upon any topic till he had studied it to the best of his ability. He did not write of the drawing of the mountains till he had made a thorough study of geology and mineralogy. He did not write of cloud forms till he had sought out laboriously, in books of science and in the clouds themselves, the nature of their being. Nor did he write of political economy till he had read with care and thought what the recognized economists had to say upon the subject. He may have been in error. If he was, his error did not spring from negligence. One should base condemnation of Ruskin's theories upon a study of what Ruskin really said, not on the fact that he wrote on both political economy and art. It is not impossible that one man might tell truths about both. This much is sure: In political economy, as in art, opinions have altered. The elements that Ruskin wished men to consider are being more and more taken into consideration. Man is regarded as having some other elements than combative acquisitiveness. Beauty in one's surroundings is becoming recognized as of advantage. Parks, recreation piers, libraries, museums, are allowed to have a certain "practical" value. It is acknowledged that a railway train need not be ugly, and that an iron bridge is not the worse for "architecture." People talk of preserving fine bits of woodland, and there is objection to the destruction of the Palisades of the Hudson River. Societies are formed to prevent the disfiguring of landscape by advertisements. Laws are passed to obviate the clouds of smoke that darken our cities. The needless noise of city life is being bit by bit suppressed. New schemes are devised almost daily for the housing of the workmen in "model tenements" and "colonies." All these reforms may have nothing to do with the teachings of the "unpractical" John Ruskin, yet, coming as they do after his writings and lectures, accompanied as they are by the building of Ruskin halls in England and America, they are suggestive. Perhaps here, as in the case of art, some are reluctant to trace an effect to its logical cause.

It is well to reflect, in this connection, upon the words of Mr. Mather, in his *Life of Ruskin:* "One of the best ways," he suggests, " of judging the work of Ruskin is to suppose the non-appearance of the man. . . . It would be the merest of commonplace to speak of the loss to English literature. There would have been other losses, however, heavier and more fatal than merely the loss to the formative thought of the century. Ruskin's books have made men, because they have made men think, and they have broadened the minds of men, because they have put them in touch with the great thought of the past. . . . They have conduced to that seriousness without which literature and life are fleeting and inane. And because of this, they have aroused wrathfulness and mockery. . . . Those whose cry is, 'Let us alone,' cannot let him alone, because his writings are as a whip to torment them. There are, however, those whom he has aroused to a better mind. They are many, and they, in their turn, have aroused a better national mind. Thus Ruskin, while not leaving behind him a school, leaves behind him a tone, a temper, and a life that is becoming as widespread in England as any of the ruling sentiments of the age."

Ruskin is often spoken of as a scold. It is true that he occasionally denounced. So does every earnest teacher. The question is, Was his scolding helpful? Did he merely abuse people for being what they inavoidably are, or did he, while blaming, point the road to improvement? To the reader of his works the question answers itself. Ruskin never blames without indicating an escape from the fault blamed. His reproaches are to rouse to action, not to confirm in despair. He has (see, for instance, Lecture I., Section 40) the deepest confidence in his fellow-countrymen. He realizes that they have the power, and the will, but he realizes, too, that, like strong and stubborn horses, they will bear a deal of lashing before one can rouse them to their true pace.

Isaiah and Jeremiah, for all the latter's "Lamentations," are not denounced as "scolds," yet their prophecy is mainly denunciation of evil. And it is evil that Ruskin reproves. He reproves ugliness and the vulgar toleration of ugliness; he reproves gross content in material prosperity; he reproves greed and hostile competition. One would hardly maintain that these things are admirable. He reproves, with peculiar bitterness, religious conceit and Pharisaical pride. Is not the reproof merited? As a boy he had been taught to regard Protestantism as the one religion, and to view Catholic worship with distrust. When, later, he came to study the early works of Italian Catholic art, and to appreciate their tender, pious beauty, he saw his error. His blame is directed at his earlier self as well as at the reader.

He shows peculiar bitterness in regard to intolerance in women. This springs not from scorn of women, — impossible in the writer of *Queens' Gardens*, — but from a high ideal of their possible power. That a woman whose charm and authority lies in her capabilities of tender compassion, should be complacently confident of the condemnation of others, — should, while unwilling to hurt a fly, rejoice in the thought of "disbelievers" agonizing in eternal fire, — this struck him as a sad incongruity, a pitiful abjuration of queenship.

It is characteristic that Ruskin's works were, in the latter part of his life, removed from the hands of the regular publishers, to whose methods Ruskin objected, and were issued by a printer whom Ruskin installed in his own neighborborhood, at Orpington, in Kent, England. The work was excellently done, the only disadvantage being that some of the works were high in price, and that all were difficult to obtain. Yet this method of independent publication has had its influence, as is shown by the work of the Kelmscott Press of William Morris in England and of the Roycroft publications in America.

Such has been Ruskin's influence, as impressed by his writings and his life. And one other lesson may well be reserved for the last — his lesson of conscientious craftsmanship, honest delight of the workman in his work, the delight of the First Great Artificer when he looked upon his handiwork and "saw that it was good," the delight of each worthy human artificer in the petty fiat of his daily task. It is this principle which is uttered in the third lecture in this volume, which underlies the teachings of the *Lamps of Architecture* and the *Stones of Venice*, and which, in his own life, guided Ruskin's own energies. From the first patient tracing of the printed letters of the *Harry and Lucy*, through the careful pencilled study of bud and branch and peak and cloud, through the patient marshalling of words till the perfect message was shaped for the future reader, through the watchful, kindly oversight of struggling genius that looked to him for help, we find this his rule of life, the spring of action, and the source of pleasure. It was this which directed, also, humbler acts. It was this which made him wash, with his own hands, unclean stairways, which made him take the street-sweeper's broom and clean the muddy crossing, which set him at work, himself, with the road-builder's pickaxe, the carpenter's plane, or the house-painter's brush. Read, in his biography, the story of the Oxford road-making, and you will get insight into the man's restless energy and his patient thoroughness. Study the minute detail of his architectural drawings and sketches of leaf and root. Then — if you think the patience came from a fussy pettiness of nature — see his freer drawings of cloud mass or mountain majesty. From these two you will get the strangely blended elements of his nature — the power that impelled him to do, and the laborious patience that insisted upon tender diligence.

The word "tender," in spite of its hint of sentiment, best sums the lesson of Ruskin's whole life and work. Tender, reverent study of God's world, tender, helpful love for fellow-man, tender patience in the well-doing of what lies nearest, tender —

yes, though the voice be stern with the sense of love's defeat — tender reproof of man that forgets he is of the spirit and that misses God's proffered inheritance.   And in his written word, in the bland, pure, soothing music of his prose, there sounds the same note of tenderness, the soft pleading of flute and hautboy, the muted softness of the gentler brass, the vibrant passion of the reed.   It is a music of peace, of all that peace brings and of all that makes for peace — beauty and noble-doing and tender charity.

ANALYSIS OF THE LECTURES

In studying these essays, as in the study of any piece of writing, the student should make it his first endeavor to get an idea of the work as a whole, to perceive the main outlines, to comprehend the general structure.   In the case of some writers, this is easy.   In the case of Ruskin, it is relatively difficult. Ruskin's habit of mind is singularly discursive ; the value of his writing lies quite as much in incidental ideas which surprise him as in his attainment of any end that he sets out to attain.

The first lecture, *Of Kings' Treasuries*, has, one might say, a compound subject, a major and a minor.   The major subject, expressed in the title, is the link that unites the first lecture with the second, *Kings' Treasuries* with *Queens' Gardens*.   The two lectures are to deal with the kingship of men and the queenly power of women — to tell how this spiritual power — for it is spiritual domination of which the author speaks — may be acquired and exercised.   The subject of the first lecture is consequently this : How may men make themselves spiritual kings among men ?   The minor subject develops the means of attaining such kingship :   One derives help from noble companionship.   The noblest companionship is that of great writers.   Reading, then, by means of their written words, which offers companionship with these great spirits, is the right road to royalty of character.

It would be unjust to say that Ruskin ever quite loses sight of this design. In his deviations into incidental subjects, however, he may perplex the reader into losing sight of it. The precise explanation of kingship does not occur till the beginning of the second lecture; the end of the first lecture is far off the main theme, and whole pages are given to the treatment of matters very remotely related to the topic under discussion.

The line of thought in the first lecture is briefly as follows: the Roman numerals representing divisions of the thought, the Arabic the sections as numbered by Ruskin:—

I. (§§ 1–5). Most men desire, next to winning praise, to obtain real good for themselves and to do good to others. To help them in this, they seek helpful friendship.

II. (§§ 6–12). The most helpful friendship is with the great of the past, revealed in their writings. Their society is always offered to us if we are willing to understand their meaning, and fitted to appreciate it.

III. (§§ 13–end). We must show our love for them in two ways: (A) by trying to understand their meaning — by entering into their *thoughts*, and (B) by trying to sympathize with their spirit — by entering into their *hearts*.

    A. (§§ 13–26). We must understand what they mean.

        1. (§§ 13–19). We must study their works closely, word by word, syllable by syllable (which involves being familiar with the meanings and history of words).

        2. (§§ 20–24). An examination of some lines from Milton will illustrate the right method.

3. (§§ 25–26). We must try humbly to find the writer's meaning, not to judge it ; we must read without prejudice.

B. (§ 27). We must accord with them in spirit.

    1. (§§ 27–29). We must cultivate fineness of feeling, as opposed to vulgarity, or coarse bluntness of feeling.

    2. (§§ 30–41). The English, as a nation, are far from the ideal mood of the reader.

        (*a*) (§ 32). We have despised literature.
        (*b*) (§ 33). We have despised science.
        (*c*) (§ 34). We have despised art.
        (*d*) (§ 35). We have despised nature.
        (*e*) (§§ 36–40). We have despised compassion.

    3. (§§ 41–42). We must acquire true kingship of heart.

    4. (§§ 43–46). Actual kings do not benefit their people, but heap up unprofitable wealth and useless armament.

    5. (§§ 47–end). Ideal kings would found libraries, etc., for the good of their people, furnishing spiritual food, the true Sesame.

This plan is coherent and logical, except in the latter part. Section 42 does not lead to Section 43, at least leads to it only by a superficial associational connection. The real subject in Section 42 is the development of self, the attainment of true kingship by companionship with the great of the past. The word "king," however, leads Ruskin off to discuss the evils of misgovernment, a theme that he develops to the end of the lecture, without any return, except very indirectly and by implication, to the main theme.

Yet, while there is no logical transition, the result is good, for the thought is led from the development of the individual to the development of the nation, and the conclusion has the inclusive largeness of subject that a peroration should have. The irregularity lies in the peculiarly subtle method of shifting to the new subject, — by mere verbal modulation through the word "king," rather than by an overt change of key. The result is that the reader is perplexed to discover how he got from one topic to the other.

The most marked irregularity in the working out of this plan is the disproportional prominence given to incidental matters. At the outset the relative importance given to motives distracts one from the main idea. In discussing the importance of close study of words, Ruskin, in Sections 16–18, is led off into the quite irrelevant subject of "masked words," and their effect upon history. In the analysis of the passage from Milton (20–24), he goes, in 23, far from his path to discuss religious conceit and spiritual pride.

In his denunciation of the English for vulgarity and lack of the finer perceptions, Ruskin seems to be carried quite away from the recollection of his main subject. Yet this portion of his lecture is by no means the least effective. This is his favorite topic, the topic toward which, no matter what his subject, we shall find him gravitating, — reproach of the world that it fails to esteem what it should esteem, and leaves unvalued, unperceived, its true treasures. And this grand denunciation (30–40) gives the lecture no small part of its prophetic dignity.

In general, the lecture has unity or oneness in purpose. Its whole appeal is for sensitiveness of perception, and, behind this, the perception of what is worth while in life. It is the kind of address fitted to summon to alertness any stagnating on the borders of the slough of Philistinism, to cry to them, "Awake, arise, or be forever fallen."

The second lecture, *Of Queens' Gardens*, is complementary to the first. It points out Ruskin's ideal of womanhood and the means by which young women should aim to advance to that ideal. The general outline is as follows : —

I. (§§ 51–53). Statement of the ideal kingship of men and queenship of women.

II. (§§ 54–69). Woman's true place and power in the world. She is to be queen of the home, her husband's companion, uplifting, helping, inspiring.

    1. (§ 54). Statement of problem.

    2. (§§ 55–62). Examination of the ideal of noble womanhood pictured by the world's great writers.

    3. (§§ 63–69). Statement of conclusions.

III. (§§ 70–85). The education of woman. Different from man's yet not less accurate.

    1. (§§ 70–71). Physical development, a life of freedom and delight.

    2. (§§ 72–81). Intellectual development, her education and man's.

    3. (§§ 82–85). Imaginative development, sense of beauty and wonder in nature. (Digression.)

IV. (§§ 86–end). Woman's duties in the larger world outside the home.

The conclusion is highly figurative, and, in the beginning of Section 95, a trifle superficial in connection, using the word "garden" just as "king" was used in the lecture preceding, to make a perplexing transition to the concluding theme.

The third lecture is the most difficult. Its relation to the others is in mood rather than in subject. Like them it tries to rouse the reader to a sense of the seriousness of life, to sting him into shaking off the clogging sense of the commonplace — to make him feel, in fact, that nothing that is, can be really commonplace. It is rather a sermon than a lecture, — a ser-

mon not inculcating any theology, but instilling that sense of
wonder and awe, that aspiration, that dissatisfaction with one's
self, one's deeds, and one's knowledge, that perception of the im-
mensity and mystery of all about us, which is the very core and
vital essence of all religion. This was the centre of Ruskin's
teaching, and in this lecture we find this in its purest expression.

The difficulty in studying this lecture is partly owing to this
subject, indefinite at the best, and leading besides to so many
related topics that a writer less discursive than Ruskin might
well be tempted to wander. In fact, so easy is it to stray
that many readers follow Ruskin through all his divagations
without the least notion that he is out of the path. This is
the easier on account of the peculiarity noted above, — the perfect coherence, the smooth, though often superficial connection
of thought.

The main theme is this : Unless a man have an awed sense
of the mystery of life, and a wholesome desire to perform his
part in life's work industriously and lovingly, there is no hope
of art. Art must spring, that is, first, from religion, a sense of
greater than ourselves ; secondly, from a desire to accomplish
diligently the nearest duty.

I. (§§ 97–98). Introduction. Statement of the subject
(though nothing is said as yet about art) in the question, "What is your life?" with quotation of the verse
from James expressing this mystery.

II. (§§ 98–107). The main thesis : Art must have a noble
motive, must be rooted in a right sense of the mystery
of life.

    1. (§§ 98–104). The mystery of failure, in other
lives, in Ruskin's own life. (Digressive discussion of architecture, art, etc.)

    2. (§§ 105–107). The lesson from this failure. Right-
ness of art can only be consistent with a right
understanding of the ends of life.

III. (§§ 108–128). From all sources we learn but two lessons, the need of self-discontented aspiration, and the need of faithful work.

    1. (§§ 108–109). We care little, as a rule, about eternal mysteries. And this carelessness is itself a mystery.

    2. (§§ 110–112). The great religious poets, Dante and Milton, can tell us nothing, or will tell us nothing.

    3. (§§ 113–115). Homer and Shakespeare offer no solution.

    4. (§§ 116–118). Practical men afford none. (Digression on the silliness of commercial rivalry. Subject temporarily forgotten.)

    5. (§§ 119–127). We must learn from the actual artists and toilers who do their work well because they (*a*) feel themselves wrong — are humble, willing to learn ; and because they (*b*) work with delight and without needless theorizing over their work.

IV. (§§ 129–end). Art, then, depends on helpful action accomplished in the right spirit. As a rule, the world has really done little.

    1. (§ 129). Our agriculture has left men unfed.

    2. (§ 130). Our weaving has left men unclad.

    3. (§ 131). Our building has left men homeless.

    4. (§§ 132–139). We must, then, take up our burden, and do the work that is undone — feeding, clothing, lodging people, and giving them happiness.

        (1) (§ 136). Feeding. (2) (§ 137). Dressing.
            (3) (§ 138). Lodging.

    5. Such work in such a spirit will prevent spiritual conceit and narrowness, and will educate in true charity.

The chief difficulty here is that while the chief lessons are that art must depend on a right sense of the mystery of life and on loving diligent work — while these are the chief lessons, yet other and minor topics — Milton's treatment of his theme, the commercial view of life, false pride in station, etc. — are made misleadingly prominent. Strictly, the fact that life is mysterious should have been presented as subordinate. The fact that the audience must be roused to recognize the mystery, excites Ruskin to a treatment in which it assumes a prominent place.

As in the lectures preceding, a large part is made up of denunciation of the selfishness of modern commercialism, and of the self-satisfied superficiality of present-day life. And these, we must recognize, quite as much as any teaching about art as such, give the lecture its value. It is these, too, that join it to the other two in a common teaching. All three lectures tell men and women of the ideals men and women should set before them : how to read and build character under the inspiration of the nobility of the past, fitting one's self for such great society ; how to develop noble womanhood in women, and, in men, ennobling reverence for womanhood ; how to bear one's self toward the wonder of life, toward one's work in the world, and toward one's duty to others.

These three lectures are, as has been said, three sermons, — lay sermons, and undoctrinal, but sermons none the less, and sermons that the world needs to read and take note of. Perhaps the world has improved since 1864. It may safely be left to the reader to answer whether it has so improved that Ruskin's denunciations no longer find a mark. It is safe to say that there is no one, young or old, who can read these without benefit, without feeling an ennobling stimulus, an inciting discontent, a new aspiration, a larger citizenship among mankind, a deeper humility before God.

SUBJECTS FOR COMPOSITION

THESE subjects, while suited for use in themselves, are intended chiefly to suggest other similar subjects fitted to the particular surroundings and interests of the class. Work of this character could be done with most advantage in the third or fourth year of the high school.

1. My favorite book. A description of some book from which you have received stimulus and help.
2. My favorite author. An attempt to make plain the reasons for your liking.
3. The public library *vs.* private ownership of books. Advantages of each.
4. Object in life. Desire of praise *vs.* desire to do duty, though unpraised.
5. Tolerance in religion. Its development in the last four centuries.
6. The preservation of beauty in nature. Discussion of local problems, — such as that of the preservation of the Palisades in New York.
7. The desirability of free public art-galleries.
8. Reasons against buying showy but cheap furniture, etc.
9. Advantages in having one's books in neat, well-printed editions.
10. Fresh-air excursions. Why city children should be taken out to see the beauty of the country.
11. "What I like in Nature." A statement of your personal preferences in natural scenery, for mountain, sea, peaceful or wild scenery, with explanation for your preference.
12. Argument for or against "organized charities."
13. How a boy or girl can help the poor.
14. Ruskin's personality, as felt in reading *Sesame and Lilies.*
15. The chief lesson that you learn from *Sesame and Lilies.*

16. Ruskin's ideal of woman. How far is it your own?
17. What should one learn in school and in life besides facts? Why?
18. Ruskin and Carlyle. Contrast their characters and teachings.
19. The Pre-Raphaelites. Their work and its influence.

BIBLIOGRAPHY

———◆———

A. RUSKIN'S WRITINGS

THE following is a list of Ruskin's chief works in the order of publication. Minor writings, short articles in magazines, etc., have been purposely omitted. The more important writings are described briefly, Ruskin's peculiar love for fanciful titles making it somewhat difficult to judge of the contents from the title-page.

1834–1846. I. Articles on science and art, under various titles, in the *Architectural Magazine* and the *Magazine of Natural History*. II. Poems in *London Monthly Miscellany* and *Friendship's Offering*, also the Newdigate Prize Poem, *Salsette and Elephanta*, printed separately, also in *Oxford Prize Poems*.

1837. **The Poetry of Architecture.** Discussing the relation between architecture and the surrounding landscape. In *Architectural Magazine*.

1843. **Modern Painters.** Vol. I. The subsequent parts issued as follows: 1846, Vol. II.; 1856, Vols. III. and IV.; 1860, Vol. V. The Autograph Edition was published in 1873, and there have been many editions and reprints since. There have also been volumes of selections, *Frondes Agrestes*, *In Montis Sanctis*, and *Cœli Enarrant*, the first, miscellaneous selections, the second, studies of mountain form, the third, studies in cloud form. For the general character of *Modern Painters*, see Introduction. The illustrations, found in all the better editions, usually drawn by, or under the direction of, Ruskin himself, add greatly to the value.

1849. **The Seven Lamps of Architecture.** These seven "lamps" are Sacrifice, Truth, Power, Beauty, Life, Memory, Obedience. The book, that is, deals with the spirit in which the architect should work, and the national spirit which makes great national architecture possible.

1850. **Poems**, by J. R. Containing poems previously mentioned, and others.

1851. **The King of the Golden River.** Written in 1841.

The Stones of Venice. Vol. I. A study of the architecture of Venice, applying to a particular case the general theories enunciated in *The Seven Lamps of Architecture.* Accompanied in the same year by *Examples of the Architecture of Venice.* Vols. II. and III. two years later.

Notes on the Construction of Sheepfolds. A plea for church unity, for bringing into union the two folds of the Presbyterians and the Established Church of England.

Pre-Raphaelitism. Discussion of the movement of this name. See page xv.

1853. **Stones of Venice.** Vols. II. and III. (See above.)

1853–1860. **Giotto and his Works in Padua.** A study and description suitable for the use of travellers.

1854. **Lectures on Architecture and Painting.**

1856. **Modern Painters.** Vols. III. and IV. (See above.)
The Harbors of England.

1857. **The Elements of Drawing.**
The Political Economy of Art. Reprinted under title *A Joy Forever (and its Price in the Market).*
Education in Art.

1859. **The Two Paths.** Lectures on art and its application to decoration and manufacture. It contrasts the spirit that seeks to represent truly and the spirit of false self-content.

Elements of Perspective.

1860. **Modern Painters.** Vol. V. (See above.)

Unto this Last. Essays on the principles of political economy. Very important in any study of Ruskin's teaching. These essays, as first published in this year, did not bear this title, but were reprinted under it two years later.

1862–1863. **Munera Pulveris.** Essays in political economy.

1865. **Sesame and Lilies.** First two lectures.

1866. **The Ethics of the Dust.** Studies in mineralogy and crystallography.

The Crown of Wild Olive. Three lectures on work, traffic, and war. A discussion of principles of political economy, and the problems of labor and of war.

1867. **Time and Tide by Weare and Tyne.** Twenty-five letters on questions of political economy and related topics.

1869. **The Queen of the Air.** A study of the Greek myths of cloud and storm. This, however, like most of Ruskin's writings, passes to the larger questions of life, and work, and art.

1871–1884. **Fors Clavigera.** A continuation of letters like those in *Time and Tide*, published in pamphlet form at sevenpence (later, tenpence) a copy, each number containing some twenty pages by Ruskin. The name is symbolic, almost defying exact explanation. Fors means Force, or Fate, and Clavigera means bearing the Key, or Club, or Nail, according as the interpretation changes. The third Fors, indeed, is simply Fortune. The object of the whole is to present to men, didactically, thoughts upon the problems of life, to rouse and to inspire. The book is varied in style, Carlylean denunciation mingling with tender idealism and sparkling wit. It is, in many respects, revolutionary, attacking commercialism as the root of all modern evils, and its appearance raised no little outcry.

1870–1872. **Aratra Pentelici.** Six lectures on elements of sculpture. Univ. of Oxford.

   The Relation between Michael Angelo and Tintoret.

   The Eagle's Nest. The relation of natural science to art.

1873. **Love's Meinie.** Parts I. and II. Part III. was issued in 1881. Lessons on Greek and English birds.

   Ariadne Florentina. Six lectures on wood and metal engraving.

1873–1874. **Val d'Arno.** Ten lectures, the Tuscan art directly antecedent to the Florentine year of victories.

1875–1877. **Mornings in Florence.** A guide to the tourist.

1875–1886. **Proserpina.** Studies of wayside flowers, taking up character of leaf, stem, and seed, with discussion of several common flowers.

1875–1878. **Deucalion.** Collected studies on the lapse of waves and life of stones.

1877–1884. **St. Mark's Rest.** "The history of Venice written for the help of the few travellers who still care for her mountains."

1877–1878. **The Laws of Fésole.** A familiar treatise on the elementary principles and practice of drawing and painting, as determined by the Tuscan masters.

1880. **Elements of English Prosody.**

   Arrows of the Chace. Various letters to newspapers on various subjects, collected and edited by A. D. O. Wedderburn.

1880–1885. **The Bible of Amiens,** or *Our Fathers have told Us.* "Sketches of the history of Christianity for boys and girls who have been held at its fonts."

1883. **The Art of England.** Lectures in Oxford. These deal with Rossetti, Burne-Jones, Holman, Hunt, Alma-Tadema, and other representative English artists.

1884. **The Storm Cloud of the Nineteenth Century.**

1884–1885. **The Pleasures of England.** Lectures in Oxford. The "Pleasures" are the pleasures of Learning, of Faith, and of Deed. They are treated in relation to early English history.

1885. **On the Old Road.** Collected magazine articles from various sources, consisting largely of early work.

    Præterita. A beginning of an autobiography or, more strictly, autobiographic notes, giving a charging view into the life and nature of the writer. (It is one of the best of autobiographical records, with something of the innocent egotism of Pepys.)

1886. **Dilecta.** Correspondence and other material illustrative of Præterita.

    Hortus Inclusus. The inclosed garden. Letters to two young ladies, collected and edited.

1890. **Ruskiana.** Collected letters.

1891. **The Poems of John Ruskin.**

B. WRITINGS ABOUT RUSKIN

Among the best biographies of Ruskin are the following: *The Life of John Ruskin,* by W. G. Collingwood (Houghton, Mifflin & Co.); *John Ruskin,* M. H. Spielmann (Lippincott & Co.); *John Ruskin, his Life and Teaching,* Mather (Warne & Co.); *Ruskin et la Religion de la Beauté,* Robert de la Sizeranne (Hachette et Cie.); *John Ruskin, Aspects of his Thought and Teaching,* Baillie; *Work of John Ruskin,* Charles Waldstein (Harper and Brothers). Ruskin is discussed also in *Modern Humanists,* John M. Robertson (Swan Sonnenschein

& Co.) — a most excellent criticism.   W. Hamilton's *Æsthetic Movement in England* casts a good deal of rather distorted light on the Pre-Raphaelites, while biographies of D. G. Rossetti, and others of Ruskin's group, bring Ruskin in as an accessory figure.   Very useful, of course, are the *Præterita*, Ruskin's autobiographical reminiscence, the *Dilecta*, and other collections of letters and biographical material.

In the periodicals, especially in the year 1900, there have appeared a great many articles upon Ruskin and his work. For these the student should consult Poole's *Index to Periodical Literature*.   The following may be of especial interest. (The numeral indicates the volume of the magazine.   For the page, see magazine index.)

Biography : — *Ruskin and his Home* (*National Magazine*, 7); *John Ruskin*, W. H. Winslow (*New England Magazine*, New Series, 21); *John Ruskin at Home* (Academy 56, *Book-Buyer*, 10).

Art Criticism : — *Ruskin as Artist*, M. H. Spielmann (*Scribner's Magazine*, 24); *Ruskin, Rossetti, and Pre-Raphaelitism*, M. S. Anderson (*Dial*, 26); *Ruskin as Art Teacher*, W. G. Kingsland (*Poet-Lore*, 5).

Political Economy : — *Lessons from Ruskin*, C. S. Devas (*Economic Journal*, 8); *Ruskin Coöperative Colony*, N. H. Casson (*Independent*, 51); *Ruskin as Political Economist*, W. J. Lhamon (*Canadian Magazine*, 8); *Ruskin as a Practical Teacher*, Kaufman (*Scottish Review*, 24); *Ruskin in Relation to Modern Problems* (*National Review*, 22); *Ruskin's Influence on English Social Thought* (*New England Magazine*, New Series, 9); *John Ruskin as Economist*, Patrick Geddes (*International Monthly*, 1).

As a Writer : — *Ruskin as Oxford Lecturer*, J. M. Bruce (*Century*, 33); *Ruskin as Writer*, M. H. Spielmann (*Book-Buyer*, 19); *Ruskin as Master of Prose*, Frederic Harrison (*Century*, 38); *Titles of Ruskin's Books*, Mrs. E. T.

Cook (*Good Words*, 34); *Ruskin's Writings*, Saintsbury (*Critic*, 25).

RUSKIN AND HIS CONTEMPORARIES

Thomas Carlyle,	1795–1881.
J. M. W. Turner (painter),	1775–1851.
Alfred Tennyson,	1809–1892.
Robert Browning,	1812–1889.
John Ruskin,	1819–1900.
Dante Gabriel Rossetti,	1828–1882.
William Morris,	1834–1890.
Algernon C. Swinburne,	1837– .

PREFACE TO EDITION OF 1882

1. THE present edition of "Sesame and Lilies," issued at the request of an aged friend, is reprinted without change of a word from the first small edition of the book, withdrawing only the irrelevant preface° respecting tours in the Alps, which however, if the reader care to see, he will find placed with more propriety in the second volume of "Deucalion." The third lecture, added in the first volume of the large edition of my works, and the gossiping introduction prefixed to that edition, are withdrawn also, not as irrelevant, but as following the subject too far, and disturbing the simplicity in which the two original lectures dwell on their several themes, — the majesty of the influence of good books,° and of good women,° if we know how to read them, and how to honor.

2. I might just as well have said, the influence of good men, and good women, since the best strength of a man is shown in his intellectual work, as that of a women in her daily deed and character; and I am somewhat tempted to involve myself in the debate which might be imagined in illustrating these relations of their several powers, because only the other day one of my friends put me in no small pet° by saying that he thought my own influence was much more in being amiable and obliging than in writing books. Admitting for argument's sake, the amiableness and obligingness, I begged him, with some warmth, to observe that there were myriads of at least equally good-natured people in the world who had merely become its slaves, if not its victims, but that the influence of my books was

distinctly on the increase, and I hoped — etc., etc., — it is no matter what more I said, or intimated; but it much matters that the young reader of the following essays should be confirmed in the assurance on which all their pleading depends, that there *is* such a thing as essential good, and as essential evil, in books, in art, and in character; — that this essential goodness and badness are independent of epochs, fashions, opinions, or revolutions; and the present extremely active and ingenious generation of young people, in thanking Providence for the advantages it has granted them in the possession of steam whistles and bicycles, need not hope materially to add to the laws of beauty in sound or grace in motion, which were acknowledged in the days of Orpheus,° and Camilla.°

3. But I am brought to more serious pause than I had anticipated in putting final accent on the main sentences in this — already, as men now count time, old — book of mine, because since it was written, not only these untried instruments ° of action, but many equally novel methods of education and systems of morality have come into vogue, not without a certain measure of prospective good in them; — college education for women, — out-of-college education ° for men: positivism ° with its religion of humanity, and negativism ° with its religion of Chaos, and the like, from the entanglement of which no young people can now escape, if they would; together with a mass of realistic,° or materialistic literature and art, founded mainly on the theory of nobody's having any will, or needing any master; and much of it extremely clever, irresistibly amusing, and enticingly pathetic; but which is all nevertheless the mere whirr and dust-cloud of a dissolutely ° reforming and vulgarly manufacturing age, which when its dissolutions are appeased, and its manufactures purified, must return in due time to the understanding of things that have been, and are, and shall be hereafter, though for the present concerned seriously with nothing beyond its dinner and its bed.

4. I must therefore, for honesty's sake, no less than intelligibility's, warn the reader of "Sesame and Lilies" that the book is wholly of the old school; that it ignores, without contention or regret, the ferment of surrounding elements, and assumes for perennial some old-fashioned conditions and existences which the philosophy of to-day imagines to be extinct with the Mammoth ° and the Dodo.°

5. Thus the second lecture, in its very title, "Queens' Gardens," takes for granted the persistency of Queenship, and therefore of Kingship, and therefore of Courtliness or Courtesy, and therefore of Uncourtliness or Rusticity. It assumes, with the ideas of higher and lower rank, those of serene authority and happy submission; of Riches and Poverty without dispute for their rights, and of Virtue and Vice without confusion of their natures.

6. And farther, it must be premised that the book is chiefly written for young people belonging to the upper, or undistressed middle, classes; who may be supposed to have choice of the objects and command of the industries of their life. It assumes that many of them will be called to occupy responsible positions in the world, and that they have leisure in preparation for these, to play tennis or read Plato.

7. Therefore also — that they have Plato to read if they choose, with lawns on which they may run, and woods in which they may muse. It supposes their father's library to be open to them, and to contain all that is necessary for their intellectual progress, without the smallest dependence on monthly parcels ° from town.

8. These presupposed conditions are not extravagant in a country that boasts of its wealth, and which, without boasting, still presents in the greater number of its landed households, the most perfect types of grace and peace which can be found in Europe.

9. I have only to add farther, respecting the book, that it

was written while my energies were still unbroken and my temper unfettered ; and that, if read in connection with " Unto this Last," it contains the chief truths I have endeavored through all my past life to display, and which, under the warnings I have received to prepare for its close, I am chiefly thankful to have learnt and taught.

AVALLON, Aug. 24th, 1882.

SESAME AND LILIES

PREFACE TO EDITION OF 1871

I. BEING now fifty-one years old, and little likely to change my mind hereafter on any important subject of thought (unless through weakness of age), I wish to publish a connected series of such parts of my works as now seem to me right, and likely to be of permanent use. In doing so I shall omit much, but not attempt to mend what I think worth reprinting. A young man necessarily writes otherwise than an old one, and it would be worse than wasted time to try to recast the juvenile language; nor is it to be thought that I am ashamed even of what I cancel, for a great part of my earlier work was rapidly written for temporary purposes, and is now unnecessary, though true, even to truism.° What I wrote about religion was, on the contrary, painstaking, and, I think, forcible, as compared with most religious writing, especially in its frankness and fearlessness; but it was wholly mistaken, for I had been educated in the doctrines of a narrow sect, and had read history as obliquely as sectarians necessarily must.

Mingled among these either unnecessary or erroneous statements, I find, indeed, some that might be still of value; but these, in my earlier books, disfigured by affected language,° partly through the desire to be thought a fine writer, and partly, as in the second volume of "Modern Painters,"° in the notion of returning as far as I could to what I thought the better style of old English literature, especially to that of my then favorite in prose, Richard Hooker.°[1]

* * * * * * * *

III. The first book of which a new edition is required chances to be "Sesame and Lilies." . . . I am glad that it should be the first of the complete series, for many reasons, though in now looking over these lectures, I am painfully struck by the waste of good work in them. They cost me much thought and much strong emotion; but it was foolish to suppose that I could rouse my audiences in a little while to any sympathy with the temper into which I had brought myself by years of thinking over subjects full of pain; while, if I missed my purpose at the time, it was little to be hoped I could attain it afterwards, since phrases written for oral delivery become ineffective when quietly read. Yet I should only take away what good is in them if I tried to translate them into the language of books;° nor, indeed, could I at all have done so at the time of their delivery, my thoughts then habitually and impatiently putting themselves into forms fit only for emphatic speech. And thus I am startled, in my review of them, to find that though there is much (forgive me the impertinence) which seems to me accurately and energetically said, there is scarcely anything put in a form to be generally convincing, or even easily intelligible; and I can well imagine a reader laying down the book without being at all moved by it, still less guided, to any definite course of action.

I think, however, if I now say briefly and clearly what I meant my hearers to understand, and what I wanted and still would fain have them to do, there may afterwards be found some better service in the passionately written text.

---

[1] Here Ruskin goes on to speak of writings not included in this edition. This passage is consequently omitted. — ED.

IV. The first lecture says,° or tries to say, that life being very short, and the quiet hours of it few, we ought to waste none of them in reading valueless books; and that valuable books should, in a civilized country, be within the reach of every one, printed in excellent form, for a just price, but not in any vile, vulgar, or, by reason of smallness of type, physically injurious form, at a vile price. For we none of us need many books, and those which we need ought to be clearly printed, on the best paper, and strongly bound. And though we are indeed now a wretched and poverty-struck nation, and hardly able to keep soul and body together, still, as no person in decent circumstances would put on his table confessedly bad wine, or bad meat, without being ashamed, so he need not have on his shelves ill-printed or loosely and wretchedly stitched books; for though few can be rich, yet every man who honestly exerts himself may, I think, still provide, for himself and his family, good shoes, good gloves, strong harness for his cart or carriage horses, and stout leather binding for his books. And I would urge upon every young man, as the beginning of his due and wise provision for his household, to obtain as soon as he can, by the severest economy, a restricted, serviceable, and steadily — however slowly — increasing series of books for use through life, — making his little library, of all the furniture in his room, the most studied and decorative piece, every volume having its assigned place, like a little statue in its niche, and one of the earliest and strictest lessons to the children of the house being how to turn the pages of their own literary possessions lightly and deliberately, with no chance of tearing or dogs' ears.

V. That is my notion of the founding of Kings' Treasuries; and the first lecture is intended to show somewhat the use and preciousness of their treasures; but the two following ones have wider scope, being written in the hope of awakening the youth of England, so far as my poor words might have any power with them, to take some thought of the purposes of the life

into which they are entering, and the nature of the world they
have to conquer.

VI. These two lectures are fragmentary and ill-arranged,
but not, I think, diffuse or much compressible. The entire
gist and conclusion° of them, however, is in the last six paragraphs, 135 to the end, of the third lecture, which I would
beg the reader to look over, not once or twice (rather than any
other part of the book), for they contain the best expression I
have yet been able to put in words of what, so far as is within
my power, I mean henceforward both to do myself, and to plead
with all over whom I have any influence, to do also, according
to their means, — the letters begun on the first day of this
year,[1] to the workmen of England, having the object of originating, if possible, this movement among them, in true alliance
with whatever trustworthy element of help they can find in the
higher classes. After these paragraphs, let me ask you to read,
by the fiery light of recent events, the fable given at §117, and
then §§ 129–131, and observe, my statement respecting the
famine of Orissa° is not rhetorical, but certified by official docu-
ments as within the truth. Five hundred thousand persons,
at least, died by starvation in our British dominions, wholly
in consequence of carelessness and want of forethought. Keep
that well in your memory, and note it as the best possible illustration of modern political economy in true practice, and of the
relations it has accomplished between Supply and Demand.
Then begin the second lecture, and all will read clear enough,
I think, to the end ; only, since that second lecture was written,
questions have arisen respecting the education and claims of
women which have greatly troubled simple minds and excited
restless ones. I am sometimes asked my thoughts on this matter, and I suppose that some girl readers of the second lecture
may at the end of it desire to be told summarily what I would

---

[1] "Fors Clavigera," begun in 1871.

have them do and desire in the present state of things. This, then, is what I would say to any girl who had confidence enough in me to believe what I told her, or do what I asked her.

VII. First, be quite sure of one thing, that, however much you may know, and whatever advantages you may possess, and however good you may be, you have not been singled out° by the God who made you from all the other girls in the world, to be especially informed respecting His own nature and character. You have not been born in a luminous° point upon the surface of the globe, where a perfect theology might be expounded to you from your youth up, and where everything you were taught would be true, and everything that was enforced upon you, right. Of all the insolent, all the foolish persuasions that by any chance could enter and hold your empty little heart, this is the proudest and foolishest, — that you have been so much the darling of the Heavens and favorite of the Fates as to be born in the very nick of time, and in the punctual place, when and where pure Divine truth had been sifted from the errors of the nations; and that your papa had been providentially disposed to buy a house in the convenient neighborhood of the steeple under which that Immaculate and final verity° would be beautifully proclaimed. Do not think it, child; it is not so. This, on the contrary, is the fact, — unpleasant you may think it; pleasant, it seems to *me*, — that you, with all your pretty dresses, and dainty looks, and kindly thoughts, and saintly aspirations, are not one whit more thought of or loved by the great Maker and Master than any poor little red, black, or blue savage, running wild in the pestilent woods, or naked on the hot sands of the earth; and that of the two, you probably know less about God than she does; the only difference being that she thinks little of Him that is right, and you, much that is wrong.

That, then, is the first thing to make sure of; — that you are not yet perfectly well informed on the most abstruse of all possible subjects,° and that if you care to behave with modesty or propriety, you had better be silent about it.

VIII. The second thing which you may make sure of is, that however good you may be, you have faults; that however dull you may be, you can find out what some of them are; and that however slight they may be, you had better make some — not too painful, but patient — effort to get quit of them. And so far as you have confidence in me at all, trust me for this, that how many soever you may find or fancy your faults to be, there are only two that are of real consequence, — Idleness and Cruelty. Perhaps you may be proud. Well, we can get much good out of pride, if only it be not religious. Perhaps you may be vain, — it is highly probable, and very pleasant for the people who like to praise you. Perhaps you are a little envious, — that is really very shocking; but then — so is everybody else. Perhaps, also, you are a little malicious, which I am truly concerned to hear, but should probably only the more, if I knew you, enjoy your conversation. But whatever else you may be, you must not be useless, and you must not be cruel. If there is any one point which, in six thousand years of thinking about right and wrong, wise and good men have agreed upon, or successively by experience discovered, it is that God dislikes idle and cruel people more than any others; — that His first order is, "Work while you have light;"° and His second, "Be merciful while you have mercy."°

"Work while you have light," especially while you have the light of morning.° There are few things more wonderful to me than that old people never tell young ones how precious their youth is. They sometimes sentimentally regret their own earlier days, sometimes prudently forget them, often foolishly rebuke the young, often more foolishly indulge, often most foolishly thwart and restrain, but scarcely ever warn or watch them. Remember, then, that I, at least, have warned *you* that the happiness of your life, and its power, and its part and rank ın earth or in heaven, depend on the way you pass your days now. They are not to be sad days, — far from that, the first duty of young people is to be delighted and delightful; but they are to be in the deepest sense solemn days. There is no solemnity so deep, to a rightly thinking creature, as that of dawn. But not only in that beautiful sense, but in all their character and method, they are to be solemn days. Take your Latin dictionary, and look out "solennis," ° and fix the sense of the word well in your mind, and remember that every day of your early life is ordaining irrevocably, for good or evil, the custom and practice of your soul, — ordaining either sacred customs of dear and lovely recurrence, or trenching deeper and deeper the furrows for seed of sorrow. Now, therefore, see that no day passes in which you do not make yourself a somewhat better creature; and in order to do that, find out, first, what you are now. Do not think vaguely about it; take pen and paper, and write down as accurate a description of yourself as you can, with the date to it. If you dare not do so, find out why you dare not, and try to get strength of heart enough to look yourself fairly in the face, in mind as well as body. I do not doubt but that the mind is a less pleasant thing to look at than the face, and for that very reason it needs more looking at; so always have two mirrors ° on your toilet-table, and see that with proper care you dress body and mind before them daily. After the dressing is once over for the day, think no more about it: as your hair will blow about your ears, so your temper and thoughts will get ruffled with the day's work, and may need, sometimes, twice dressing; but I don't want you to carry about a mental pocket-comb, only to be smooth braided ° always in the morning.

IX. Write down, then, frankly, what you are, or at least what you think yourself, not dwelling upon those inevitable faults which I have just told you are of little consequence, and which the action of a right life will shake or smooth away; but

that you may determine to the best of your intelligence what
you are good for, and can be made into. You will find that
the mere resolve not to be useless, and the honest desire to help
other people, will, in the quickest and delicatest ways, improve
yourself. Thus, from the beginning, consider all your accomplishments as means of assistance to others; read attentively,
in this volume, paragraphs 74, 75, 19, and 79, and you will
understand what I mean, with respect to languages and music.
In music especially you will soon find what personal benefit
there is in being serviceable: it is probable that, however
limited your powers, you have voice and ear enough to sustain
a note of moderate compass in a concerted piece; — that, then,
is the first thing to make sure you can do. Get your voice disciplined and clear, and think only of accuracy, never of effect
or expression: if you have any soul worth expressing, it will
show itself in your singing; but most likely there are very few
feelings in you, at present, needing any particular expression, and
the one thing you have to do is to make a clear-voiced little
instrument ° of yourself, which other people can entirely depend
upon for the note wanted. So, in drawing, as soon as you can
set down the right shape of anything, and thereby explain its
character to another person, or make the look of it clear and
interesting to a child, you will begin to enjoy the art vividly
for its own sake, and all your habits of mind and powers of
memory will gain precision; but if you only try to make showy
drawings for praise, or pretty ones for amusement, your drawing
will have little of real interest for you, and no educational power
whatever.

Then, besides this more delicate work, resolve to do every
day some that is useful in the vulgar ° sense. Learn first
thoroughly the economy of the kitchen, — the good and bad
qualities of every common article of food, and the simplest and
best modes of their preparation; when you have time, go and
help in the cooking of poorer families, and show them how to

make as much of everything as possible, and how to make little, nice ; — coaxing and tempting them into tidy and pretty ways, and pleading for well-folded table-cloths, however coarse, and for a flower or two out of the garden to strew on them. If you manage to get a clean table-cloth, bright plates on it, and a good dish in the middle, of your own cooking, you may ask leave to say a short grace ; and let your religious ministries be confined to that much for the present.

X. Again, let a certain part of your day (as little as you choose, but not to be broken in upon) be set apart for making strong and pretty dresses for the poor. Learn the sound qualities of all useful stuffs, and make everything of the best you can get, whatever its price. I have many reasons for desiring you to do this, — too many to be told just now ; — trust me, and be sure you get everything as good as can be. And if in the villanous state of modern trade, you cannot get it good at any price, buy its raw material, and set some of the poor women about you to spin and weave, till you have got stuff that can be trusted ; and then, every day, make some little piece of useful clothing, sewn with your own fingers as strongly as it can be stitched ; and embroider it or otherwise beautify it moderately with fine needlework, such as a girl may be proud of having done. And accumulate these things by you until you hear of some honest persons in need of clothing, which may often too sorrowfully be ; and even though you should be deceived, and give them to the dishonest, and hear of their being at once taken to the pawnbroker's, never mind that, for the pawnbroker must sell them to some one who has need of them. That is no business of yours ; what concerns you is only that when you see a half-naked child, you should have good and fresh clothes to give it, if its parents will let it be taught to wear them. If they will not, consider how they came to be of such a mind, which it will be wholesome for you beyond most subjects of inquiry to ascertain. And after you have gone on doing this a little while, you will begin to understand the meaning of at least one chapter of your Bible, — Proverbs xxxi.,° — without need of any labored comment, sermon, or meditation.

XI. In these, then (and of course in all minor ways besides, that you can discover in your own household), you must be to the best of your strength usefully employed during the greater part of the day, so that you may be able at the end of it to say as proudly as any peasant that you have not eaten the bread of idleness.

Then, secondly, I said you are not to be cruel. Perhaps you think there is no chance of your being so, and indeed I hope it is not likely that you should be deliberately unkind to any creature ; but unless you are deliberately kind to every creature, you will often be cruel to many. Cruel, partly through want of imagination (a far rarer and weaker faculty in women than men), and yet more, at the present day, through the subtle encouragement of your selfishness by the religious doctrine that all which we now suppose to be evil will be brought to a good end, — doctrine practically issuing, not in less earnest efforts that the immediate unpleasantness may be averted from ourselves, but in our remaining satisfied in the contemplation of its ultimate objects, when it is inflicted on others.

It is not likely that the more accurate methods of recent mental education will now long permit young people to grow up in the persuasion that in any danger or distress they may expect to be themselves saved by the providence of God, while those around them are lost by His improvidence ; but they may be yet long restrained from rightly kind action, and long accustomed to endure both their own pain occasionally, and the pain of others always, with an unwise patience, by misconception of the eternal and incurable nature of real evil. Observe, therefore, carefully in this matter : there are degrees of pain, as degrees of faultfulness, which are altogether conquerable, and which seem to be merely forms of wholesome trial or discipline.

Your fingers tingle when you go out on a frosty morning, and are all the warmer afterwards; your limbs are weary with wholesome work, and lie down in the pleasanter rest; you are tried for a little while by having to wait for some promised good, and it is all the sweeter when it comes. But you cannot carry the trial past a certain point. Let the cold fasten on your hand in an extreme degree, and your fingers will moulder from their sockets. Fatigue yourself, but once, to utter exhaustion, and to the end of life you shall not recover the former vigor of your frame. Let heart-sickness pass beyond a certain bitter point, and the heart loses its life forever.

Now, the very definition of evil is in this irremediableness. It means sorrow, or sin, which end in death; and assuredly, as far as we know, or can conceive, there are many conditions both of pain and sin which cannot but so end. Of course we are ignorant and blind creatures, and we cannot know what seeds of good may be in present suffering, or present crime; but with what we cannot know, we are not concerned. It is conceivable that murderers and liars may in some distant world be exalted into a higher humanity than they could have reached without homicide or falsehood; but the contingency is not one by which our actions should be guided. There is indeed a better hope that the beggar who lies at our gates in misery, may, within gates of pearl,° be comforted; but the Master, whose words are our only authority for thinking so, never Himself inflicted disease as a blessing, nor sent away the hungry unfed, or the wounded unhealed.

XII. Believe me then, the only right principle of action here, is to consider good and evil as defined by our natural sense of both, and to strive to promote the one, and to conquer the other, with as hearty endeavor as if there were, indeed, no other world than this. Above all, get quit of the absurd idea that Heaven will interfere to correct great errors, while allowing its laws to take their course in punishing small ones. If you prepare a dish of food carelessly, you do not expect Providence to make it palatable; neither if through years of folly you misguide your own life, need you expect° Divine interference to bring round everything at last for the best. I tell you positively, the world is not so constituted: the consequences of great mistakes are just as sure as those of small ones, and the happiness of your whole life, and of all the lives over which you have power, depends as literally on your own common-sense and discretion as the excellence and order of the feast of a day.

XIII. Think carefully and bravely over these things, and you will find them true; having found them so, think also carefully over your own position in life. I assume that you belong to the middle or upper classes, and that you would shrink from descending into a lower sphere. You may fancy you would not, — nay, if you are very good, strong-hearted, and romantic, perhaps you really would not; but it is not wrong that you should. You have, then, I suppose, good food, pretty rooms to live in, pretty dresses to wear, power of obtaining every rational and wholesome pleasure: you are moreover, probably gentle and grateful, and in the habit of every day thanking God for these things. But why do you thank Him? Is it because, in these matters, as well as in your religious knowledge, you think He has made a favorite of you? Is the essential meaning of your thanksgiving, "Lord, I thank thee° that I am not as other girls are, not in that I fast twice in the week while they feast, but in that I feast seven times a week, while they fast"? And are you quite sure this is a pleasing form of thanksgiving to your Heavenly Father? Suppose you saw one of your own true earthly sisters, Lucy or Emily, cast out of your mortal father's house, starving, helpless, heartbroken; and that every morning when you went into your father's room, you said to him, "How good you are, father, to give me what you don't give Lucy!"° are you sure that, what ever anger your parent might have just cause for, against your sister, he would be pleased by that thanksgiving, or flattered by that praise? Nay, are you even sure that you *are* so much the favorite? — suppose that all this while he loves poor Lucy just as well as you, and is only trying you through her pain, and perhaps not angry with her in anywise, but deeply angry with you, and all the more for your thanksgivings? Would it not be well that you should think, and earnestly too, over this standing of yours; and all the more if you wish to believe that text, which clergymen so much dislike preaching on,° "How hardly shall they that have riches enter into the Kingdom of God"?° You do not believe it now, or you would be less complacent in your state; — and you cannot believe it at all, until you know that the Kingdom of God means, — "not meat and drink, but justice, peace, and joy in the Holy Ghost," nor until you know also that such joy is not by any means, necessarily, in going to church, or in singing hymns, but may be joy in a dance, or joy in a jest,° or joy in anything you have deserved to possess, or that you are willing to give; but joy in nothing that separates you, as by any strange favor, from your fellow-creatures, that exalts you through their degradation, — exempts you from their toil, — or indulges you in time of their distress.

XIV. Think, then, and some day, I believe, you will feel also, — no morbid passion of pity such as would turn you into a black Sister of Charity, but the steady fire of perpetual kindness, which will make you a bright one. I speak in no disparagement of them. I know well how good the Sisters of Charity are, and how much we owe to them; but all these professional pieties (except so far as distinction or association may be necessary for effectiveness of work) are in their spirit wrong, and in practice merely plaster the sores of disease that ought never have been permitted to exist, — encouraging at the same time the herd of less excellent women in frivolity, by leading them to think that they must either be good up to the black stand ard, or **cannot** be good for anything.   Wear a costume, by all means, if you like ; but let it be a cheerful and becoming one; and be in your heart a Sister of Charity always, without either veiled or voluble declaration of it.

XV. As I pause, before ending my preface, — thinking of one or two more points that are difficult to write of, — I find a letter in "The Times," from a French lady, which says all I want so beautifully that I will print it just as it stands : —

Sir, — It is often said that one example is worth many sermons. Shall I be judged presumptuous if I point out one which seems to me so striking just now that, however painful, I cannot help dwelling upon it ?

It is the share, the sad and large share, that French society and its recent habits of luxury, of expenses, of dress, of indulgence in every kind of extravagant dissipation, has to lay to its own door in its actual crisis of ruin, misery and humiliation. If our *ménagères*° can be cited as an example to English housewives, so, alas ! can other classes of our society be set up as an example — *not* to be followed.

Bitter must be the feelings of many a Frenchwoman whose days of luxury and expensive habits are at an end, and whose bills of bygone splendor lie with a heavy weight on her conscience, if not on her purse !

With us the evil has spread high and low. Everywhere have the examples given by the highest ladies in the land been followed but too successfully. Every year did dress become more extravagant, entertainments more costly, expenses of every kind more considerable. Lower and lower became the tone of society, its good-breeding, its delicacy. More and more were *monde* and *demi-monde* associated in newspaper accounts of fashionable doings, in scandalous gossip, on race-courses, in *premières représentations*, in imitation of each other's costumes, *mobiliers*, and slang.

Living beyond one's means became habitual — almost necessary — for every one to keep up with, if not to go beyond, every one else.

What the result of all this has been we now see in the wreck of our prosperity, in the downfall of all that seemed brightest and highest.

Deeply and fearfully impressed by what my own country has incurred and is suffering, I cannot help feeling sorrowful when I see in England signs of our besetting sins appearing also. Paint and chignons, slang and vaudevilles, knowing "Anonymas" by name, and reading doubtfully moral novels, are in themselves small offences, although not many years ago they would have appeared very heinous ones, yet they are quick and tempting conveyances on a very dangerous high-road.

I would that all English women knew how they are looked up to from abroad, — what a high opinion, what honor and reverence we foreigners have for their principles, their truthfulness, the fresh and pure innocence of their daughters, the healthy youthfulness of their lovely children.

May I illustrate this by a short example which happened very near me? During the days of the *émeutes*° of 1848, all the houses in Paris were being searched for fire-arms by the mob. The one I was living in contained none, as the master of the house repeatedly assured the furious and incredulous Republicans. They were going to lay violent hands on him, when his wife, an English lady, hearing the loud discussion, came bravely forward and assured them that no arms were concealed. "Vous êtes anglaise, nous vous croyons ; les anglaises disent toujours la vérité,"° was the immediate answer ; and the rioters quietly left.

Now, Sir, shall I be accused of unjustified criticism, if, loving and admiring your country, as these lines will prove, certain new features strike me as painful discrepancies in English life?

Far be it from me to preach the contempt of all that can make life lovable and wholesomely pleasant. I love nothing better than to see a woman nice, neat, elegant, looking her best in the prettiest dress that her taste and purse can afford, or your bright, fresh young girls fearlessly and perfectly sitting their horses, or adorning their houses as pretty [*sic* ;° it is not quite grammar, but it is better than if it were] as care, trouble, and refinement can make them.

It is the degree *beyond* that which to us has proved so fatal, and that I would our example could warn you from, as a small repayment for your hospitality and friendliness to us in our days of trouble.

May English women accept this in a kindly spirit as a new-year's wish from

                A FRENCH LADY.

DECEMBER 29.

That, then, is the substance of what I would fain say convincingly, if it might be, to my girl friends; at all events with certainty in my own mind that I was thus far a safe guide to them.

XVI. For other and older readers it is needful I should write a few words more, respecting what opportunity I have had to judge, or right I have to speak, of such things; for indeed too much of what I have said about women has been said in faith only.   A wise and lovely English lady told me, when "Sesame and Lilies" first appeared, that she was sure the "Sesame" would be useful, but that in the "Lilies" I had been writing of what I knew nothing about.   Which was in a measure too true, and also that it is more partial than my writings are usually; for as Ellesmere ° spoke his speech on the —— intervention, not indeed otherwise than he felt, but yet altogether for the sake of Gretchen, so I wrote the "Lilies" to please one girl, and were it not for what I remember of her, and a few besides, should now perhaps recast some of the sentences in the "Lilies" in a very different tone; — for as years have gone by, it has chanced to me, untowardly in some respects, fortunately in others (because it enables me to read history more clearly), to see the utmost evil that is in women, while I have but to believe the utmost good.   The best women are indeed necessarily the most difficult to know; they are recognized chiefly in the happiness of their husbands and the nobleness of their children.   They are only to be divined, not discerned, by the stranger, and sometimes seem almost helpless except in their homes; yet without the help of one of them,[1] to whom this book is dedicated, the day would probably have come before now, when I should have written and thought no more.

XVII. On the other hand, the fashion of the time renders whatever is forward, coarse, or senseless in feminine nature,

---

[1] φίλη.°

too palpable to all men: the weak picturesqueness of my earlier writings brought me acquainted with much of their emptiest enthusiasm; and the chances of later life gave me opportunities of watching women in states of degradation and vindictiveness which opened to me the gloomiest secrets of Greek and Syrian tragedy.° I have seen them betray their household charities to lust, their pledged love to devotion; I have seen mothers dutiful to their children as Medea° and children dutiful to their parents as the daughter of Herodias; but my trust is still unmoved in the preciousness of the natures that are so fatal in their error, and I leave the words of the "Lilies" unchanged; believing, yet, that no man ever lived a right life who had not been chastened by a woman's love, strengthened by her courage, and guided by her discretion.

XVIII. What I might myself have been, so helped, I rarely indulge in the idleness of thinking; but what I am, since I take on me the function of a teacher, it is well that the reader should know, as far as I can tell him:—

Not an unjust person;° not an unkind one; not a false one; a lover of order, labor, and peace. That, it seems to me, is enough to give me right to say all I care to say on ethical subjects; more, I could only tell definitely through details of autobiography such as none but prosperous and (in the simple sense of the word) faultless lives could justify,—and mine has been neither. Yet if any one, skilled in reading the torn manuscripts of the human soul, cares for more intimate knowledge of me, he may have it by knowing with what persons in past history I have most sympathy.

I will name three:—

In all that is strongest and deepest in me,—that fits me for my work, and gives light or shadow to my being,—I have sympathy with Guido Guinicelli.°

In my constant natural temper, and thoughts of things and of people, with Marmontel.°

In my enforced and accidental temper, and thoughts of things and of people, with Dean Swift.°

Any one who can understand the natures of those three men, can understand mine; and having said so much, I am content to leave both life and work to be remembered or forgotten, as their uses may deserve.

DENMARK HILL, Jan. 1, 1871.

I

OF KINGS' TREASURIES

SESAME AND LILIES

LECTURE I

SESAME°

OF KINGS' TREASURIES

You shall each have a cake of sesame, —and ten pound.

LUCIAN: The Fisherman.

1. MY first duty this evening is to ask your pardon for the ambiguity of title under which the subject of lecture has been announced: for indeed I am not going to talk of kings, known as regnant,° nor of treasuries, understood to contain wealth; but of quite another order of royalty, and another material of riches, than those usually acknowledged. I had even intended to ask your attention for a little while on trust, and (as sometimes one contrives, in taking a friend to see a favorite piece of scenery) to hide what I wanted most to show,° with such imperfect cunning as I might, until we unexpectedly reached the best point of view by winding paths. But — and as also I have heard it said, by men practised in public address, that hearers are never so much fatigued as by the endeavor to follow a speaker who gives them no clue to his purpose, — I will take the slight mask off° at once, and tell you plainly that I want to speak to you about the treasures hidden in books; and about the way we find them, and the way we lose them.

3

A grave subject, you will say, and a wide one! Yes; so wide that I shall make no effort to touch the compass° of it. I will try only to bring before you a few simple thoughts about reading, which press themselves upon me every day more deeply, as I watch the course of the public mind with respect to our daily enlarging means of education, and the answeringly wider spreading on the levels, of the irrigation of literature.°

2. It happens that I have practically some connection with schools° for different classes of youth; and I receive many letters° from parents respecting the education of their children. In the mass of these letters I am always struck by the precedence which the idea of a "position in life" takes above all other thoughts in the parents'— more especially in the mothers'— minds. "The education befitting such and such a *station in life*,"— this is the phrase, this the object, always. They never seek, as far as I can make out, an education good in itself; even the conception of abstract rightness in training rarely seems reached by the writers. But, an education "which shall keep a good coat on my son's back; which shall enable him to ring with confidence the visitors' bell at double-belled doors;° which shall result ultimately in the establishment of a double-belled door to his own house,— in a word, which shall lead to advancement in life,— *this* we pray for on bent knees and this is *all* we pray for." It never seems to occur to the parents that there may be an education° which in itself *is* advancement in Life;° that any other than that may perhaps be advancement in Death;° and that this essential education might be more easily got, or given, than they fancy, if they set about it in the right way, while it is for no price and by no favor to be got, if they set about it in the wrong.

3. Indeed, among the ideas most prevalent and effective in the mind of this busiest of countries, I suppose the first— at least that which is confessed with the greatest frankness, and put forward as the fittest stimulus to youthful exertion— is

tnis of "Advancement in life." May I ask you to consider with me, what this idea practically includes, and what it should include?

Practically, then, at present, "advancement in life" means, becoming conspicuous in life, — obtaining a position which shall be acknowledged by others to be respectable or honorable. We do not understand by this advancement, in general, the mere making of money, but the being known to have made it; not the accomplishment of any great aim, but the being seen to have accomplished it. In a word, we mean the gratification of our thirst for applause. That thirst, if the last infirmity ° of noble minds, is also the first infirmity of weak ones, and on the whole, the strongest impulsive influence of average humanity. The greatest efforts of the race have always been traceable to the love of praise, as its greatest catastrophes ° to the love of pleasure.

4. I am not about to attack or defend this impulse. I want you only to feel how it lies at the root of effort, especially of all modern effort. It is the gratification of vanity which is, with us, the stimulus of toil and balm of repose; so closely does it touch the very springs of life that the wounding of our vanity is always spoken of (and truly) as in its measure *mortal;* ° we call it "mortification," using the same expression which we should apply to a gangrenous and incurable bodily hurt. And although a few of us may be physicians enough to recognize the various effect of this passion upon health and energy, ° I believe most honest men know, and would at once acknowledge, its leading power with them as a motive. The seaman does not commonly desire to be made captain only because he knows he can manage the ship better than any other sailor on board; he wants to be made captain that he may be *called* captain. ° The clergyman does not usually want to be made a bishop only because he believes that no other hand can, as firmly as his, direct the diocese through its difficulties; he

wants to be made bishop primarily that he may be called " My
Lord." °   And a prince does not usually desire to enlarge, or a
subject to gain, a kingdom because he believes that no one else
can as well serve the State upon its throne, but, briefly, because
he wishes to be addressed as " Your Majesty " by as many lips
as may be brought to such utterance.

5. This, then, being the main idea of "advancement in
life," the force of it applies for all of us, according to our station, particularly to that secondary result of such advancement
which we call " getting into good society."   We want to get
into good society, not that we may have it,° but that we may
be seen in it ; and our notion of its goodness depends primarily
on its conspicuousness.

Will you pardon me if I pause for a moment to put what I
fear you may think an impertinent question ?   I never can go
on with an address unless I feel or know that my audience are
either with me or against me.   I do not much care which, in
beginning ; but I must know where they are.   And I would
fain find out at this instant whether you think I am putting
the motives of popular action too low.°   I am resolved, to-night,
to state them low enough to be admitted as probable ; for
whenever, in my writings on Political Economy,° I assume
that a little honesty, or generosity, — or what used to be
called.° " virtue," — may be calculated upon as a human motive
of action, people always answer me, saying, " You must not
calculate on that : that is not in human nature.°   You must
not assume anything to be common to men but acquisitiveness
and jealousy ; no other feeling ever has influence on them,
except accidentally, and in matters out of the way of business."   I begin, accordingly, to-night low in the scale of
motives ; but I must know if you think me right in doing so.
Therefore, let me ask those who admit the love of praise to be
usually the strongest motive in men's minds in seeking advancement, and the honest desire of doing any kind of duty to be

an entirely secondary one, to hold up their hands.° (*About a dozen hands held up, — the audience, partly, not being sure the lecturer is serious, and, partly, shy of expressing opinion.*) I am quite serious, — I really do want to know what you think ; however, I can judge by putting the reverse question. Will those who think that duty is generally the first, and love of praise the second, motive, hold up their hands? (*One hand reported to have been held up, behind the lecturer.*) Very good; I see you are with me, and that you think I have not begun too near the ground. Now, without teasing you by putting farther question, I venture to assume that you will admit duty as at least a secondary or tertiary motive. You think that the desire of doing something useful, or obtaining some real good, is indeed an existent collateral idea, though a secondary one, in most men's desire of advancement. You will grant that moderately honest men desire place and office, at least in some measure, for the sake of beneficent power, and would wish to associate rather with sensible and well-informed persons than with fools and ignorant persons, whether they are seen in the company of the sensible ones or not. And finally, without being troubled by repetition of any common truisms about the preciousness of friends and the influence of companions, you will admit, doubtless, that according to the sincerity of our desire that our friends may be true, and our companions wise, and in proportion to the earnestness and discretion with which we choose both, will be the general chances of our happiness and usefulness.

6. But granting that we had both the will and the sense to choose our friends well, how few of us have the power! or at least, how limited, for most, is the sphere of choice! Nearly all our associations are determined by chance or necessity, and restricted within a narrow circle. We cannot know whom we would; and those whom we know, we cannot have at our side when we most need them. All the higher circles of human

intelligence are, to those beneath, only momentarily and par- tially open. We may by good fortune obtain a glimpse of a great poet, and hear the sound of his voice, or put a question to a man of science, and be answered good-humoredly. We may intrude ten minutes' talk on a cabinet minister, answered probably with words worse than silence, being deceptive, or snatch, once or twice in our lives, the privilege of throwing a bouquet in the path of a princess,° or arresting the kind glance of a queen. And yet these momentary chances we covet, and spend our years and passions and powers in pursuit of little more than these ; while, meantime, there is a society continually open to us of people who will talk to us as long as we like, whatever our rank or occupation, — talk to us in the best words they can choose, and of the things nearest their hearts. And this society, because it is so numerous and so gentle, and can be kept waiting round us all day long, kings and states- men lingering patiently, not to grant audience, but to gain it ! in those plainly furnished and narrow anterooms, our book- case shelves, — we make no account of that company, perhaps never listen to a word they would say, all day long.

7. You may tell me, perhaps, or think within yourselves, that the apathy with which we regard this company of the noble, who are praying us to listen to them, and the passion with which we pursue the company probably of the ignoble, who despise us, or who have nothing to teach us, are grounded in this, — that we can see the faces of the living men ; and it is themselves, and not their sayings, with which we desire to become familiar. But it is not so. Suppose you never were to see their faces ; suppose you could be put behind a screen in the statesman's cabinet or the prince's chamber, would you not be glad to listen to their words, though you were forbidden to advance beyond the screen? And when the screen is only a little less, folded in two ° instead of four, and you can be hidden behind the cover of the two boards that bind a book, and listen

all day long, not to the casual talk, but to the studied, determined, chosen addresses of the wisest of men, — this station of
audience and honorable privy council ° you despise !

8. But perhaps you will say that it is because the living
people talk of things that are passing, and are of immediate
interest to you, that you desire to hear them. Nay, that cannot be so ; for the living people will themselves tell you about
passing matters much better in their writings than in their
careless talk. But I admit that this motive does influence you,
so far as you prefer those rapid and ephemeral ° writings to slow
and enduring writings, — books, properly so-called. For all
books are divisible into two classes, — the books of the hour, °
and the books of all time. Mark this distinction ; it is not
one of quality only. It is not merely the bad book that does
not last, and the good one that does ; it is a distinction of species. There are good books for the hour, and good ones for all
time ; bad books for the hour, and bad ones for all time. I
must define the two kinds before I go farther.

9. The good book of the hour, then, — I do not speak of
the bad ones, — is simply the useful or pleasant talk of some
person whom you cannot otherwise converse with, printed for
you. Very useful often, telling you what you need to know ;
very pleasant often, as a sensible friend's present talk would
be. These bright accounts of travels ; good-humored and witty
discussions of question ; lively or pathetic story-telling in the
form of novel ; firm fact-telling, by the real agents concerned
in the events of passing history, — all these books of the hour,
multiplying among us as education becomes more general, are a
peculiar possession of the present age. We ought to be entirely
thankful for them, and entirely ashamed of ourselves if we make
no good use of them. But we make the worst possible use if
we allow them to usurp the place of true books ; for strictly
speaking, they are not books at all, but merely letters or newspapers in good print. Our friend's letter may be delightful or

necessary to-day, — whether worth keeping or not, is to be considered. The newspaper may be entirely proper° at breakfast-time, but assuredly it is not reading for all day; so, though bound up in a volume,° the long letter which gives you so pleasant an account of the inns and roads and weather last year at such a place, or which tells you that amusing story, or gives you the real circumstances of such and such events, however valuable for occasional reference, may not be in the real sense of the word, a "book" at all, nor, in the real sense, to be "read." A book is essentially not a talked thing, but a written thing, and written not with a view of mere communication, but of permanence. The book of talk is printed only because its author cannot speak to thousands of people at once; if he could he would, — the volume is mere *multiplication* of his voice. You cannot talk to your friend in India; if you could, you would. You write instead; that is mere *conveyance* of voice. But a book is written, not to multiply the voice merely, not to carry it merely, but to perpetuate it. The author has something to say which he perceives to be true and useful, or helpfully beautiful. So far as he knows, no one has yet said it; so far as he knows, no one else can say it. He is bound to say it clearly and melodiously if he may; clearly, at all events. In the sum of his life he finds this to be the thing or group of things manifest to him, — this, the piece of true knowledge or sight which his share of sunshine and earth has permitted him to seize. He would fain set it down forever, engrave it on rock if he could, saying, "This is the best of me; for the rest, I ate and drank and slept, loved and hated, like another. My life was as the vapor, and is not; but this I saw and knew, — this, if anything of mine, is worth your memory." This is his "writing"; it is in his small human way, and with whatever degree of true inspiration is in him, his inscription or scripture. That is a "Book."°

10. Perhaps you think no books were ever so written?

But, again, I ask you, do you at all believe in honesty or at all in kindness, or do you think there is never any honesty or benevolence in wise people? None of us, I hope, are so unhappy as to think that. (Well, whatever bit of a wise man's work is honestly and benevolently done, that bit is his book,° or his piece of art.[1] It is mixed always with evil fragments, — ill done, redundant, affected work. But if you read rightly, you will easily discover the true bits, and those *are* the book.

11. Now, books of this kind have been written in all ages by their greatest men, — by great readers, great statesmen, and great thinkers. These are all at your choice; and Life is short. You have heard as much before; yet have you measured and mapped out this short life and its possibilities? Do you know, if you read this, that you cannot read that; that what you lose to-day you cannot gain to-morrow? Will you go and gossip with your housemaid or your stable-boy,° when you may talk with queens and kings;° or flatter yourselves that it is with any worthy consciousness of your own claims to respect that you jostle with the hungry and common crowd for *entrée*° here, and audience there, when all the while this eternal court is open to you, with its society, wide as the world, multitudinous as its days, — the chosen and the mighty of every place and time? Into that you may enter always; in that you may take fellowship and rank according to your wish; from that, once entered into it, you can never be an outcast but by your own fault; by your aristocracy of companionship there, your own inherent aristocracy° will be assuredly tested, and the motives with which you strive to take high place in the society of the living, measured, as to all the truth and sincerity that are in them, by the place you desire to take in this company of the dead.

12. "The place you desire," and the place *you fit yourself for*, I must also say, because, observe, this court of the past

[1] Note this sentence carefully, and compare "Queen of the Air," § 106

differs from all living aristocracy in this, — it is open to labor and to merit, but to nothing else. No wealth will bribe, no name overawe, no artifice deceive, the guardian of those Elysian gates.° In the deep sense, no vile or vulgar person ever enters there. At the portières ° of that silent Faubourg St. Germain,° there is but brief question : "Do you deserve to enter? Pass. Do you ask to be the companion of nobles? Make yourself noble, and you shall be. Do you long for the conversation of the wise? Learn to understand it, and you shall hear it. But on other terms? — No. If you will not rise to us, we cannot stoop to you. The living lord may assume courtesy, the living philosopher explain his thought to you with considerate pain ; but here we neither feign nor interpret. You must rise to the level of our thoughts if you would be gladdened by them, and share our feelings if you would recognize our presence."

13. This, then, is what you have to do,° and I admit that it is much. You must, in a word, love these people, if you are to be among them. No ambition is of any use. They scorn your ambition. You must love them, and show your love in these two following ways : —

(a) First, by a true desire to be taught by them, and to enter into their thoughts. To enter into theirs, observe, not to find your own expressed by them. If the person who wrote the book is not wiser than you, you need not read it ; if he be, he will think differently from you in many respects.

Very ready we are to say of a book, "How good this is, — that's exactly what I think!" But the right feeling is, "How strange that is ! I never thought of that before, and yet I see it is true ; or if I do not now, I hope I shall some day." But whether thus submissively or not, at least be sure that you go to the author to get at *his* meaning, not to find yours. Judge it afterward if you think yourself qualified to do so ; but ascertain it first. And be sure also, if the author is worth anything, that you will not get at his meaning all at once, — nay, that at his whole meaning you will not for a long time arrive in any wise. Not that he does not say what he means, and in strong words too; but he cannot say it all, and what is more strange, *will* not, but in a hidden way and in parable, in order that he may be sure you want it. I cannot quite see the reason of this, nor analyze that cruel reticence° in the breasts of wise men which makes them always hide their deeper thought. They do not give it you by way of help, but of reward, and will make themselves sure that you deserve it before they allow you to reach it. But it is the same with the physical type of wisdom, gold. There seems, to you and me, no reason why the electric forces of the earth should not carry whatever there is of gold within it at once to the mountain-tops; so that kings and people might know that all the gold they could get was there, and without any trouble of digging, or anxiety, or chance, or waste of time, cut it away, and coin as much as they needed. But Nature does not manage it so. She puts it in little fissures in the earth, nobody knows where; you may dig long and find none; you must dig painfully to find any.

14. And it is just the same with men's best wisdom. When you come to a good book, you must ask yourself, "Am I inclined to work as an Australian miner would? Are my pickaxes and shovels in good order, and am I in good trim, myself, my sleeves well up to the elbow, and my breath good, and my temper?" And keeping the figure a little longer, even at a cost of tiresomeness, for it is a thoroughly useful one, the metal you are in search of being the author's mind or meaning, his words are as the rock which you have to crush and smelt in order to get at it. And your pickaxes are your own care, wit, and learning; your smelting furnace is your own thoughtful soul. Do not hope to get at any good author's meaning without those tools and that fire; often you will need sharpest, finest chiselling and patientest fusing, before you can gather one grain of the metal.

15. And, therefore, first of all, I tell you earnestly and authoritatively (I *know* I am right in this), you must get into the habit of looking intensely at words, and assuring yourself of their meaning, syllable by syllable° — nay, letter by letter. For though it is only by reason of the opposition of letters in the function of signs to sounds in the function of signs, that the study of books is called "literature,"° and that a man versed in it is called, by the consent of nations, a man of letters instead of a man of books or of words, you may yet connect with that accidental nomenclature this real fact, — that you might read all the books in the British Museum° (if you could live long enough) and remain an utterly "illiterate," uneducated person ; but that if you read ten pages of a good book, letter by letter, — that is to say, with real accuracy, — you are forevermore in some measure an educated person. The entire difference between education and non-education (as regards the merely intellectual part of it) consists in this accuracy. A well-educated gentleman may not know many languages, may not be able to speak any but his own, may have read very few books. But whatever language he knows, he knows precisely ;° whatever word he pronounces, he pronounces rightly. Above all, he is learned in the *peerage*° of words, knows the words of true descent and ancient blood, at a glance, from the words of modern *canaille*,° remembers all their ancestry, their inter-marriages, distant relationships, and the extent to which they were admitted, and offices they held, among the national *noblesse*° of words at any time and in any country. But an uneducated person may know, by memory, many languages, and talk them all, and yet truly know not a word of any, — not a word even of his own. An ordinarily clever and sensible seaman° will be able to make his way ashore at most ports, yet he has only to speak a sentence of any language to be known for an illiterate person ; so also the accent, or turn of expression of a single sentence, will at once mark a scholar.

And this is so strongly felt, so conclusively admitted, by educated persons, that a false accent or a mistaken syllable ° is enough in the parliament of any civilized nation, to assign to a man a certain degree of inferior standing forever.

16. ° And this is right; but it is a pity that the accuracy insisted on is not greater, and required to a serious purpose. It is right that a false Latin quantity should excite a smile in the House of Commons; but it is wrong that a false English *meaning* should *not* excite a frown there. Let the accent of words be watched, and closely; let their meaning be watched more closely still, and fewer will do the work. A few words, well chosen and distinguished, will do work that a thousand cannot, when every one is acting, equivocally, in the function of another. Yes; and words, if they are not watched, will do deadly work sometimes. There are masked ° words droning and skulking about us in Europe just now (there never were so many, owing to the spread of a shallow, blotching, blundering, infectious "information," or rather deformation, everywhere, and to the teaching of catechism and phrases at schools instead of human meanings) — there are masked words abroad, I say, which nobody understands, but which everybody uses, and most people will also fight for, live for, or even die for, fancying they mean this or that or the other of things dear to them; for such words wear chameleon cloaks, ° — "ground-lion " cloaks, of the color of the ground of any man's fancy; on that ground they lie in wait, and rend him with a spring from it. There never were creatures of prey so mischievous, never diplomatists so cunning, never poisoners so deadly, as these masked words; they are the unjust stewards ° of all men's ideas. Whatever fancy or favorite instinct a man most cherishes, he gives to his favorite masked words to take care of for him. The word at last comes to have an infinite power over him, — you cannot get at him but by its ministry.

17. And in languages so mongrel in breed ° as the English,

there is a fatal power of equivocation put into men's hands, almost whether they will or no, in being able to use Greek or Latin words for an idea when they want it to be awful, and Saxon or otherwise common words when they want it to be vulgar. What a singular and salutary effect, for instance, would be produced on the minds of people who are in the habit of taking the form of the "Word" they live by for the Power of which that Word tells them, if we always either retained, or refused, the Greek form "biblos," or "biblion," as the right expression for "book," instead of employing it only in the one instance in which we wish to give dignity to the idea, and translating it into English everywhere else. How wholesome it would be for many simple persons if in such places (for instance) as Acts xix. 19, we retained the Greek expression, instead of translating it, and they had to read: "Many of them also which used curious arts, brought their Bibles together, and burned them before all men; and they counted the price of them, and found it fifty thousand pieces of silver"! Or if, on the other hand, we translated where we retain it, and always spoke of "the Holy Book," instead of "Holy Bible," it might come into more heads than it does at present, that the Word of God, by which the heavens ° were of old, and by which they are now kept in store,[1] cannot be made a present of to anybody in morocco ° binding, nor sown on any wayside ° by help either of steam plough or steam press, but is nevertheless being offered to us daily, and by us with contumely refused, and sown in us daily, and by us, as instantly as may be, choked.

18. So, again, consider what effect has been produced on the English vulgar mind by the use of the sonorous Latin form "damno," in translating the Greek κατακρίνω, when people charitably wish to make it forcible; and the substitu-

[1] 2 Peter iii. 5–7.

tion of the temperate "condemn"° for it, when they choose to
keep it gentle; and what notable sermons have been preached
by illiterate clergymen on — "He that believeth not shall be
damned," though they would shrink with horror from translating Heb. xi. 7, "The saving of his house, by which he
damned the world," or John viii. 10–11, "Woman, hath no
man damned thee? She said, No man, Lord. Jesus answered
her, Neither do I damn thee; go, and sin no more." And
divisions in the mind of Europe, ° which have cost seas of blood,
and in the defence of which the noblest souls of men have been
cast away in frantic desolation, countless as forest-leaves, —
though, in the heart of them, founded on deeper causes, —
have nevertheless been rendered practically possible mainly, by
the European adoption of the Greek word for a public meeting,
"ecclesia,"° to give peculiar respectability to such meetings,
when held for religious purposes; and other collateral equivo-
cations, such as the vulgar English one of using the word
"priest" as a contraction for "presbyter."

19. Now, in order to deal with words rightly, this is the
habit you must form. Nearly every word in your language
has been first a word of some other language, — of Saxon, German, French, Latin, or Greek; (not to speak of Eastern and
primitive dialects). And many words have been all these;
that is to say, have been Greek first,° Latin next, French
or German next, and English last, — undergoing a certain change
of sense and use on the lips of each nation, but retaining a
deep vital meaning, which all good scholars feel in employing
them, even at this day. If you do not know the Greek alphabet, learn it. Young or old, girl or boy, whoever you may be,
if you think of reading seriously (which, of course, implies that
you have some leisure at command), learn your Greek alphabet;
then get good dictionaries of all these languages, and whenever
you are in doubt about a word, hunt it down patiently. Read
Max Müller's ° lectures thoroughly, to begin with; and after

c

that never let a word escape you that looks suspicious. It is severe work ; but you will find it, even at first, interesting, and at last, endlessly amusing. And the general gain to your character, in power and precision, will be quite incalculable.

Mind, this does not imply knowing, or trying to know, Greek, or Latin, or French. It takes a whole life ° to learn any language perfectly. But you can easily ascertain the meanings through which the English word has passed, and those which in a good writer's work it must still bear.

20. And now, merely for example's sake, I will, with your permission, read a few lines of a true book with you carefully, and see what will come out of them. I will take a book perfectly known to you all. No English words are more familiar to us, yet few perhaps have been read with less sincerity. I will take these few following lines of " Lycidas " : — °

> " Last came, and last did go,
>   The pilot of the Galilean lake.
>   Two massy keys he bore of metals twain,
>   (The golden opes, the iron shuts amain,)
>   He shook his mitred locks, and stern bespake :
>   ' How well could I have spared for thee, young swain,
>   Enow of such as for their bellies' sake
>   Creep, and intrude, and climb into the fold !
>   Of other care they little reckoning make
>   Than how to scramble at the shearers' feast,
>   And shove away the worthy bidden guest ;
>   Blind mouths ! that scarce themselves know how to hold
>   A sheep-hook, or have learned aught else, the least
>   That to the faithful herdsman's art belongs !
>   What recks it them ?   What need they ?   They are sped ;
>   And when they list, their lean and flashy songs
>   Grate on their scrannel pipes of wretched straw.
>   The hungry sheep look up, and are not fed,
>   But swoln with wind, and the rank mist they draw,
>   Rot inwardly, and foul contagion spread,
>   Besides what the grim wolf with privy paw
>   Daily devours apace, and nothing said.' "

Let us think over this passage, and examine its words.

First, is it not singular to find Milton assigning to Saint Peter not only his full episcopal function,° but the very types of it which Protestants usually refuse most passionately? His " mitred " locks ! Milton was no bishop-lover;° how comes Saint Peter to be "mitred"? "Two massy keys he bore." Is this, then, the power of the keys claimed ° by the bishops of Rome, and is it acknowledged here by Milton only in a poetical license, for the sake of its picturesqueness, that he may get the gleam of the golden keys to help his effect? Do not think it. Great men do not play stage tricks with the doctrines of life and death ; only little men do that. Milton means what he says, and means it with his might, too, — is going to put the whole strength of his spirit presently into the saying of it. For though not a lover of false bishops, he *was* a lover of true ones ; and the Lake-pilot is here, in his thoughts, the type and head of true episcopal power. For Milton reads that text, " I will give unto thee the keys of the kingdom of Heaven " quite honestly. Puritan though he be, he would not blot it out of the book because there have been bad bishops, — nay, in order to understand *him*, we must understand that verse first ; it will not do to eye it askance, or whisper it under our breath, as if it were a weapon of an adverse sect. It is a solemn, universal assertion, deeply to be kept in mind by all sects. But perhaps we shall be better able to reason on it if we go a little farther and come back to it. For clearly this marked insistence on the power of the true episcopate is to make us feel more weightily what is to be charged against the false claimants of episcopate, or generally, against false claimants of power and rank in the body of the clergy, they who "for their bellies' sake creep, and intrude, and climb into the fold."

21. Never think Milton uses those three words to fill up his verse, as a loose writer would. He needs all the three, — specially those three, and no more than those, — " creep " and

"intrude" and "climb"; no other words would or could serve
the turn, and no more could be added.   For they exhaustively
comprehend the three classes, correspondent to the three characters, of men who dishonestly seek ecclesiastical power.   First,
those who "creep" into the fold, who do not care for office, nor
name, but for secret influence, and do all things occultly and
cunningly, consenting to any servility of office or conduct, so
only that they may intimately discern, and unawares direct,
the minds of men.   Then those who "intrude" (thrust, that is)
themselves into the fold, who by natural insolence of heart, and
stout eloquence of tongue, and fearlessly perseverant self-assertion,
obtain hearing and authority with the common crowd.   Lastly,
those who "climb," who, by labor and learning both stout and
sound, but selfishly exerted in the cause of their own ambition,
gain high dignities and authorities, and become "lords over
the heritage," though not "ensamples to the flock."°

22. Now go on : —

> "Of other care they little reckoning make
>   Than how to scramble at the shearers' feast.
>   *Blind mouths* — "

I pause again, for this is a strange expression, — a broken
metaphor,° one might think, careless and unscholarly.

Not so ; its very audacity and pithiness are intended to
make us look close at the phrase and remember it. Those two
monosyllables express the precisely accurate contraries of right
character in the two great offices of the Church, — those of
bishop and pastor.

A "bishop" means° "a person who sees."

A "pastor" means° "a person who feeds."

The most unbishoply character a man can have is therefore
to be blind.

The most unpastoral is, instead of feeding, to want to be
fed, — to be a mouth.

Take the two reverses together, and you have "blind mouths." We may advisably follow out this idea a little. Nearly all the evils in the Church have arisen from bishops desiring *power* more than *light*.° They want authority, not outlook; whereas their real office is not to rule, though it may be vigorously to exhort and rebuke. It is the king's office to rule; the bishop's office is to *oversee* the flock, to number it, sheep by sheep, to be ready always to give full account of it. Now, it is clear he cannot give account of the souls, if he has not so much as numbered the bodies, of his flock. The first thing, therefore, that a bishop has to do is at least to put himself in a position in which, at any moment, he can obtain the history, from childhood, of every living soul in his diocese, and of its present state. Down in that back street, Bill and Nancy knocking each other's teeth out, — does the bishop know° all about it? Has he his eye upon them? Has he *had* his eye upon them? Can he circumstantially explain to us how Bill got into the habit of beating Nancy about the head? If he cannot, he is no bishop, though he had a mitre as high as Salisbury steeple;° he is no bishop, — he has sought to be at the helm° instead of the masthead; he has no sight of things. "Nay," you say, "it is not his duty to look after Bill in the back street." What! the fat sheep that have full fleeces, — you think it is only those he should look after while (go back to your Milton) "the hungry sheep look up, and are not fed, besides what the grim wolf, with privy paw" (bishops knowing nothing about it) "daily devours apace, and nothing said"?

"But that's not our idea of a bishop."[1] Perhaps not; but it was St. Paul's, and it was Milton's. They may be right, or we may be; but we must not think we are reading either one or the other by putting our meaning into their words.

---

[1] Compare the 13th Letter in "Time and Tide."

23. I go on.

" But swoln with wind, and the rank mist they draw."

This is to meet the vulgar answer that " if the poor are not looked after in their bodies, they are in their souls; they have spiritual food."

And Milton says, " They have no such thing as spiritual food; they are only swollen with wind." At first you may think that is a coarse type, and an obscure one. But again, it is a quite literally accurate one. Take up your Latin and Greek dictionaries and find out the meaning of " Spirit." It is only a contraction° of the Latin word " breath," and an indistinct translation of the Greek word for " wind." The same word is used in writing, " The wind bloweth where it listeth," and in writing, " So is every one that is born of the Spirit; " born of the *breath*, that is, for it means the breath of God in soul and body. We have the true sense of it in our words " inspiration" and " expire." Now, there are two kinds of breath with which the flock may be filled, — God's breath and man's. The breath of God is health and life and peace to them, as the air of heaven is to the flocks on the hills; but man's breath — the word which *he* calls spiritual — is disease and contagion to them, as the fog of the fen. They rot inwardly with it; they are puffed up by it, as a dead body by the vapors of its own decomposition. This is literally true of all false religious teaching; the first and last and fatalest sign of it is that " puffing up." ° Your converted children, who teach their parents; your converted convicts, who teach honest men; your converted dunces, who, having lived in cretinous° stupefaction half their lives, suddenly awaking to the fact of there being a God, fancy themselves therefore His peculiar people and messengers; your sectarians of every species, small and great, Catholic or Protestant, of High Church or Low, ° in so far as they think themselves exclusively in the right and others wrong ; and pre-eminently, in every sect, those who hold that men can be saved by thinking rightly instead of doing rightly, by work instead of act, and wish instead of work, — these are the true fog children ; clouds, these, without water ;° bodies, these, of putrescent vapor and skin without blood or flesh, blown bagpipes for the fiends to pipe with, corrupt and corrupting, "Swoln with wind, and the rank mist they draw."

24. Lastly, let us return to the lines respecting the power of the keys, for now we can understand them. Note the difference between Milton and Dante,° in their interpretation of this power ; for once the latter is weaker in thought. He supposes *both* the keys° to be of the gate of heaven ; one is of gold, the other of silver. They are given by Saint Peter to the sentinel angel ; and it is not easy to determine the meaning either of the substances of the three steps of the gate, or of the two keys. But Milton makes one, of gold, the key of heaven, the other, of iron, the key of the prison in which the wicked teachers are to be bound who "have taken away the key° of knowledge, yet entered not in themselves."

We have seen that the duties of bishop and pastor are to see and feed, and of all who do so it is said, "He that watereth,° shall be watered also himself." But the reverse is truth also. He that watereth not, shall be *withered* himself ; and he that seeth not, shall himself be shut out of sight, — shut into the perpetual prison-house. And that prison opens here as well as hereafter ; he who is to be bound in heaven must first be bound on earth. That command° to the strong angels, of which the rock-apostle° is the image, "Take him, and bind him hand and foot, and cast him out," issues, in its measure, against the teacher, for every help withheld, and for every truth refused, and for every falsehood enforced ; so that he is

more strictly fettered the more he fetters, and farther outcast
as he more and more misleads, till at last the bars of the iron
cage close upon him, and as "the golden opes, the iron shuts
amain."

25. We have got something out of the lines, I think, and
much more is yet to be found in them; but we have done
enough by way of example of the kind of word-by-word examination of your author which is rightly called "reading," —
watching every accent and expression, and putting ourselves
always in the author's place, annihilating our own personality,°
and seeking to enter into his, so as to be able assuredly to say,
"Thus Milton thought," not "Thus *I* thought, in misreading
Milton." And by this process you will gradually come to
attach less weight to your own "Thus I thought" at other
times. You will begin to perceive that what *you* thought was
a matter of no serious importance; that your thoughts on any
subject are not perhaps the clearest and wisest that could be
arrived at thereupon; in fact, that unless you are a very
singular person, you cannot be said to have any "thoughts"
at all; that you have no materials for them in any serious
matters,[1]° — no right to "think," but only to try to learn more
of the facts. Nay, most probably all your life (unless, as I
said, you are a singular person) you will have no legitimate
right to an "opinion" on any business, except that instantly
under your hand. What must of necessity be done you can
always find out, beyond question, how to do. Have you a
house to keep in order, a commodity to sell, a field to plough,
a ditch to cleanse?° There need be no two opinions about the
proceedings; it is at your peril if you have not much more
than an "opinion" on the way to manage such matters. And
also, outside of your own business, there are one or two sub-

---

[1] Modern "education" for the most part signifies giving people the
faculty of thinking wrong on every conceivable subject of importance
to them.

jects on which you are bound to have but one opinion, — that roguery and lying ° are objectionable, and are instantly to be flogged out of the way whenever discovered ; that covetousness and love of quarrelling are dangerous dispositions even in children, and deadly dispositions in men and nations ; that in the end, the God of heaven and earth loves active, modest, and kind people, and hates idle, proud, greedy, and cruel ones. On these general facts you are bound to have but one, and that a very strong, opinion. For the rest, respecting religions, governments, sciences, arts, you will find that on the whole you can know NOTHING,° judge nothing ; that the best you can do, even though you may be a well-educated person, is to be silent, and strive to be wiser every day, and to understand a little more of the thoughts of others, which so soon as you try to do honestly, you will discover that the thoughts even of the wisest ° are very little more than pertinent questions. To put the difficulty into a clear shape, and exhibit to you the grounds for *in*decision, that is all they can generally do for you ; and well for them and for us if indeed they are able " to mix the music ° with our thoughts, and sadden us with heavenly doubts." This writer ° from whom I have been reading to you is not among the first or wisest : he sees shrewdly as far as he sees, and therefore it is easy to find out his full meaning ; but with the greater men you cannot fathom their meaning ; they do not even wholly measure it themselves, it is so wide. Suppose I had asked you, for instance, to seek for Shakespeare's opinion instead of Milton's on this matter of church authority, — or of Dante's ? Have any of you at this instant the least idea what either thought about it ? Have you ever balanced the scene with the bishops ° in Richard III. against the character of Cranmer ? the description of Saint Francis and Saint Dominic ° against that of him who made Virgil wonder ° to gaze upon him, — " disteso, tanto vilmente, nell' eterno esilio ;" or of him whom Dante stood beside,

"come 'l frate che confessa lo perfido assassin"?[1] Shakespeare
and Alighieri knew men better than most of us, I presume.
They were both in the midst of the main struggle between the
temporal and spiritual powers. They had an opinion, we may
guess. But where is it? Bring it into court! Put Shakespeare's or Dante's creed into articles,° and send it up for trial
by the Ecclesiastical Courts!

26. You will not be able, I tell you again, for many and
many a day, to come at the real purposes and teaching of these
great men; but a very little honest study of them will
enable you to perceive that what you took for your own
"judgment" was mere chance prejudice,° and drifted, helpless,
entangled weed of castaway thought, — nay, you will see that
most men's minds are indeed little better than rough heath
wilderness, neglected and stubborn, partly barren, partly over-
grown with pestilent brakes° and venomous, wind-sown herb-
age of evil surmise; that the first thing you have to do for
them, and yourself, is eagerly and scornfully to set fire to *this*,
burn all the jungle into wholesome ashheaps, and then plough
and sow. All the true literary work before you, for life, must
begin with obedience to that order, "Break up° your fallow
ground, and *sow not among thorns.*"

27.° (*b*)[2] Having then faithfully listened to the great
teachers, that you may enter into their Thoughts, you have yet
this higher advance to make, — you have to enter into their
Hearts. As you go to them first for clear sight, so you must
stay with them that you may share at last their just and
mighty Passion. Passion, or "sensation."° I am not afraid of
the word, still less of the thing. You have heard many out-
cries against sensation lately, but, I can tell you, it is not less
sensation we want, but more. The ennobling difference between
one man and another — between one animal and another — is

---

precisely in this, that one feels more than another. If we were sponges, perhaps sensation might not be easily got for us; if we were earth-worms, liable at every instant to be cut in two by the spade, perhaps too much sensation might not be good for us. But being human creatures, *it is* good for us; nay, we are only human in so far as we are sensitive, and our honor is precisely in proportion to our passion.

28. You know I said of that great and pure society of the Dead, that it would allow "no vain or vulgar person to enter there." What do you think I meant by a "vulgar" person? What do you yourself mean by "vulgarity"? You will find it a fruitful subject of thought; but, briefly, the essence of all vulgarity° lies in want of sensation. Simple and innocent vulgarity is merely an untrained and undeveloped bluntness of body and mind; but in true inbred vulgarity there is a dreadful callousness, which in extremity becomes capable of every sort of bestial habit and crime, without fear, without pleasure, without horror, and without pity. It is in the blunt hand and the dead heart, in the diseased habit, in the hardened conscience, that men become vulgar; they are forever vulgar, precisely in proportion as they are incapable of sympathy, of quick understanding, of all that, in deep insistence on the common but most accurate term, may be called the "tact"° or "touch-faculty" of body and soul; that tact which the Mimosa° has in trees, which the pure woman has above all creatures, — fineness and fulness of sensation, beyond reason, the guide and sanctifier of reason itself. Reason can but determine what is true, — it is the God-given passion° of humanity which alone can recognize what God has made good.

29. We come then to that great concourse of the Dead, not merely to know from them what is true, but chiefly to feel° with them what is just. Now, to feel with them, we must be like them; and none of us can become that without pains. As

the true knowledge is disciplined and tested knowledge, — not the first thought that comes, — so the true passion is disciplined and tested passion, — not the first passion that comes. The first that come are the vain, the false, the treacherous ; if you yield to them, they will lead you wildly and far, in vain pursuit, in hollow enthusiasm, till you have no true purpose and no true passion left.   Not that any feeling possible to humanity is in itself wrong, but only wrong when undisciplined. Its nobility is in its force and justice ; it is wrong when it is weak, and felt for paltry cause.   There is a mean wonder, as of a child who sees a juggler tossing golden balls, and this is base, if you will.   But do you think that the wonder is ignoble, or the sensation less, with which every human soul is called to watch the golden balls of heaven° tossed through the night by the Hand that made them ?   There is a mean curiosity, as of a child opening a forbidden door, or a servant prying into her master's business ; — and a noble curiosity, questioning, in the front of danger, the source of the great river beyond the sand, — the place of the great continent beyond the sea, — a nobler curiosity still, which questions of the source of the River of Life,° and of the space of the Continent of Heaven — things which "the angels desire to look into."°   So the anxiety is ignoble, with which you linger over the course and catastrophe° of an idle tale ; but do you think the anxiety is less, or greater, with which you watch, or *ought* to watch, the dealings of fate and destiny with the life of an agonized nation ?°   Alas ! it is the narrowness, selfishness, minuteness of your sensation that you have to deplore in England at this day ; — sensation which spends itself in bouquets and speeches ; in revellings and junketings ;° in sham fights and gay puppet shows, while you can look on and see noble nations murdered,° man by man, without an effort or a tear.

30. I said "minuteness" and "selfishness" of sensation, but it would have been enough to have said "injustice" or

" unrighteousness " of sensation. For as in nothing is a gentleman better to be discerned from a vulgar person, so in nothing
is a gentle nation (such nations have been) better to be discerned from a mob, than in this, — that their feelings are constant and just, results of due contemplation, and of equal
thought. You can talk a mob ° into anything; its feelings
may be — usually are — on the whole, generous and right ;
but it has no foundation for them, no hold of them ; you may
tease or tickle it into any, at your pleasure ; it thinks by infec-
tion, for the most part, catching an opinion like a cold, and
there is nothing so little that it will not roar itself wild about,
when the fit is on ; — nothing so great but it will forget in an
hour, when the fit is past. But a gentleman's, or a gentle
nation's, passions are just, measured, and continuous. A great
nation, for instance, does not spend its entire national wits ° for
a couple of months in weighing evidence of a single ruffian's
having done a single murder ; and for a couple of years see
its own children ° murder each other by their thousands or tens
of thousands a day, considering only what the effect is likely
to be on the price of cotton,° and caring nowise to determine
which side of battle is in the wrong. Neither does a great
nation send its poor little boys to jail for stealing six walnuts ; °
and allow its bankrupts to steal their hundreds of thousands
with a bow, and its bankers, rich with poor men's savings, to
close their doors " under circumstances ° over which they have
no control," with a " by your leave " ; and large landed estates
to be bought by men who have made their money ° by going
with armed steamers up and down the China Seas, selling
opium at the cannon's mouth, and altering, for the benefit of
the foreign nation, the common highwayman's demand of
" your money *or* your life," into that of " your money *and*
your life." Neither does a great nation allow the lives of its
innocent poor to be parched out of them by fog fever, and
rotted out of them by dunghill plague, for the sake of six

pence a life ° extra per week to its landlords ;[1] and then debate,
with drivelling tears, and diabolical sympathies, whether it
ought not piously to save, and nursingly cherish, the lives of
its murderers.°　　Also, a great nation having made up its mind
that hanging is quite the wholesomest process for its homicides
in general, can yet with mercy distinguish between the degrees
of guilt in homicides, and does not yelp like a pack of frost-
pinched wolf-cubs on the blood track of an unhappy crazed
boy,° or gray-haired clodpate Othello,° "perplexed i' the extreme,"° at the very moment that it is sending a Minister of
the Crown ° to make polite speeches to a man who is bayonet-
ing young girls in their fathers' sight, and killing noble youths
in cool blood, faster than a country butcher kills lambs in
spring.　　And, lastly, a great nation does not mock Heaven
and its Powers, by pretending belief in a revelation which
asserts ° the love of money to be the root of *all* evil, and declaring, at the same time,° that it is actuated, and intends to
be actuated, in all chief national deeds and measures, by no
other love.

31.　My friends, I do not know why any of us should talk
about reading.　We want some sharper discipline than that
of reading ; but, at all events, be assured, we cannot read.
No reading is possible for a people with its mind in this state.
No sentence of any great writer is intelligible to them.　It is
simply and sternly impossible for the English public, at this
moment, to understand any thoughtful writing, — so incapable
of thought has it become in its insanity of avarice.　Happily,
our disease is, as yet, little worse than this incapacity of
thought ; it is not corruption of the inner nature ; we ring
true still,° when anything strikes home to us ; and though the
idea that everything should "pay" has infected our every pur-

---

[1] See note at end of lecture.　I have put it in large type, because
the course of matters since it was written has made it perhaps better
worth attention.

pose so deeply, that even when we would play the good Samaritan, we never take out our two-pence° and give them to the host, without saying, "When I come again, thou shalt give me four-pence," there is a capacity of noble passion° left in our hearts' core. We show it in our work — in our war — even in those unjust domestic affections which make us furious at a small private wrong, while we are polite to a boundless public one; we are still industrious to the last hour of the day, though we add the gambler's fury to the laborer's patience; we are still brave to the death, though incapable of discerning true cause for battle; and are still true in affection to our own flesh, to the death, as the sea-monsters are, and the rock-eagles.° And there is hope for a nation while this can be still said of it. As long as it holds its life in its hand, ready to give it for its honor (though a foolish honor), for its love (though a selfish love), and for its business (though a base business), there is hope for it. But hope only; for this instinctive, reckless virtue cannot last. No nation can last, which has made a mob of itself, however generous at heart. It must discipline its passions, and direct them, or they will discipline *it*, one day, with scorpion-whips.° Above all, a nation cannot last as a money-making mob;° it cannot with impunity, — it cannot with existence, — go on despising literature, despising science, despising art, despising nature, despising compassion, and concentrating its soul on Pence. Do you think these are harsh or wild words? Have patience with me but a little longer. I will prove their truth to you, clause by clause.

32. I. I say first we have despised literature. What do we, as a nation, care about books? How much do you think we spend altogether on our libraries, public or private, as compared with what we spend on our horses? If a man spends lavishly on his library, you call him mad — a bibliomaniac.° But you never call any one a horse-maniac, though men ruin themselves every day by their horses, and you do not hear of

people ruining themselves by their books. Or, to go lower
still, how much do you think the contents of the book shelves
of the United Kingdom, public or private, would fetch, as
compared with the contents of its wine-cellars? What position would its expenditure on literature take, as compared
with its expenditure on luxurious eating? We talk of food
for the mind, as of food for the body: now a good book contains such food inexhaustibly; it is a provision for life, and
for the best part of us; yet how long most people would look
at the best book before they would give the price of a large
turbot for it! Though there have been men who have pinched
their stomachs and bared their backs to buy a book, whose
libraries were cheaper to them, I think, in the end, than most
men's dinners are. We are few of us put to such trial, and
more the pity; for, indeed, a precious thing is all the more
precious to us if it has been won by work or economy; and if
public libraries were half as costly as public dinners, or books
cost the tenth part of what bracelets do, even foolish men and
women might sometimes suspect there was good in reading, as
well as in munching° and sparkling;° whereas the very cheap-
ness of literature is making even wise people forget that if a
book is worth reading, it is worth buying. No book is worth
anything which is not worth *much;* nor is it serviceable until
it has been read, and re-read, and loved, and loved again; and
marked, so that you can refer to the passages you want in it,
as a soldier can seize the weapon he needs in an armory, or a
house-wife bring the spice she needs from her store. Bread of
flour is good; but there is bread, sweet as honey, if we would
eat it, in a good book; and the family must be poor indeed,
which, once in their lives, cannot for such multipliable barley-
loaves,° pay their baker's bill. We call ourselves a rich nation,
and we are filthy and foolish enough to thumb each other's
books out of circulating libraries!°

  33. II. I say we have despised° science.

"What!" you exclaim, "are we not foremost in all discovery,[1] and is not the whole world giddy by reason, or unreason, of our inventions?" Yes, but do you suppose that is national work? That work is all done *in spite* of the nation; by private people's zeal and money. We are glad enough, indeed, to make our profit of science; we snap up anything in the way of a scientific bone that has meat on it, eagerly enough; but if the scientific man comes for a bone or a crust to *us*, that is another story. What have we publicly done for science? We are obliged to know what o'clock it is, for the safety of our ships,° and therefore we pay for an Observatory; and we allow ourselves, in the person of our Parliament, to be annually tormented into doing something, in a slovenly way, for the British Museum;° sullenly apprehending that to be a place for keeping stuffed birds in, to amuse our children. If anybody will pay for their own telescope, and resolve another nebula,° we cackle over the discernment as if it were our own; if one in ten thousand of our hunting squires suddenly perceives that the earth was indeed made to be something else than a portion for foxes,° and burrows in it himself, and tells us where the gold is, and where the coals, we understand that there is some use in that; and very properly knight him: but is the accident of his having found out how to employ himself usefully any credit to *us*? (The negation of such discovery° among his brother squires may perhaps be some *dis*credit to us, if we would consider of it.) But if you doubt these generalities, here is one fact for us all to meditate upon, illustrative of our love of science. Two years ago there was a collection of the fossils of Solenhofen° to be sold in Bavaria; the best in existence, containing many specimens unique for perfectness, and one, unique as an example of a species (a whole kingdom

---

[1] Since this was written, the answer has become definitely — No; we having surrendered the field of Arctic discovery to the Continental nations, as being ourselves too poor to pay for ships.

D

of unknown living creatures being announced by that fossil). This collection, of which the mere market worth, among private buyers, would probably have been some thousand or twelve hundred pounds, was offered to the English nation for seven hundred : but we would not give seven hundred, and the whole series would have been in the Munich museum at this moment, if Professor Owen [10] had not, with loss of his own time, and patient tormenting of the British public in person of its representatives, got leave to give four hundred pounds at once, and himself become answerable for the other three ! which the said public will doubtless pay him eventually, but sulkily, and caring nothing about the matter all the while ; only always ready to cackle if any credit comes of it. Consider, I beg of you, arithmetically, what this fact means. Your annual expenditure for public purposes (a third of it for military apparatus) is at least fifty millions. Now £700 is to £50,000,000, roughly, as seven-pence to two thousand pounds. Suppose, then, a gentleman of unknown income, but whose wealth was to be conjectured from the fact that he spent two thousand a year on his park walls and footmen only, professes himself fond of science ; and that one of his servants comes eagerly to tell him that an unique collection of fossils, giving clue to a new era of creation, is to be had for the sum of seven-pence sterling ; and that the gentleman, who is fond of science, and spends two thousand a year on his park, answers, after keeping his servant waiting several months, "Well ! I'll give you four-pence for them, if you will be answerable for the extra three-pence yourself, till next year !"

34. III. I say you have despised Art ! "What !" you again answer, "have we not Art exhibitions, miles long ? and

---

[1] I state this fact without Professor Owen's permission, which of course he could not with propriety have granted, had I asked it ; but I consider it so important that the public should be aware of the fact, that I do what seems to me right, though rude.

do not we pay thousands of pounds for single pictures? and
have we not Art schools and institutions, more than ever nation
had before?" Yes, truly, but all that is for the sake of the
shop. You would fain sell canvas as well as coals, and crock-
ery as well as iron; you would take every other nation's bread
out of its mouth if you could;[1]° not being able to do that,
your ideal of life is to stand in the thoroughfares of the world,
like Ludgate apprentices,° screaming to every passer-by,
"What d' ye lack?" You know nothing of your own faculties or circumstances; you fancy that, among your damp, flat,
fat fields of clay you can have as quick art-fancy as the Frenchman among his bronzed vines, or the Italian under his volcanic
cliffs;°— that Art may be learned as book-keeping is, and
when learned, will give you more books to keep. You care
for pictures, absolutely, no more than you do for the bills
pasted on your dead walls. There is always room on the walls
for the bills to be read,— never for the pictures to be seen.
You do not know what pictures you have (by repute) in the
country, nor whether they are false or true, nor whether they
are taken care of or not; in foreign countries, you calmly see
the noblest existing pictures in the world rotting in abandoned
wreck — (in Venice you saw the Austrian guns° deliberately
pointed at the palaces containing them), and if you heard that
all the fine pictures in Europe were made into sandbags
to-morrow on the Austrian forts, it would not trouble you
so much as the chance of a brace or two of game less in your
own bags, in a day's shooting. That is your national love of
Art.

35. IV. You have despised nature; that is to say, all the
deep and sacred sensations of natural scenery. The French

---

[1] That was our real idea of "Free Trade"°—"All the trade to myself." You find now that by "competition" other people can manage
to sell something as well as you—and now we call for Protection
again. Wretches!

revolutionists made stables ° of the cathedrals of France ; you have made race-courses of the cathedrals of the earth. Your *one* conception of pleasure is to drive in railroad carriages round their aisles, and eat off their altars.[1] You have put a railroad-bridge over the falls of Schaffhausen.° You have tunnelled the cliffs of Lucerne ° by Tell's chapel ; ° you have destroyed the Clarens shore ° of the Lake of Geneva ; there is not a quiet valley in England that you have not filled with bellowing fire ; ° there is no particle left of English land which you have not trampled coal ashes into[2] — nor any foreign city in which the spread of your presence is not marked among its fair old streets and happy gardens by a consuming white leprosy of new hotels and perfumers' shops : the Alps themselves, which your own poets used to love so reverently, you look upon as soaped poles° in a bear-garden, which you set yourselves to climb and slide down again, with "shrieks of delight." When you are past shrieking, having no human articulate voice to say you are glad with, you fill the quietude of their valleys with gunpowder blasts, and rush home, red with cutaneous eruption of conceit,° and voluble with convulsive hiccough of self-satisfaction.° I think nearly the two sorrowfullest spectacles I have ever seen in humanity, taking the deep inner significance of them, are the English mobs ° in the valley of Chamouni, amusing themselves with firing rusty howitzers ; ° and the Swiss vintagers of Zurich expressing their Christian thanks for the gift of the vine, by assembling in knots in the "towers of the vineyards," ° and slowly loading and firing horse-pistols from morning till evening. It is pitiful, to have dim conceptions of duty ; more

---

[1] I meant that the beautiful places of the world — Switzerland, Italy, South Germany, and so on — are, indeed, the truest cathedrals — places to be reverent in, and to worship in ; and that we only care to drive through them ; and to eat and drink at their most sacred places.

[2] I was singularly struck, some years ago, by finding all the river shore at Richmond, in Yorkshire, black in its earth, from the mere drift of soot-laden air from places many miles away.

pitiful, it seems to me, to have conceptions like these, of mirth.

36. Lastly. You despise compassion. There is no need of words of mine for proof of this. I will merely print one of the newspaper paragraphs which I am in the habit of cutting out and throwing into my store-drawer;° here is one from a "Daily Telegraph" of an early date this year (1864)° (date which, though by me carelessly left unmarked, is easily discoverable; for on the back of the slip, there is the announcement that "yesterday the seventh of the special services of this year was performed by the Bishop of Ripon in St. Paul's"); it relates only one of such facts as happen now daily; this by chance having taken a form in which it came before the coroner. I will print the paragraph in red. Be sure, the facts themselves are written in that color, in a book which we shall all of us, literate or illiterate, have to read our page of, some day.

An inquiry was held on Friday by Mr. Richards, deputy coroner, at the White Horse tavern, Christ Church, Spital-fields, respecting the death of Michael Collins, aged 58 years. Mary Collins, a miserable looking woman, said that she lived with the deceased and his son in a room at 2, Cobb's Court, Christ Church. Deceased was a "translator"° of boots. Witness went out and bought old boots; deceased and his son made them into good ones, and then witness sold them for what she could get at the shops, which was very little indeed. Deceased and his son used to work night and day to try and get a little bread and tea, and pay for the room (2*s*. a week),° so as to keep the home together. On Friday-night week, deceased got up from his bench and began to shiver. He threw down the boots, saying, "Somebody else must finish them when I am gone, for I can do no more." There was no fire, and he said, "I would be better if I was warm." Witness therefore took two pairs of " translated " boots [1] to sell at the shop, but she could only get 14*d.* for the two pairs, for the people at the shop said, " We must have our profit." Witness got 14 lb. of coal, and a little tea and bread. Her son sat up the whole night to make the " translations," to get money, but deceased died on Saturday morning. The family never had enough to eat. — Coroner : " It seems to me deplorable that you did not go into the workhouse." Witness : " We wanted the comforts of our little home." A juror asked what the comforts were, for he only saw a little straw in the corner of the room, the windows of which were broken. The witness began to cry, and said that they had a quilt and other little things. The deceased said he never would go into the workhouse. In summer, when the season was good, they sometimes made as much as 10*s.* profit in the week. They then always saved toward the next week, which was generally a bad one. In winter they made not half so much. For three years they had been getting from bad to worse. — Cornelius Collins said that he had assisted his father since 1847. They used to work so far into the night that both nearly lost their eyesight. Witness now had a film over his eyes. Five years ago deceased applied to the parish for aid. The relieving officer gave him a 4 lb. loaf, and told him if he came again he should get the " stones." [2] °

---

[1] One of the things which we must very resolutely enforce, for the good of all classes, in our future arrangements, must be that they wear no " translated " article of dress. See the preface.

[2] This abbreviation of the penalty of useless labor is curiously coincident in verbal form with a certain passage which some of us may remember. It may perhaps be well to preserve beside this paragraph another cutting out of my store-drawer, from the " Morning Post," of about a parallel date, Friday, March 10, 1865 : — " The *salons*° of Mme. C——, who did the honors with clever imitative grace and elegance, were crowded with princes, dukes, marquises, and counts — in fact, with the same *male* company as one meets at the parties of the Princess Metternich and Madame Drouyn de Lhuys.° Some English peers and members of Parliament were present, and appeared to

That disgusted deceased, and he would have nothing to do with them since. They got worse and worse until last Friday week, when they had not even a half-penny to buy a candle. Deceased then lay down on the straw, and said he could not live till morning. — A juror: "You are dying of starvation yourself, and you ought to go into the house until the summer." — Witness: "If we went in, we should die. When we come out in the summer, we should be like people dropped from the sky. No one would know us, and we would not have even a room. I could work now if I had food, for my sight would get better." Dr. G. P. Walker said deceased died from syncope, from exhaustion from want of food. The deceased had had no bedclothes. For four months he had had nothing but bread to eat. There was not a particle of fat in the body. There was no disease, but if there had been medical attendance, he might have survived the syncope, or fainting. The coroner having remarked upon the painful nature of the case, the jury returned the following verdict, "That deceased died from exhaustion from want of food and the common necessaries of life; also through want of medical aid."

enjoy the animated and dazzling improper scene. On the second floor the supper tables were loaded with every delicacy of the season. That your readers may form some idea of the dainty fare of the Parisian demi-monde, I copy the menu of the supper, which was served to all the guests (about 200) seated at four o'clock. Choice Yquem, Johannisberg, Laffitte, Tokay, and champagne of the finest vintages were served most lavishly throughout the morning. After supper dancing was resumed with increased animation, and the ball terminated with a *chaine diabolique*° and a *cancan d'enfer*° at seven in the morning. (Morning service°— 'Ere the fresh lawns appeared, under the opening eyelids of the Morn.') Here is the menu:—'Consommé de volaille à la Bagration: 16 hors-d'œuvres variés. Bouchées à la Talleyrand. Saumons froids, sauce Ravigote. Filets de bœuf en Bellevue, timbales milanaises, chaudfroid de gibier. Dindes truffées. Pâtés de foies gras, buissons d'écrevisses, salades vénétiennes, gelées blanches aux fruits, gateaux mancini, parisiens et parisiennes. Fromages glacés Ananas. Dessert.'"

37. "Why would witness not go into the workhouse?" you ask. Well, the poor seem to have a prejudice against the workhouse which the rich have not; for of course every one who takes a pension ° from Government goes into the workhouse on a grand scale :[1] only the workhouses for the rich do not involve the idea of work, and should be called play-houses. But the poor like to die independently, it appears; perhaps if we made the play-houses for them pretty and pleasant enough, or gave them their pensions at home, and allowed them a little introductory peculation ° with the public money, their minds might be reconciled to the conditions. Meantime, here are the facts : we make our relief either so insulting to them, or so painful, that they rather die than take it at our hands; or, for third alternative, we leave them so untaught and foolish that they starve like brute creatures, wild and dumb, not knowing what to do, or what to ask. I say, you despise compassion; if you did not, such a newspaper paragraph would be as impossible in a Christian country as a deliberate assassination permitted in its public streets.[2] "Christian" did I

[1] Please observe this statement, and think of it, and consider how it happens that a poor old woman will be ashamed to take a shilling a week from the country — but no one is ashamed to take a pension of a thousand a year.

[2] I am heartily glad to see such a paper as the "Pall Mall Gazette" established; for the power of the press in the hands of highly educated men, in independent position, and of honest purpose, may indeed, become all that it has been hitherto vainly vaunted to be. Its editor will therefore, I doubt not, pardon me, in that, by very reason of my respect for the journal, I do not let pass unnoticed an article in its third number, page 5, which was wrong in every word of it, with the intense wrongness which only an honest man can achieve who has taken a false turn of thought in the outset, and is following it, regardless of consequences. It contained at the end this notable passage : —

"The bread of affliction, and the water of affliction ° — aye, and the bedstead and blankets of affliction, are the very utmost that the law ought to give to *outcasts merely as outcasts.*" I merely put beside this expression of the gentlemanly mind of England in 1865, a part of the message which Isaiah was ordered to "lift up his voice like a trumpet" in declaring to the gentlemen of his day : " Ye fast for strife, and

say? Alas, if we were but wholesomely *un*-Christian, it would be impossible: it is our imaginary Christianity that helps us to commit these crimes, for we revel and luxuriate in our faith, for the lewd sensation of it; dressing *it* up, like everything else, in fiction. The dramatic Christianity of the organ and aisle, of dawn-service and twilight-revival, — the Christianity which we do not fear to mix the mockery of, pictorially, with our play about the devil, in our Satanellas,° — Roberts, — Fausts;° chanting hymns through traceried windows for background effect, and artistically modulating the "Dio"° through variation on variation of mimicked prayer (while we distribute tracts next day, for the benefit of uncultivated swearers, upon what we suppose to be the signification of the Third Commandment); — this gas-lighted, and gas-inspired, Christianity, we are triumphant in, and draw back the hem° of our robes from the touch of the heretics who dispute it. But to do a piece of common Christian righteousness in a plain English word or deed; to make Christian law any rule of life and found one National act or hope thereon, — we know too well what our faith comes to for that! You might sooner get lightning out of incense smoke than true action or passion out

---

to smite with the fist of wickedness. Is not this the fast that I have chosen, to deal thy bread to the hungry, and that thou bring the poor *that are cast out* [margin, 'afflicted'] to thy house?" The falsehood on which the writer had mentally founded himself, as previously stated by him, was this: "To confound the functions of the dispensers of the poor-rates with those of the dispensers of a charitable institution is a great and pernicious error." This sentence is so accurately and exquisitely wrong, that its substance must be thus reversed in our minds before we can deal with any existing problem of national distress. "To understand that the dispensers of the poor-rates are the almoners of the nation, and should distribute its alms with a gentleness and freedom of hand as much greater and franker than that possible to individual charity as the collective national wisdom and power may be supposed greater than those of any single person, is the foundation of all law respecting pauperism." (Since this was written the "Pall Mall Gazette" has become a mere party-paper — like the rest; but it writes well, and does more good than mischief on the whole.)

of your modern English religion. You had better get rid of
the smoke, and the organ pipes, both : leave them, and the
Gothic windows, and the painted glass, to the property man ;°
give up your carburetted hydrogen ghost° in one healthy expiration, and look after Lazarus° at the doorstep. For there is
a true Church wherever° one hand meets another helpfully,
and that is the only holy or Mother Church which ever was,
or ever shall be.

38. All these pleasures° then, and all these virtues, I repeat,
you nationally despise. You have, indeed, men among you who
do not ; by whose work, by whose strength, by whose life, by
whose death, you live, and never thank them. Your wealth,
your amusement, your pride, would all be alike impossible, but
for those whom you scorn or forget. The policeman, who is
walking up and down the black lane all night to watch the
guilt you have created there ; and may have his brains beaten
out, and be maimed for life, at any moment, and never be
thanked ; the sailor wrestling with the sea's rage ; the quiet
student poring over his book or his vial ; the common worker,
without praise, and nearly without bread, fulfilling his task as
your horses drag your carts, hopeless, and spurned of all : these
are the men by whom England lives ; but they are not the
nation ; they are only the body and nervous force of it, acting
still from old habit in a convulsive perseverance, while the
mind is gone. Our National wish and purpose are only to be
amused ; our National religion is the performance of church
ceremonies, and preaching of soporific truths (or untruths) to
keep the mob quietly at work, while we amuse ourselves ; and
the necessity for this amusement is fastening on us, as a fever-
ous disease of parched throat and wandering eyes — senseless,
dissolute, merciless. How literally that word *Dis*-Ease, the
Negation and possibility of Ease, expresses the entire moral
state of our English Industry and its Amusements !

39. When men are rightly occupied, their amusement grows

out of their work,° as the color-petals out of a fruitful flower; — when they are faithfully helpful and compassionate, all their emotions become steady, deep, perpetual, and vivifying to the soul as the natural pulse to the body. But now, having no true business, we pour our whole masculine energy into the false business of money-making; and having no true emotion, we must have false emotions dressed up for us to play with, not innocently, as children with dolls, but guiltily and darkly, as the idolatrous Jews° with their pictures on cavern walls, which men had to dig to detect. The justice we do not execute, we mimic in the novel and on the stage; for the beauty we destroy in nature, we substitute the metamorphosis of the pantomime, and (the human nature of us imperatively requiring awe and sorrow of *some* kind) for the noble grief we should have borne with our fellows, and the pure tears we should have wept with them, we gloat over the pathos of the police court, and gather the night-dew of the grave.

40. It is difficult to estimate the true significance of these things; the facts are frightful enough; — the measure of national fault involved in them is perhaps not as great as it would at first seem. We permit, or cause, thousands of deaths daily, but we mean no harm; we set fire to houses, and ravage peasants' fields, yet we should be sorry to find we had injured anybody. We are still kind at heart; still capable of virtue, but only as children are. Chalmers,° at the end of his long life, having had much power with the public, being plagued in some serious matter by a reference to "public opinion," uttered the impatient exclamation, "The public is just a great baby!" And the reason that I have allowed all these graver subjects of thought to mix themselves up with an inquiry into methods of reading, is that, the more I see of our national faults or miseries, the more they resolve themselves into conditions of childish illiterateness and want of education in the most ordinary habits of thought. It is, I repeat, not vice, not

selfishness, not dulness of brain, which we have to lament; but an unreachable schoolboy's recklessness, only differing from the true schoolboy's in its incapacity of being helped, because it acknowledges no master.

41. There is a curious type of us given in one of the lovely, neglected works of the last of our great painters.° It is a drawing of Kirkby Lonsdale° churchyard, and of its brook, and valley, and hills, and folded morning sky beyond. And unmindful alike of these, and of the dead who have left these for other valleys and for other skies, a group of schoolboys have piled their little books upon a grave, to strike them off with stones. So, also, we play with the words of the dead that would teach us, and strike them far from us with our bitter, reckless will; little thinking that those leaves which the wind scatters had been piled, not only upon a gravestone, but upon the seal of an enchanted vault — nay, the gate of a great city of sleeping kings, who would awake for us, and walk with us, if we knew but how to call them by their names. How often, even if we lift the marble entrance gate, do we but wander among those old kings in their repose, and finger the robes they lie in, and stir the crowns on their foreheads; and still they are silent to us, and seem but a dusty imagery, because we know not the incantation° of the heart that would wake them; — which, if they once heard, they would start up to meet us, in their power of long ago, narrowly to look upon us, and consider us; and as the fallen kings of Hades° meet the newly fallen, saying, "Art thou also become weak as we — art thou also become one of us?" so would these kings, with their undimmed, unshaken diadems, meet us, saying, "Art thou also become pure and mighty of heart as we? art thou also become one of us?"

42. Mighty of heart, mighty of mind — "magnanimous" — to be this, is, indeed, to be great in life; to become this increasingly, is, indeed, to "advance in life," — in life itself, not in the trappings of it. My friends, do you remember that old

Scythian custom,° when the head of a house died? How he was dressed in his finest dress, and set in his chariot, and carried about to his friends' houses; and each of them placed him at his table's head, and all feasted in his presence? Suppose it were offered to you in plain words, as it *is* offered to you in dire facts, that you should gain this Scythian honor gradually, while you yet thought yourself alive. Suppose the offer were this: You shall die slowly; your blood shall daily grow cold, your flesh petrify, your heart beat at last only as a rusted group of iron valves. Your life shall fade from you, and sink through the earth into the ice of Caina;° but, day by day, your body shall be dressed more gaily, and set in higher chariots, and have more orders on its breast — crowns on its head, if you will. Men shall bow before it, stare and shout round it, crowd after it up and down the streets; build palaces for it; feast with it at their tables' heads all the night long; your soul shall stay enough within it to know what they do, and feel the weight of the golden dress on its shoulders, and the furrow of the crown-edge on the skull; — no more. Would you take the offer, verbally made by the death-angel? Would the meanest among us take it, think you? Yet practically and verily we grasp at it every one of us, in a measure; many of us grasp at it in its fulness of horror. Every man accepts it, who desires to advance in life without knowing what life is; who means only that he is to get more horses, and more footmen, and more fortune, and more public honor, and — *not* more personal soul. He only is advancing in life, whose heart is getting softer, whose blood warmer, whose brain quicker, whose spirit is entering into Living [1] peace.° And the men who have this life in them are the true lords or kings of the earth — they, and they only. All other kingships, so far as they are true, are only the practical issue and expression of theirs;

---

[1] " τὸ δὲ φρόνημα τοῦ πνεύματος ζωὴ καὶ εἰρήνη."

if less than this, they are either dramatic royalties, — costly
shows, set off, indeed, with real jewels instead of tinsel — but
still only the toys of nations, or else they are no royalties at
all, but tyrannies, or the mere active and practical issue of
national folly; for which reason I have said of them elsewhere,°
"Visible governments are the toys of some nations, the disease
of others, the harness of some, the burdens of more."

43. But I have no words for the wonder with which I hear
Kinghood still spoken of, even among thoughtful men, as if
governed nations were a personal property, and might be
bought and sold, or otherwise acquired, as sheep, of whose
flesh their king was to feed, and whose fleece he was to gather;
as if Achilles'° indignant epithet of base kings, "people-eating," were the constant and proper title of all monarchs; and
enlargement of a king's dominion meant the same thing as the
increase of a private man's estate! Kings who think so, however powerful, can no more be the true kings of the nation
than gadflies are the kings of a horse; they suck it, and may
drive it wild, but do not guide it. They and their courts and
their armies are, if one could see clearly, only a large species
of marsh mosquito, with bayonet proboscis and melodious,
bandmastered trumpeting, in the summer air; the twilight
being, perhaps, sometimes fairer, but hardly more wholesome,
for its glittering mists of midge companies. The true kings,
meanwhile, rule quietly, if at all, and hate ruling; too many of
them make *il gran rifiuto;*° and if they do not, the mob, as
soon as they are likely to become useful to it, is pretty sure to
make *its gran rifiuto* of *them.*

44. Yet the visible king may also be a true one, some day,
if ever day comes when he will estimate his dominion by the
force of it, — not the geographical boundaries. It matters
very little whether Trent cuts you a cantel out° here, or Rhine
rounds you a castle less there. But it does matter to you, king
of men, whether you can verily say to this man° "Go," and he

goeth, and to another, "Come," and he cometh. Whether you can turn your people, as you can Trent — and where it is that you bid them come, and where go. It matters to you, king of men, whether your people hate you, and die by you, or love you, and live by you. You may measure your dominion by multitudes, better than by miles ; and count degrees of love-latitude, not from, but to, a wonderfully warm and infinite equator.

45. Measure ! — nay, you cannot measure. Who shall measure the difference between the power of those who "do and teach," ° and who are greatest in the kingdoms of earth, as of heaven — and the power of those who undo, and consume — whose power, at the fullest, is only the power of the moth and the rust ? Strange ! to think how the Moth-kings lay up treasures for the moth ; and the Rust-kings, who are to their people's strength as rust to armor, lay up treasures for the rust ; and the Robber-kings,° treasures for the robber ; but how few kings have ever laid up treasures that needed no guarding — treasures of which, the more thieves there were, the better ! Broidered robe,° only to be rent ; helm and sword, only to be dimmed ; jewel and gold, only to be scattered ; — there have been three kinds of kings who have gathered these. Suppose there ever should arise a Fourth order of kings, who had read, in some obscure writing of long ago, that there was a Fourth kind of treasure,° which the jewel and gold could not equal, neither should it be valued with pure gold. A web made fair in the weaving, by Athena's shuttle ; an armor, forged in divine fire by Vulcanian force ; a gold to be mined in the very sun's red heart, where he sets over the Delphian cliffs,° — deep pictured tissue ;° — impenetrable armor ; — potable gold ; — the three great Angels of Conduct, Toil, and Thought, still calling to us, and waiting at the posts of our doors, to lead us, with their winged power, and guide us, with their unerring eyes, by the path which no fowl knoweth, and which the vulture's eye has not seen ! Suppose kings should ever arise, who heard and

believed this word, and at last gathered and brought forth treasures of — Wisdom — for their people?

46. Think what an amazing business *that* would be! How inconceivable, in the state of our present national wisdom! That we should bring up our peasants to a book exercise instead of a bayonet exercise! — organize, drill, maintain with pay, and good generalship, armies of thinkers, instead of armies of stabbers!° — find national amusement in reading-rooms as well as rifle-grounds; give prizes for a fair shot at a fact, as well as for a leaden splash on a target. What an absurd idea it seems, put fairly in words, that the wealth of the capitalists of civilized nations should ever come to support literature instead of war!

47. Have yet patience with me, while I read you a single sentence out of the only book,° properly to be called a book, that I have yet written myself, the one that will stand (if anything stand) surest and longest of all work of mine : —

" It is one very awful form of the operation of wealth in Europe that it is entirely capitalists' wealth which supports unjust wars. Just wars do not need so much money to support them; for most of the men who wage such, wage them gratis; but for an unjust war, men's bodies and souls have both to be bought, and the best tools of war for them besides, which makes such war costly to the maximum; not to speak of the cost of base fear, and angry suspicion, between nations which have not grace nor honesty enough in all their multitudes to buy an hour's peace of mind with; as, at present, France and England, purchasing of each other ten millions sterling worth of consternation, annually (a remarkably light crop, half thorns and half aspen leaves,° sown, reaped, and granaried by the 'science' of the modern political economists, teaching covetousness instead of truth). And all unjust war being supportable, if not by pillage of the enemy, only by loans from capitalists, these loans are repaid by subsequent taxation of the people, who appear to have no will in the matter, the capitalists' will being the primary root of the war; but its real root is the covetousness of the whole nation, rendering it incapable of faith, frankness, or justice, and bringing about, therefore, in due time, his own separate loss and punishment to each person."

48. France and England° literally, observe, buy *panic* of each other; they pay, each of them, for ten thousand-thousand pounds' worth of terror, a year. Now suppose, instead of buying these ten millions' worth of panic annually, they made up their minds to be at peace with each other, and buy ten millions' worth of knowledge annually; and that each nation spent its ten thousand-thousand pounds a year in founding royal libraries, royal art galleries, royal museums, royal gardens, and places of rest. Might it not be better somewhat for both French and English?

49. It will be long, yet, before that comes to pass. Nevertheless, I hope it will not be long before royal or national libraries will be founded in every considerable city, with a royal series° of books in them; the same series in every one of them, chosen books, the best in every kind, prepared for that national series in the most perfect way possible; their text printed all on leaves of equal size, broad of margin, and divided into pleasant volumes, light in the hand, beautiful, and strong, and thorough as examples of binders' work; and that these great libraries will be accessible to all clean and orderly persons at all times of the day and evening; strict law being enforced for this cleanliness and quietness.

50. I could shape for you other plans, for art galleries, and for natural history galleries, and for many precious — many, it seems to me, needful — things; but this book plan is the easiest and needfullest, and would prove a considerable tonic to what we call our British Constitution,° which has fallen dropsical of late, and has an evil thirst, and evil hunger, and wants healthier feeding. You have got its corn laws° repealed for it; try if you cannot get corn laws established for it, dealing in a better bread; — bread made of that old enchanted Arabian grain, the Sesame, which opens doors; — doors, not of robbers',° but of Kings' Treasuries.

E

Note to § 30°

Respecting the increase of rent by the deaths of the poor, for evidence of which, see the preface to the Medical Officer's report to the Privy Council, just published, there are suggestions in its preface which will make some stir among us, I fancy, respecting which let me note these points following: —

There are two theories on the subject of land now abroad, and in contention; both false.

The first is that, by Heavenly law, there have always existed, and must continue to exist, a certain number of hereditarily sacred persons to whom the earth, air, and water of the world belong, as personal property; of which earth, air, and water, these persons may, at their pleasure, permit or forbid the rest of the human race to eat, to breathe, or to drink. This theory is not for many years longer tenable. The adverse theory is that a division of the land of the world among the mob of the world would immediately elevate the said mob into sacred personages; that houses would then build themselves, and corn grow of itself; and that everybody would be able to live without doing any work for his living. This theory would also be found highly untenable in practice.

It will, however, require some rough experiments and rougher catastrophes, before the generality of persons will be convinced that no law concerning anything — least of all concerning land, for either holding or dividing it, or renting it high, or renting it low — would be of the smallest ultimate use to the people, so long as the general contest for life, and for the means of life, remains one of mere brutal competition. That contest, in an unprincipled nation, will take one deadly form or another, whatever laws you make against it. For instance, it would be an entirely wholesome law for England, if it could be carried, that maximum limits should be assigned to incomes according to classes; and that every nobleman's income should be paid to him as a fixed salary or pension by the nation; and not squeezed by him in variable sums, at discretion, out of the tenants of his land. But if you could get such a law passed to-morrow, and if, which would be further necessary, you could fix the value of the assigned incomes by making a given weight of pure bread for a given sum, a twelve-month would not pass before another currency would have been tacitly established, and the power of accumulated wealth would have re-asserted itself in some other article, or some other imaginary sign. There is only one cure for public distress, and that is public education, directed to make men thoughtful, merciful, and just. There are, indeed, many laws conceivable which would gradually better and strengthen the national temper; but for the most part, they are such as the national temper must be much bettered before it would bear. A nation in its youth may be helped by laws, as a weak child by back-boards, but when it is old it cannot that way strengthen its crooked spine.

And besides; the problem of land, at its worst, is a bye one;° distribute the earth as you will, the principal question remains inexorable,°— Who is to dig it? Which of us, in brief word, is to do the hard and dirty work for the rest — and for what pay? Who is to do the pleasant and clean work, and for what pay? Who is to do no work, and for what pay? And there are curious moral and religious questions connected with these. How far is it lawful to suck a portion of the soul out of a great many persons, in order to put the abstracted physical quantities together and make one very beautiful or ideal soul? If we had to deal with mere blood instead of spirit (and the thing might literally be done — as it has been done with infants before now) — so that it were possible by taking a certain quantity of blood from the arms of a given number of the mob and putting it all into one person, to make a more azure-blooded° gentleman of him, the thing would of course be managed; but secretly, I should conceive.　But now, because it is brain and soul that we abstract, not visible blood, it can be done quite openly, and we live, we gentlemen, on delicatest prey, after the manner of weasels ;° that is to say, we keep a certain number of clowns° digging and ditching, and generally stupefied, in order that we, being fed gratis,° may have all the thinking and feeling to ourselves. Yet there is a great deal to be said for this.　A highly-bred and trained English, French, Austrian, or Italian gentleman (much more a lady), is a great production, — a better production than most statues ; being beautifully colored as well as shaped, and plus all the brains ; a glorious thing to look at, a wonderful thing to talk to ; and you cannot have it, any more than a pyramid or a church, but by sacrifice° of much contributed life.　And it is, perhaps, better to build a beautiful human creature than a beautiful dome or steeple — and more delightful to look up reverently to a creature far above us, than to a wall ; only the beautiful human creature will have some duties to do in return — duties of living belfry and rampart — of which presently.°

II

OF QUEENS' GARDENS

LECTURE II

LILIES

OF QUEENS' GARDENS

"Be thou glad, oh thirsting Desert; let the desert be made cheerful, and bloom as a lily; and the barren places of Jordan shall run wild with wood."—ISAIAH xxxv. 1.   (Septuagint.)°

51.° It will, perhaps, be well, as this Lecture is the sequel of one previously given, that I should shortly state to you my general intention in both.   The questions specially proposed to you in the first, namely, How and What to Read, rose out of a far deeper one, which it was my endeavor to make you propose earnestly to yourselves, namely, *Why* to Read.   I want you to feel,° with me, that whatever advantage we possess in the present day in the diffusion of education and of literature, can only be rightly used by any of us when we have apprehended clearly what education is to lead to, and literature to teach.   I wish you to see that both well-directed moral training and well-chosen reading lead to the possession of a power over the ill-guided and illiterate, which is, according to the measure of it, in the truest sense, *kingly;* conferring indeed the purest kingship that can exist among men.   Too many other kingships (however distinguished by visible insignia° or material power) being either spectral, or tyrannous;—spectral—that is to say, aspects and shadows only of royalty, hollow as death, and which only the "likeness of a kingly crown° have on"; or

else tyrannous — that is to say, substituting their own will for
the law of justice and love by which all true kings rule.

52. There is, then, I repeat — and as I want to leave this
idea with you, I begin with it, and shall end with it, — only
one pure kind of kingship; ° an inevitable and eternal kind,
crowned or not : the kingship, namely, which consists in a
stronger moral state, and a truer thoughtful state,° than that
of others ; enabling you, therefore, to guide, or to raise them.
Observe that word "State" ; we have got into a loose way of
using it. It means literally the standing and stability of a
thing ; and you have the full force of it in the derived word
"statue" — "the immovable thing." A king's majesty or
"state," then, and the right of his kingdom to be called a
state, depends on the movelessness of both : — without tremor,
without quiver of balance ; established and enthroned upon a
foundation of eternal law which nothing can alter, nor overthrow.

53. Believing that all literature and all education are only
useful so far as they tend to confirm this calm, beneficent, and
therefore kingly, power, — first, over ourselves, and, through
ourselves, over all around us, — I am now going to ask you to
consider with me, farther, what special portion or kind of this
royal authority, arising out of noble education, may rightly be
possessed by women ; and how far they also are called to a true
queenly power, — not in their households merely, but over all
within their sphere. And in what sense, if they rightly understood and exercised this royal or gracious influence, the order
and beauty induced by such benignant power would justify us
in speaking of the territories over which each of them reigned,
as "Queens' Gardens." °

54. And here, in the very outset, we are met by a far deeper
question, which — strange though this may seem — remains
among many of us yet quite undecided, in spite of its infinite
importance.

We cannot determine what the queenly power of women should be, until we are agreed ° what their ordinary power should be. We cannot consider how education may fit them for any widely-extending duty, until we are agreed what is their true constant duty. And there never was a time when wilder words were spoken, or more vain imagination permitted, respecting this question — quite vital to all social happiness. The relations of the womanly to the manly nature, their different capacities of intellect or of virtue, seem never to have been yet estimated with entire consent. We hear of the "mission" and of the "rights" of Woman, as if these could ever be separate from the mission and the rights of Man ; — as if she and her lord were creatures of independent kind, and of irreconcilable claim. This, at least, is wrong. And, not less wrong — perhaps even more foolishly wrong (for I will anticipate thus far what I hope to prove) — is the idea that woman is only the shadow and attendant image of her lord, owing him a thoughtless and servile obedience, and supported altogether in her weakness, by the pre-eminence of his fortitude.

This, I say, is the most foolish of all errors respecting her who was made to be the helpmate ° of man. As if he could be helped effectively by a shadow, or worthily by a slave !

55. Let us try, then, whether we cannot get at some clear and harmonious idea (it must be harmonious if it is true) of what womanly mind and virtue are in power and office, with respect to man's ; and how their relations, rightly accepted, aid, and increase, the vigor, and honor, and authority of both.

And now I must repeat one thing I said in the last lecture : namely, that the first use of education was to enable us to consult with the wisest and the greatest men on all points of earnest difficulty. That to use books rightly, was to go to them for help : to appeal to them when our own knowledge and power of thought failed : to be led by them into wider sight, — purer conception, — than our own, and receive from them the united sentence of the judges and councils of all time, against our solitary and unstable opinion.

Let us do this now. Let us see whether the greatest, the wisest, the purest-hearted of all ages, are agreed in any wise on this point : let us hear the testimony they have left respecting what they held to be the true dignity of woman, and her mode of help to man.

56. And first let us take Shakespeare.

Note broadly in the outset, Shakespeare has no heroes ;° — he has only heroines. There is not one entirely heroic figure in all his plays, except the slight sketch of Henry the Fifth,° exaggerated for the purposes of the stage ; and the still slighter Valentine° in "The Two Gentlemen of Verona." In his labored and perfect plays you have no hero. Othello° would have been one, if his simplicity had not been so great as to leave him the prey of every base practice round him ; but he is the only example even approximating to the heroic type. Coriolanus° — Cæsar — Antony° stand in flawed strength, and fall by their vanities ; — Hamlet° is indolent, and drowsily speculative ; Romeo° an impatient boy ; the Merchant of Venice° languidly submissive to adverse fortune ; Kent,° in "King Lear," is entirely noble at heart, but too rough and unpolished to be of true use at the critical time, and he sinks into the office of a servant only. Orlando,° no less noble, is yet the despairing toy of chance, followed, comforted, saved, by Rosalind.° Whereas there is hardly a play that has not a perfect woman in it, steadfast in grave hope, and errorless purpose ; Cordelia,° Desdemona,° Isabella,° Hermione,° Imogen,° Queen Catherine,° Perdita,° Sylvia,° Viola,° Rosalind,° Helena,° and last, and perhaps loveliest, Virgilia,° are all faultless ; conceived in the highest heroic type of humanity.

57. Then observe, secondly,

The catastrophe° of every play is caused always by the folly or fault of a man ; the redemption, if there be any, is by the wisdom and virtue of a woman, and, failing that, there is none. The catastrophe of King Lear° is owing to his want of judgment, his impatient vanity, his misunderstanding of his children ; the virtue of his one true daughter would have saved him from all the injuries of the others, unless he had cast her away from him ; as it is, she all but saves him.

Of Othello° I need not trace the tale ; nor the one weakness of his so mighty love ; nor the inferiority of his perceptive intellect to that even of the second woman character in the play, the Emilia who dies in wild testimony against his error : —

> "O murderous coxcomb !° what should such a fool
> Do with so good a wife ? "

In "Romeo and Juliet," the wise and brave stratagem of the wife is brought to ruinous issue by the reckless impatience° of her husband. In "The Winter's Tale,"° and in "Cymbeline,"° the happiness and existence of two princely households, lost through long years, and imperilled to the death by the folly and obstinacy of the husbands, are redeemed at last by the queenly patience and wisdom of the wives. In "Measure for Measure,"° the foul injustice of the judge, and the foul cowardice of the brother, are opposed to the victorious truth and adamantine purity of a woman. In "Coriolanus,"° the mother's counsel, acted upon in time, would have saved her son from all evil ; his momentary forgetfulness of it is his ruin ; her prayer, at last, granted, saves him — not, indeed, from death, but from the curse of living as the destroyer of his country.

And what shall I say of Julia,° constant against the fickleness of a lover who is a mere wicked child ? — of Helena, against the petulance and insult of a careless youth ? — of the patience of Hero, the passion of Beatrice,° and the calmly devoted wisdom of the "unlessoned girl,"° who appears among the helplessness, the blindness, and the vindictive passions of men, as a gentle angel, bringing courage and safety by her presence, and

defeating the worst malignities of crime by what women are
fancied most to fail in, — precision and accuracy of thought?

58. Observe, further, among all the principal figures in
Shakespeare's plays, there is only one weak woman —
Ophelia; ° and it is because she fails Hamlet at the critical
moment, and is not, and cannot in her nature be, a guide to
him when he needs her most, that all the bitter catastrophe
follows. Finally, though there are three wicked women among
the principal figures, Lady Macbeth, ° Regan, ° and Goneril, °
they are felt at once to be frightful exceptions to the ordinary
laws of life ; fatal in their influence also, in proportion to the
power for good which they have abandoned.

Such, in broad light, is Shakespeare's testimony to the position and character of women in human life. He represents
them as infallibly faithful and wise counsellors, — incorruptibly
just and pure examples, — strong always to sanctify, even when
they cannot save.

59. Not as in any wise comparable in knowledge of the
nature of man, — still less in his understanding of the causes
and courses of fate, — but only as the writer who has given
us the broadest view of the conditions and modes of ordinary
thought in modern society, I ask you next to receive the witness
of Walter Scott. °

I put aside his merely romantic prose writings ° as of no
value ; and though the early romantic poetry is very beautiful,
its testimony is of no weight, other than that of a boy's ideal.
But his true works, studied from Scottish life, bear a true witness ; and, in the whole range of these, there are but three men
who reach the heroic type [1] — Dandie Dinmont, ° Rob Roy, °

---

[1] I ought, in order to make this assertion fully understood, to have
noticed the various weaknesses which lower the ideal of other great
characters of men in the Waverley novels — the selfishness and narrowness of thought in Redgauntlet, the weak religious enthusiasm in
Edward Glendinning, and the like ; and I ought to have noticed that
there are several quite perfect characters sketched sometimes in the

and Claverhouse;° of these, one is a border farmer; another a
freebooter; the third a soldier in a bad cause. And these
touch the ideal of heroism only in their courage and faith,
together with a strong, but uncultivated, or mistakenly applied,
intellectual power; while his younger men are the gentlemanly
playthings of fantastic fortune, and only by aid (or accident) of
that fortune, survive, not vanquish, the trials they involuntarily
sustain. Of any disciplined or consistent character, earnest in
a purpose wisely conceived, or dealing with forms of hostile
evil, definitely challenged and resolutely subdued, there is no
trace in his conceptions of young men. Whereas, in his imaginations of women, — in the characters of Ellen Douglas,° of
Flora MacIvor,° Rose Bradwardine,° Catherine Seyton,° Diana
Vernon,° Lilias Redgauntlet,° Alice Bridgenorth,° Alice Lee,°
and Jeanie Deans,° — with endless varieties of grace, tenderness, and intellectual power, we find in all a quite infallible
sense of dignity and justice; a fearless, instant, and untiring
self-sacrifice, to even the appearance of duty, much more to its
real claims; and, finally, a patient wisdom of deeply-restrained
affection, which does infinitely more than protect its objects
from a momentary error; it gradually forms, animates, and
exalts the characters of the unworthy lovers, until, at the close
of the tale, we are just able, and no more, to take patience in
hearing of their unmerited success.

So that, in all cases, with Scott as with Shakespeare, it is
the woman who watches over, teaches, and guides the youth;
it is never, by any chance, the youth who watches over, or
educates, his mistress.

60. Next, take, though more briefly, graver testimony —
that of the great Italians and Greeks. You know well the
plan of Dante's° great poem — that it is a love-poem to his

backgrounds; three — let us accept joyously this courtesy to England
and her soldiers — are English officers: Colonel Gardiner,° Colonel
Talbot,° and Colonel Mannering.°

dead lady; a song of praise for her watch over his soul. Stooping only to pity, never to love, she yet saves him from destruction — saves him from hell. He is going eternally astray in despair; she comes down from heaven to his help, and throughout the ascents of Paradise is his teacher, interpreting for him the most difficult truths, divine and human; and leading him, with rebuke upon rebuke, from star to star.

I do not insist upon Dante's conception; if I began, I could not cease: besides, you might think this a wild imagination of one poet's heart. So I will rather read to you a few verses of the deliberate writing of a knight of Pisa° to his living lady, wholly characteristic of the feeling of all the noblest men of the thirteenth, or early fourteenth, century, preserved among many other such records of knightly honor and love, which Dante Rossetti has gathered for us from among the early Italian poets.

> "For lo! thy law is passed
> That this my love should manifestly be
> To serve and honor thee:
> And so I do; and my delight is full,
> Accepted for the servant of thy rule.

> "Without almost, I am all rapturous,
> Since thus my will was set:
> To serve, thou flower of joy, thine excellence:
> Nor ever seems it anything could rouse
> A pain or a regret.
> But on thee dwells my every thought and sense
> Considering that from thee all virtues spread
> As from a fountain head, —
> *That in thy gift is wisdom's best avail,*
> *And honor without fail;*
> With whom each sovereign good dwells separate,
> Fulfilling the perfection of thy state.

> "Lady, since I conceived
> Thy pleasurable aspect in my heart,
> *My life has been apart*

> *In shining brightness and the place of truth;*
>   Which till that time, good sooth,
> Groped among shadows in a darkened place,
>   Where many hours and days
> It hardly ever had remembered good.
>   But now my servitude
> Is thine, and I am full of joy and rest.
>   A man from a wild beast
> Thou madest me, since for thy love I lived."

61. You may think, perhaps, a Greek knight° would have had a lower estimate of women than this Christian lover. His spiritual subjection to them was indeed not so absolute; but as regards their own personal character, it was only because you could not have followed me so easily, that I did not take the Greek women instead of Shakespeare's; and instance, for chief ideal types of human beauty and faith, the simple mother's and wife's heart of Andromache;° the divine, yet rejected wisdom of Cassandra;° the playful kindness and simple princess-life of happy Nausicaa;° the housewifely calm of that of Penelope,° with its watch upon the sea; the ever patient, fearless, hopelessly devoted piety of the sister and daughter, in Antigone;° the bowing down of Iphigenia,° lamb-like and silent; and finally, the expectation of the resurrection, made clear to the soul of the Greeks in the return from her grave of that Alcestis,° who, to save her husband, had passed calmly through the bitterness of death.

62. Now I could multiply witness upon witness of this kind upon you if I had time. I would take Chaucer,° and show you why he wrote a Legend of Good Women, but no Legend of Good Men. I would take Spenser,° and show you how all his fairy knights are sometimes deceived and sometimes vanquished; but the soul of Una° is never darkened, and the spear of Britomart° is never broken. Nay, I could go back into the mythical teaching of the most ancient times, and show you how the great people, — by one of whose princesses it was appointed that the

Lawgiver of all the earth ° should be educated, rather than by his own kindred : — how that great Egyptian people,° wisest then of nations, gave to their Spirit of Wisdom the form of a woman ; and into her hand, for a symbol, the weaver's shuttle ; and how the name and the form of that spirit, adopted, believed, and obeyed by the Greeks, became that Athena of the olive-helm,° and cloudy shield, to faith in whom you owe, down to this date, whatever you hold most precious in art, in literature, or in types of national virtue.

63. But I will not wander into this distant and mythical element ; I will only ask you to give its legitimate value to the testimony of these great poets and men of the world, — consistent, as you see it is, on this head. I will ask you whether it can be supposed that these men, in the main work of their lives, are amusing themselves with a fictitious and idle view of the relations between man and woman ; nay, worse than fictitious or idle ; for a thing may be imaginary, yet desirable, if it were possible ; but this, their ideal of woman, is, according to our common idea of the marriage relation, wholly undesirable. The woman, we say, is not to guide, nor even to think for herself. The man is always to be the wiser ; he is to be the thinker, the ruler, the superior in knowledge and discretion, as in power.

64. Is it not somewhat important to make up our minds on this matter? Are all these great men mistaken, or are we? Are Shakespeare and Æschylus, Dante and Homer, merely dressing dolls for us ; or, worse than dolls, unnatural visions, the realization of which, were it possible, would bring anarchy into all households and ruin into all affections? Nay, if you can suppose this, take lastly the evidence of facts given by the human heart itself. In all Christian ages ° which have been remarkable for their purity of progress, there has been absolute yielding of obedient devotion, by the lover, to his mistress. I say *obedient ;* — not merely enthusiastic and worshipping in

imagination, but entirely subject, receiving from the beloved woman, however young, not only the encouragement, the praise, and the reward of all toil, but, so far as any choice is open, or any question difficult of decision, the *direction* of all toil. That chivalry,° to the abuse and dishonor of which are attributable primarily whatever is cruel in war, unjust in peace, or corrupt and ignoble in domestic relations ; and to the original purity and power of which we owe the defence alike of faith, of law, of love ; — that chivalry, I say, in its very first conception of honorable life, assumes the subjection of the young knight to the command — should it even be the command in caprice ° — of his lady. It assumes this, because its masters knew that the first and necessary impulse of every truly taught and knightly heart is this of blind service to its lady : that where that true faith and captivity are not, all wayward and wicked passion must be ; and that in this rapturous obedience to the single love of his youth, is the sanctification of all man's strength, and the continuance of all his purposes. And this, not because such obedience would be safe, or honorable, were it ever rendered to the unworthy ; but because it ought to be impossible for every noble youth — it *is* impossible for every one rightly trained — to love any one whose gentle counsel he cannot trust, or whose prayerful command he can hesitate to obey.

65. I do not insist by any farther argument on this, for I think it should commend itself at once to your knowledge of what has been, and to your feeling of what should be. You cannot think that the buckling on ° of the knight's armor by his lady's hand was a mere caprice of romantic fashion. It is the type of an eternal truth — that the soul's armor is never well set to the heart unless a woman's hand has braced it ; and it is only when she braces it loosely that the honor of manhood fails. Know you not those lovely lines — I would they were learned by all youthful ladies of England —

F

> " Ah, wasteful woman !°— she who may
>   On her sweet self set her own price,
> Knowing she cannot choose but pay —
>   How has she cheapened Paradise !
> How given for naught her priceless gift,
>   How spoil'd the bread and spill'd the wine,
> Which, spent with due respective thrift,
>   Had made brutes men, and men divine !" [1]

66. Thus much, then, respecting the relations of lovers I believe you will accept. But what we too often doubt is the fitness of the continuance of such a relation throughout the whole of human life. We think it right in the lover and mistress, not in the husband and wife. That is to say, we think that a reverent and tender duty is due to one whose affection we still doubt, and whose character we as yet do but partially and distantly discern ; and that this reverence and duty are to be withdrawn, when the affection has become wholly and limitlessly our own, and the character has been so sifted and tried that we fear not to entrust it with the happiness of our lives. Do you not see how ignoble this is, as well as how unreasonable ? Do you not feel that marriage, — when it is marriage at all, — is only the seal which marks the vowed transition of temporary into untiring service, and of fitful into eternal love ?

67. But how, you will ask, is the idea of this guiding function of the woman reconcilable with a true wifely subjection ? Simply in that it is a *guiding*, not a determining, function. Let me try to show you briefly how these powers seem to be rightly distinguishable.

We are foolish, and without excuse foolish, in speaking of the " superiority " of one sex to the other, as if they could be compared in similar things. Each has what the other has not :

[1] Coventry Patmore. You cannot read him too often or too carefully ; as far as I know, he is the only living poet who always strengthens and purifies ; the others sometimes darken, and nearly always depress, and discourage, the imagination they deeply seize.

each completes the other, and is completed by the other : they are in nothing alike, and the happiness and perfection of both depends on each asking and receiving from the other what the other only can give.°

68. Now their separate characters are briefly these. (The man's power is active, progressive, defensive. He is eminently the doer, the creator, the discoverer, the defender. His intellect is for speculation and invention ; his energy for adventure, for war, and for conquest wherever war is just, wherever conquest necessary.) But the woman's power is for rule, not for battle, — and her intellect is not for invention or creation, but for sweet ordering, arrangement, and decision. She sees the qualities of things, their claims, and their places. Her great function is Praise; she enters into no contest, but infallibly adjudges the crown of contest.) By her office, and place, she is protected from all danger and temptation. The man, in his rough work in the open world, must encounter all peril and trial : — to him, therefore, must be the failure, the offence, the inevitable error : often he must be wounded, or subdued; often misled ; and *always* hardened. But he guards the woman from all this ; within his house, as ruled by her, unless she herself has sought it, need enter no danger, no temptation, no cause of error or offence. This is the true nature of home — it is the place of Peace ; the shelter, not only from all injury, but from all terror, doubt, and division. In so far as it is not this, it is not home ; so far as the anxieties of the outer life penetrate into it, and the inconsistently-minded, unknown, unloved, or hostile society of the outer world is allowed by either husband or wife to cross the threshold, it ceases to be home ; it is then only a part of that outer world which you have roofed over, and lighted fire in. But so far as it is a sacred place, a vestal temple,° a temple of the hearth watched over by Household Gods,° before whose faces none may come but those whom they can receive with love, — so far as it is this, and roof and fire

are types only of a nobler shade and light, — shade as of the rock in a weary land,° and light as of the Pharos ° in the stormy sea ; — so far it vindicates the name, and fulfils the praise, of Home.

And wherever a true wife comes, this home is always round her. The stars only may be over her head ; the glow-worm in the night-cold grass may be the only fire at her foot : but home is yet wherever she is ; and for a noble woman it stretches far round her, better than ceiled with cedar, or painted with vermilion,° shedding its quiet light far, for those who else were homeless.

69. This, then, I believe to be, — will you not admit it to be ? — the woman's true place and power. But do not you see that to fulfil this, she must — as far as one can use such terms of a human creature — be incapable of error ? So far as she rules, all must be right, or nothing is. She must be enduringly, incorruptibly good ; instinctively, infallibly wise — wise, not for self-development, but for self-renunciation : wise, not that she may set herself above her husband, but that she may never fail from his side : wise, not with the narrowness of insolent and loveless pride, but with the passionate gentleness of an infinitely variable, because infinitely applicable, modesty of service — the true changefulness of woman. In that great sense — "La donna è mobile,"° not "Qual piúm' al vento ; "° no, nor yet "Variable as the shade,° by the light quivering aspen made ; " but variable as the *light*,° manifold in fair and serene division, that it may take the color of all that it falls upon, and exalt it.

70.° II. I have been trying, thus far, to show you what should be the place, and what the power, of woman. Now, secondly, we ask, What kind of education is to fit her for these ?

And if you indeed think this a true conception of her office and dignity, it will not be difficult to trace the course of education which would fit her for the one, and raise her to the other.

The first of our duties to her — no thoughtful persons now

and making her happy

doubt this — is to secure for her such physical training and exercise as may confirm her health, and perfect her beauty; the highest refinement of that beauty being unattainable without splendor of activity and of delicate strength. To perfect her beauty, I say, and increase its power; it cannot be too powerful, nor shed its sacred light too far: only remember that all physical freedom is vain to produce beauty without a corresponding freedom of heart. There are two passages of that poet,° who is distinguished, it seems to me, from all others — not by power, but by exquisite *right*ness — which point you to the source, and describe to you in a few syllables, the completion of womanly beauty. I will read the introductory stanzas, but the last is the one I wish you specially to notice: —

" Three years she grew in sun and shower,
　　Then Nature said, ' A lovelier flower
　　　　' On earth was never sown:
　　' This child I to myself will take;
　　' She shall be mine, and I will make
　　　　' A lady of my own.

" ' Myself will to my darling be
　　' Both law and impulse; and with me
　　　　' The girl, in rock and plain,
　　' In earth and heaven, in glade and bower,
　　' Shall feel an overseeing power,
　　　　' To kindle, or restrain.

" ' The floating clouds their state shall lend
　　' To her; for her the willow bend;
　　　　' Nor shall she fail to see
　　' Even in the motions of the storm,
　　' Grace that should mould the maiden's form
　　　　' By silent sympathy.

" ' And *vital feelings of delight*
　　' Shall rear her form to stately height,
　　　　' Her virgin bosom swell;

Wordsworth

> 'Such thoughts to Lucy I will give,
> 'While she and I together live,
> 'Here in this happy dell.' " [1]

"*Vital* feeling of delight," observe. There are deadly feelings of delight, but the natural ones are vital, necessary to very life. And they must be feelings of delight, if they are to be vital. Do not think you can make a girl lovely, if you do not make her happy. There is not one restraint you put on a good girl's nature — there is not one check you give to her instincts of affection or of effort — which will not be indelibly written on her features, with a hardness which is all the more painful because it takes away the brightness from the eyes of innocence, and the charm from the brow of virtue.

71. This for the means : now note the end. Take from the same poet, in two lines, a perfect description of womanly beauty —

> " A countenance in which did meet
> Sweet records, promises as sweet."

The perfect loveliness of a woman's countenance can only consist in that majestic peace which is founded in the memory of happy and useful years, — full of sweet records ; and from the joining of this with that yet more majestic childishness, which is still full of change and promise ; — opening always — modest at once, and bright, with hope of better things to be won, and to be bestowed. There is no old age where there is still that promise.

72. Thus, then, you have first to mould her physical frame, and then, as the strength she gains will permit you, to fill and temper her mind with all knowledge and thoughts which tend to confirm its natural instincts of justice, and refine its natural tact of love.

---

[1] Observe, it is "Nature" who is speaking throughout, and who says, "while she and I together live."

All such knowledge should be given her as may enable her to understand, and even to aid, the work of men : and yet it should be given, not as knowledge, — not as if it were, or could be, for her, an object to know ; but only to feel, and to judge. It is of no moment, as a matter of pride or perfectness in herself, whether she knows many languages or one ; but it is of the utmost, that she should be able to show kindness to a stranger, and to understand the sweetness of a stranger's tongue. It is of no moment to her own worth or dignity that she should be acquainted with this science or that ; but it is of the highest that she should be trained in habits of accurate thought ; that she should understand the meaning, the inevitableness, and the loveliness of natural laws ; and follow at least some one path of scientific attainment, as far as to the threshold of that bitter Valley of Humiliation,° into which only the wisest and bravest of men can descend, owning themselves forever children, gathering pebbles on a boundless shore. It is of little consequence how many positions of cities she knows, or how many dates of events, or names of celebrated persons — it is not the object of education ° to turn the woman into a dictionary ; but it is deeply necessary that she should be taught to enter with her whole personality into the history she reads ; to picture the passages of it vitally in her own bright imagination ; to apprehend, with her fine instincts, the pathetic circumstances and dramatic relations, which the historian too often only eclipses by his reasoning, and disconnects by his arrangement : it is for her to trace the hidden equities of divine reward,° and catch sight, through the darkness, of the fateful threads of woven fire that connect error with retribution. But, chiefly of all, she is to be taught to extend the limits of her sympathy with respect to that history which is being forever determined as the moments pass in which she draws her peaceful breath ; and to the contemporary calamity, which, were it but rightly mourned by her, would recur no more hereafter. She is to exercise herself in imagining what would be the effects upon her mind and conduct, if she were daily brought into the presence of the suffering which is not the less real because shut from her sight. She is to be taught somewhat to understand the nothingness of the proportion which that little world in which she lives and loves, bears to the world in which God lives and loves ; — and solemnly she is to be taught to strive that her thoughts of piety may not be feeble in proportion to the number they embrace, nor her prayer more languid than it is for the momentary relief from pain of her husband or her child, when it is uttered for the multitudes of those who have none to love them, and is, "for all who are desolate and oppressed."°

73. Thus far, I think, I have had your concurrence ; perhaps you will not be with me in what I believe is most needful for me to say. There *is* one dangerous science° for women — one which they must indeed beware how they profanely touch — that of theology. Strange, and miserably strange, that while they are modest enough to doubt their powers, and pause at the threshold of sciences where every step is demonstrable and sure, they will plunge headlong, and without one thought of incompetency, into that science in which the greatest men have trembled, and the wisest erred. Strange, that they will complacently and pridefully bind up whatever vice or folly there is in them, whatever arrogance, petulance, or blind incomprehensiveness, into one bitter bundle of consecrated myrrh.° Strange in creatures born to be Love visible, that where they can know least, they will condemn first, and think to recommend themselves to their Master, by crawling up the steps of His judgment-throne, to divide it° with Him. Strangest of all, that they should think they were led by the Spirit of the Comforter° into habits of mind which have become in them the unmixed elements of home discomfort ; and that they dare to turn the Household Gods of Christianity into ugly idols of their own ; — spiritual dolls, for them to dress according to their

caprice; and from which their husbands must turn away in grieved contempt, lest they should be shrieked at for breaking them.

74. I believe, then, with this exception, that a girl's education should be nearly, in its course and material of study, the same as a boy's; but quite differently directed. A woman, in any rank of life, ought to know whatever her husband is likely to know, but to know it in a different way. His command of it should be foundational and progressive; hers, general° and accomplished for daily and helpful use. Not but that it would often be wiser in men to learn things in a womanly sort of way, for present use, and to seek for the discipline and training of their mental powers in such branches of study as will be afterwards fitted for social service; but, speaking broadly, a man ought to know any language or science he learns, thoroughly — while a woman ought to know the same language, or science, only so far as may enable her to sympathize in her husband's pleasures, and in those of his best friends.

75. Yet, observe, with exquisite° accuracy as far as she reaches. There is a wide difference between elementary knowledge and superficial knowledge — between a firm beginning, and an infirm attempt at compassing. A woman may always help her husband by what she knows, however little; by what she half-knows, or mis-knows, she will only tease him.

And indeed, if there were to be any difference between a girl's education and a boy's, I should say that of the two the girl should be earlier led, as her intellect ripens faster, into deep and serious subjects: and that her range of literature should be, not more, but less frivolous; calculated to add the qualities of patience and seriousness to her natural poignancy of thought and quickness of wit; and also to keep her in a lofty and pure element of thought. I enter not now into any question of choice of books: only let us be sure that her books are not heaped up in her lap as they fall out of the package of the cir

culating library,° wet with the last and lightest spray of the
fountain of folly.

76. Or even of the fountain of wit; for with respect to the
sore temptation of novel reading, it is not the badness of a
novel that we should dread, so much as its overwrought interest. The weakest romance is not so stupefying as the lower
forms of religious exciting literature, and the worst romance is
not so corrupting as false history, false philosophy, or false
political essays. But the best romance becomes dangerous, if,
by its excitement, it renders the ordinary course of life uninter-
esting, and increases the morbid thirst for useless acquaintance
with scenes in which we shall never be called upon to act.

77. I speak, therefore, of good novels only; and our modern
literature is particularly rich in types of such. Well read,
indeed, these books have serious use, being nothing less than
treatises on moral anatomy and chemistry;° studies of human
nature in the elements of it. But I attach little weight to
this function; they are hardly ever read with earnestness
enough to permit them to fulfil it. The utmost they usually
do is to enlarge somewhat the charity of a kind reader, or the
bitterness of a malicious one; for each will gather, from the
novel, food for her own disposition. Those who are naturally
proud and envious will learn from Thackeray° to despise humanity; those who are naturally gentle, to pity it; those who
are naturally shallow, to laugh at it. So, also, there might be
a serviceable power in novels to bring before us, in vividness, a
human truth which we had before dimly conceived; but the
temptation to picturesqueness of statement is so great, that
often the best writers of fiction cannot resist it; and our views
are rendered so violent and one sided, that their vitality is
rather a harm than a good.

78. Without, however, venturing here on any attempt at
decision how much novel reading should be allowed, let me at
least clearly assert this, that whether novels, or poetry, or his-

tory be read, they should be chosen, not for their freedom from evil, but for their possession of good. The chance and scattered evil that may here and there haunt, or hide itself in, a powerful book, never does any harm to a noble girl; but the emptiness of an author oppresses her, and his amiable folly degrades her. And if she can have access to a good library of old and classical books, there need be no choosing at all. Keep the modern magazine and novel out of your girl's way; turn her loose into the old library every wet day, and let her alone. She will find what is good for her; you cannot; for there is just this difference between the making of a girl's character and a boy's — you may chisel a boy into shape, as you would a rock, or hammer him into it, if he be of a better kind, as you would a piece of bronze. But you cannot hammer a girl into anything. She grows as a flower does, — she will wither without sun; she will decay in her sheath, as a narcissus ° will, if you do not give her air enough; she may fall, and defile her head in dust, if you leave her without help at some moments of her life; but you cannot fetter her; she must take her own fair form and way, if she take any, and in mind as in body, must have always

> "Her household motions° light and free,
> And steps of virgin liberty."

Let her loose in the library, I say, as you do a fawn in the field. It knows the bad weeds twenty times better than you; and the good ones too, and will eat some bitter and prickly ones, good for it, which you had not the slightest thought would have been so.

79. Then, in art, keep the finest models before her, and let her practice in all accomplishments be accurate and thorough, so as to enable her to understand more than she accomplishes. I say the finest models — that is to say, the truest, simplest, usefullest. Note those epithets; they will range through all the arts. Try them in music, where you might think them

the least applicable. I say the truest, that in which the notes most closely and faithfully express the meaning of the words, or the character of intended emotion; again, the simplest, that in which the meaning and melody are attained with the fewest and most significant notes possible; and finally, the usefullest, that music which makes the best words most beautiful, which enchants them in our memories each with its own glory of sound, and which applies them closest to the heart at the moment we need them.

80. And not only in the material and in the course, but yet more earnestly in the spirit of it, let a girl's education be as serious as a boy's. You bring up your girls as if they were meant for sideboard ornaments, and then complain of their frivolity. Give them the same advantages that you give their brothers—appeal to the same grand instincts of virtue in them; teach *them*, also, that courage and truth are the pillars of their being:—do you think that they would not answer that appeal, brave and true as they are even now, when you know that there is hardly a girl's school in this Christian kingdom where the children's courage or sincerity would be thought of half so much importance as their way of coming in at a door; and when the whole system of society, as respects the mode of establishing them in life, is one rotten plague of cowardice and imposture—cowardice, in not daring to let them live, or love, except as their neighbors choose; and imposture, in bringing, for the purposes of our own pride, the full glow of the world's worst vanity upon a girl's eyes, at the very period when the whole happiness of her future existence depends upon her remaining undazzled?

81. And give them, lastly, not only noble teachings, but noble teachers. You consider somewhat, before you send your boy to school, what kind of a man the master is;—whatsoever kind of a man he is, you at least give him full authority over your son, and show some respect to him yourself:—if he comes

to dine with you, you do not put him at a side table : you know also that, at college, your child's immediate tutor will be under the direction of some still higher tutor, for whom you have absolute reverence. You do not treat the Dean of Christ Church or the Master of Trinity° as your inferiors.

But what teachers do you give your girls, and what reverence do you show to the teachers you have chosen? Is a girl likely to think her own conduct, or her own intellect, of much importance, when you trust the entire formation of her character, moral and intellectual, to a person whom you let your servants treat with less respect than they do your housekeeper (as if the soul of your child were a less charge than jams and groceries), and whom you yourself think you confer an honor upon by letting her sometimes sit in the drawing-room in the evening?

82. Thus, then, of literature as her help and thus of art. There is one more help which she cannot do without — one which, alone, has sometimes done more than all other influences besides, — the help of wild and fair nature. Hear this of the education of Joan of Arc :° —

"The education of this poor girl was mean, according to the present standard ; was ineffably grand, according to a purer philosophical standard ; and only not good for our age, because for us it would be unattainable. . . .

"Next after her spiritual advantages, she owed most to the advantages of her situation. The fountain of Domrémy° was on the brink of a boundless forest ; and it was haunted to that degree by fairies, that the parish priest (*curé*) was obliged to read mass there once a year, in order to keep them in decent bounds. . . .

"But the forests of Domrémy — those were the glories of the land ; for in them abode mysterious powers and ancient secrets that towered into tragic strength. Abbeys there were, and abbey windows — 'like Moorish temples of the Hindoos,' — that exercised even princely power both in Touraine and in the German Diets.° These had their sweet bells that pierced the forests for many a league at matins or vespers, and each its own dreamy legend. Few enough, and scattered enough, were these abbeys, so as in no degree to disturb the deep solitude of the region; yet many enough to spread a network or awning of Christian sanctity over what else might have seemed a heathen wilderness."[1]

Now, you cannot, indeed, have here in England, woods eighteen miles deep to the centre; but you can, perhaps, keep a fairy or two for your children yet, if you wish to keep them. But *do* you wish it? Suppose you had each, at the back of your houses, a garden, large enough for your children to play in, with just as much lawn as would give them room to run, — no more — and that you could not change your abode; but that, if you chose, you could double your income, or quadruple it, by digging a coal shaft in the middle of the lawn, and turning the flower-beds into heaps of coke. Would you do it? I hope not. I can tell you, you would be wrong if you did, though it gave you income sixty-fold instead of four-fold.

83. Yet this is what you are doing with all England. The whole country is but a little garden, not more than enough for your children to run on the lawns of, if you would let them *all* run there. And this little garden you will turn into furnace ground, and fill with heaps of cinders, if you can; and those children of yours, not you, will suffer for it. For the fairies will not be all banished; there are fairies of the furnace as of the wood, and their first gift seems to be "sharp arrows of the mighty";° but their last gifts are "coals of juniper."°

84. And yet I cannot — though there is no part of my subject that I feel more — press this upon you; for we made so little use of the power of nature while we had it that we shall hardly feel what we have lost. Just on the other side of the Mersey° you have your Snowdon, and your Menai Straits, and that mighty granite rock beyond the moors of Anglesea, splendid in its heathery crest, and foot planted in the deep sea, once thought of as sacred — a divine promontory, looking westward;

---

[1] "Joan of Arc: in reference to M. Michelet's° 'History of France'" — De Quincey's° Works, vol. iii., p. 217.

the Holy Head or Headland, still not without awe when its red light° glares first through storm. These are the hills, and these the bays and blue inlets, which, among the Greeks, would have been always loved, always fateful in influence on the national mind. That Snowdon is your Parnassus; but where are its Muses? That Holyhead mountain is your island of Ægina; but where is its Temple to Minerva?

85. Shall I read you what the Christian Minerva° had achieved under the shadow of our Parnassus° up to the year 1848? — Here is a little account of a Welsh school, from page 261 of the Report on Wales, published by the Committee of Council on Education. This a school close to a town containing 5,000 persons:—

"I then called up a larger class, most of whom had recently come to the school. Three girls repeatedly declared they had never heard of Christ, and two that they had never heard of God. Two out of six thought Christ was on earth now" (they might have had a worse thought perhaps), "three knew nothing about the Crucifixion. Four out of seven did not know the names of the months nor the number of days in a year. They had no notion of addition; beyond two and two, or three and three, their minds were perfect blanks."

Oh, ye women of England! from the Princess of that Wales to the simplest of you, do not think your own children can be brought into their true fold of rest, while these are scattered on the hills, as sheep having no shepherd. And do not think your daughters can be trained to the truth of their own human beauty, while the pleasant places, which God made at once for their school-room and their play-ground, lie desolate and defiled. You cannot baptize them rightly in those inch-deep fonts of yours,° unless you baptize them also in the sweet waters which the great Lawgiver° strikes forth forever from the rocks of your native land — waters which a Pagan would have worshipped in their purity, and you worship only with pollution. You cannot lead your children faithfully to those narrow axe-hewn church altars of yours, while the dark azure altars in heaven — the mountains that sustain your island throne, mountains on which a Pagan would have seen the powers of heaven rest in every wreathed cloud — remain for you without inscription; altars built, not to, but by an Unknown God.°

86. III. Thus far, then, of the nature, thus far of the teaching, of woman, and thus of her household office, and queenliness. We come now to our last, our widest question, — What is her queenly office with respect to the state?

Generally, we are under an impression that a man's duties are public, and a woman's private. But this is not altogether so. A man has a personal work or duty, relating to his own home, and a public work or duty, which is the expansion of the other, relating to the state. So a woman has a personal work or duty, relating to her own home, and a public work or duty, which is also the expansion of that.

Now, the man's work for his own home is, as has been said, to secure its maintenance, progress, and defence; the woman's to secure its order, comfort, and loveliness.

Expand both these functions. The man's duty, as a member of a commonwealth, is to assist in the maintenance, in the advance, in the defence of the state. The woman's duty, as a member of the commonwealth, is to assist in the ordering, in the comforting, and in the beautiful adornment of the state.

What the man is at his own gate, defending it, if need be, against insult and spoil, that also, not in a less, but in a more devoted measure, he is to be at the gate of his country, leaving his home, if need be, even to the spoiler, to do his more incumbent work there.

And, in like manner, what the woman is to be within her gates, as the centre of order, the balm of distress, and the mirror of beauty: that she is also to be without her gates, where order is more difficult, distress more imminent, loveliness more rare.

And as within the human heart there is always set an instinct for all its real duties, — an instinct which you cannot quench, but only warp and corrupt if you withdraw it from its true purpose ; — as there is the intense instinct of love, which, rightly disciplined, maintains all the sanctities of life, and, misdirected, undermines them ; and *must* do either the one or the other ; — so there is in the human heart an inextinguishable instinct, — the love of power, which, rightly directed, maintains all the majesty of law and life, and misdirected, wrecks them.

87. Deep rooted in the innermost life of the heart of man, and of the heart of woman, God set it there, and God keeps it there. Vainly, as falsely, you blame or rebuke the desire of power ! For Heaven's sake, and for Man's sake, desire it all you can. But *what* power ? That is all the question. Power to destroy ? the lion's limb, and the dragon's breath ? Not so. Power to heal, to redeem, to guide, and to guard. Power of the sceptre and shield ; the power of the royal hand that heals in touching, — that binds the fiend, and looses the captive ; the throne that is founded on the rock of Justice, and descended from only by steps of Mercy. Will you not covet such power as this, and seek such throne as this, and be no more housewives, but queens ?

88. It is now long since the women of England arrogated, universally, a title which once belonged to nobility only ; and, having once been in the habit of accepting the simple title of gentlewoman, as correspondent to that of gentleman, insisted on the privilege of assuming the title of "Lady,"[1] which properly corresponds only to the title of "Lord."

---

[1] I wish there were a true order of chivalry instituted for our English youth of certain ranks, in which both boy and girl should receive, at a given age, their knighthood and ladyhood by true title ; attainable only by certain probation and trial both of character and accomplish-

I do not blame them for this; but only for their narrow motive in this. I would have them desire and claim the title of Lady, provided they claim, not merely the title, but the office and duty signified by it. (Lady° means "bread-giver" or "loaf-giver," and Lord° means "maintainer of laws"; and both titles have reference, not to the law which is maintained in the house, nor to the bread which is given to the household; but to law maintained for the multitude, and to bread broken among the multitude. So that a Lord has legal claim only to his title in so far as he is the maintainer of the justice of the Lord of Lords; and a Lady has legal claim to her title, only so far as she communicates that help to the poor representatives of her Master, which women once, ministering to Him of their substance, were permitted to extend to that Master Himself; and when she is known, as He Himself once was, in breaking of bread.°

89. And this beneficent and legal dominion, this power of the Dominus,° or House-Lord, and of the Domina, or House-Lady, is great and venerable, not in the number of those through whom it has lineally descended, but in the number of those whom it grasps within its sway; it is always regarded with reverent worship wherever its dynasty is founded on its duty, and its ambition correlative with its beneficence. Your fancy is pleased with the thought of being noble ladies, with a train of vassals? Be it so; you cannot be too noble, and your train cannot be too great; but see to it that your train is of vassals whom you serve and feed, not merely of slaves who serve and feed *you*; and that the multitude which obeys you is of those whom you have comforted, not oppressed, — whom you have redeemed, not led into captivity.

ment; and to be forfeited, on conviction, by their peers, of any dishonorable act. Such an institution would be entirely, and with all noble results, possible, in a nation which loved honor. That it would not be possible among us, is not to the discredit of the scheme.

90. And this, which is true of the lower or household dominion, is equally true of the queenly dominion; that highest dignity is open to you, if you will also accept that highest duty. Rex et Regina — Roi et Reine — "*Right*-doers";° they differ but from the Lady and Lord, in that their power is supreme over the mind as over the person — that they not only feed and clothe, but direct and teach. And whether consciously or not, you must be, in many a heart, enthroned: there is no putting by that crown; queens you must always be: queens to your lovers; queens to your husbands and your sons; queens of higher mystery to the world beyond, which bows itself, and will forever bow, before the myrtle crown,° and the stainless sceptre of womanhood. But, alas! you are too often idle and careless queens, grasping at majesty in the least things, while you abdicate it in the greatest; and leaving misrule and violence to work their will among men, in defiance of the power which, holding straight in gift from the Prince of all Peace,° the wicked among you betray, and the good forget.

91. "Prince of Peace." Note that name. When kings rule in that name, and nobles, and the judges of the earth, they also, in their narrow place, and mortal measure, receive the power of it. There are no other rulers than they : other rule than theirs is but *mis*rule; they who govern verily "Dei gratia"° are all princes, yes, or princesses, of Peace. There is not a war in the world, no, nor an injustice, but you women are answerable for it ; not in that you have provoked, but in that you have not hindered. Men, by their nature, are prone to fight ; they will fight for any cause, or for none. It is for you to choose their cause for them, and to forbid them when there is no cause. There is no suffering, no injustice, no misery in the earth, but the guilt of it lies with you. Men can bear the sight of it, but you should not be able to bear it. Men may tread it down without sympathy in their own struggle ; but men are feeble in sympathy, and contracted in hope ; it is you only who can

feel the depths of pain, and conceive the way of its healing. Instead of trying to do this, you turn away from it; you shut yourselves within your park walls° and garden gates; and you are content to know that there is beyond them a whole world in wilderness — a world of secrets which you dare not penetrate, and of suffering which you dare not conceive.

92. I tell you that this is to me quite the most amazing among the phenomena of humanity. I am surprised at no depths to which, when once warped from its honor, that humanity can be degraded. I do not wonder at the miser's death, with his hands, as they relax, dropping gold. I do not wonder at the sensualist's life, with the shroud wrapped about his feet.° I do not wonder at the single-handed murder of a single victim, done by the assassin in the darkness of the railway, or reed-shadow of the marsh. I do not even wonder at the myriad-handed murder of multitudes, done boastfully in the daylight, by the frenzy of nations, and the immeasurable, unimaginable guilt, heaped up from hell to heaven, of their priests, and kings. But this is wonderful to me — oh, how wonderful! — to see the tender and delicate woman among you, with her child at her breast, and a power, if she would wield it, over it, and over its father, purer than the air of heaven, and stronger than the seas of earth — nay, a magnitude of blessing which her husband would not part with for all that earth itself, though it were made of one entire and perfect chrysolite:° — to see her abdicate this majesty to play at precedence° with her next-door neighbor! This is wonderful — oh, wonderful! — to see her, with every innocent feeling fresh within her, go out in the morning into her garden to play with the fringes of its guarded flowers, and lift their heads when they are drooping, with her happy smile upon her face, and no cloud upon her brow, because there is a little wall around her place of peace; and yet she knows, in her heart, if she would only look for its knowledge, that, outside of that little rose-covered wall, the wild grass, to

the horizon, is torn up ° by the agony of men, and beat level by the drift of their life-blood.

93. Have you ever considered what a deep under-meaning there lies, or at least may be read, if we choose, in our custom of strewing flowers before those whom we think most happy? Do you suppose it is merely to deceive them into the hope that happiness is always to fall thus in showers at their feet?— that whenever they pass they will tread on herbs of sweet scent, and that the rough ground will be made smooth for them by depth of roses? So surely as they believe that, they will have, instead, to walk on bitter herbs and thorns; and the only softness to their feet will be of snow. But it is not thus intended they should believe; there is a better meaning in that old custom. The path of a good woman is indeed strewn with flowers; but they rise behind her steps, not before them. "Her feet have touched ° the meadows, and left the daisies rosy."

94. You think that only a lover's fancy;— false and vain! How if it could be true? You think this also, perhaps, only a poet's fancy—

> "Even the light harebell ° raised its head
>   Elastic from her airy tread."

But it is little to say of a woman, that she only does not destroy where she passes. She should revive; the harebells should bloom, not stoop, as she passes. You think I am rushing into hyperbole?° Pardon me, not a whit—I mean what I say in calm English, spoken in resolute truth. You have heard it said—(and I believe there is more than fancy even in that saying, but let it pass for a fanciful one)—that flowers only flourish rightly ° in the garden of some one who loves them. I know you would like that to be true; you would think it a pleasant magic if you could flush your flowers into brighter bloom by a kind look upon them: nay, more, if your look had the power, not only to cheer, but to guard;—if you could bid

the black blight° turn away, and the knotted caterpillar spare —
if you could bid the dew fall upon them in the drouth, and say
to the south wind, in frost, "Come, thou south,° and breathe
upon my garden, that the spices of it may flow out." This
you would think a great thing? And do you think it not a
greater thing, that all this (and how much more than this!)
you *can* do, for fairer flowers than these — flowers that could
bless you for having blessed them; and will love you for having
loved them; — flowers that have thoughts like yours, and lives
like yours; and which, once saved, you save forever? Is this
only a little power? Far among the moorlands and the rocks, —
far in the darkness of the terrible streets, — these feeble florets°
are lying, with all their fresh leaves torn, and their stems broken
— will you never go down to them, nor set them in order in
their little fragrant beds, nor fence them, in their trembling,
from the fierce wind? Shall morning follow morning, for you,
but not for them; and the dawn rise to watch, far away, those
frantic Dances of Death;[1] but no dawn rise to breathe upon
these living banks of wild violet, and woodbine, and rose; nor
call to you, through your casement, — call (not giving you the
name of the English poet's lady,° but the name of Dante's great
Matilda,° who on the edge of happy Lethe, stood, wreathing
flowers with flowers), saying, —

> "Come into the garden, Maud,°
>   For the black bat, night, has flown,
> And the woodbine spices are wafted abroad
>   And the musk of the roses blown"?

Will you not go down among them? — among those sweet
living things, whose new courage, sprung from the earth with
the deep color of heaven upon it, is starting up in strength of
goodly spire; and whose purity, washed from the dust, is opening, bud by bud, into the flower of promise: — and still they

[1] See note 2, page 38.

turn to you, and for you, "The Larkspur° listens — I hear, I hear! And the Lily whispers — I wait."

95. Did you notice that I missed two lines when I read you that first stanza; and think that I had forgotten them? Hear them now: —

> "Come into the garden, Maud,
>   For the black bat, night, has flown.
> Come into the garden, Maud,
>   I am here at the gate, alone."

Who is it, think you,° who stands at the gate of this sweeter garden, alone, waiting for you? Did you ever hear, not of a Maud, but a Madeleine,° who went down to her garden in the dawn, and found One waiting at the gate, whom she supposed to be the gardener? Have you not sought Him often; sought Him in vain, all through the night; sought Him in vain at the gate of that old garden where the fiery sword° is set? He is never there; but at the gate of *this* garden He is waiting always — waiting to take your hand — ready to go down to see the fruits of the valley, to see whether the vine has flourished, and the pomegranate budded.° There you shall see with Him the little tendrils of the vines that His hand is guiding — there you shall see the pomegranate springing where His hand cast the sanguine° seed; — more: you shall see the troops of the angel keepers that, with their wings, wave away the hungry birds from the pathsides where He has sown, and call to each other between the vineyard rows, "Take us the foxes, the little foxes,° that spoil the vines, for our vines' have tender grapes." Oh — you queens — you queens; among the hills and happy greenwood of this land of yours, shall the foxes have holes,° and the birds of the air have nests; and in your cities shall the stones cry out against you, that they are the only pillows where the Son of Man can lay His head?

III

OF THE MYSTERY OF LIFE

LECTURE III

THE MYSTERY OF LIFE AND ITS ARTS°

Lecture delivered in the Theatre of the Royal College of Science, Dublin, 1868.

96. WHEN I accepted the privilege of addressing you to-day, I was not aware of a restriction° with respect to the topics of discussion which may be brought before this Society,°[1] — a restriction which, though entirely wise and right under the circumstances contemplated in its introduction, would necessarily have disabled me, thinking as I think, from preparing any lecture for you on the subject of art in a form which might be permanently useful. Pardon me, therefore, in so far as I must transgress such limitation; for indeed my infringement will be of the letter — not of the spirit — of your commands. In whatever I may say touching the religion which has been the foundation of art, or the policy which has contributed to its power, if I offend one, I shall offend all; for I shall take no note of any separations in creeds, or antagonisms in parties: neither do I fear that ultimately I shall offend any, by proving — or at least stating as capable of positive proof — the connection° of all that is best in the crafts and arts of man, with the simplicity of his faith, and the sincerity of his patriotism.

97. But I speak to you under another disadvantage, by which I am checked in frankness of utterance, not here only, but everywhere: namely, that I am never fully aware how far

---

[1] That no reference should be made to religious questions.

my audiences are disposed to give me credit for real knowledge
of my subject, or how far they grant me attention only because
I have been sometimes thought an ingenious or pleasant essay-
ist° upon it.   For I have had what, in many respects, I boldly
call the misfortune, to set my words sometimes prettily together ;
not without a foolish vanity in the poor knack that I had of
doing so : until I was heavily punished for this pride, by finding
that many people thought of the words only, and cared nothing
for their meaning.   Happily, therefore, the power of using such
pleasant language — if indeed it ever were mine — is passing
away from me : and whatever I am now able to say at all, I find
myself forced to say with great plainness.   For my thoughts
have changed also, as my words have ; and whereas in earlier
life, what little influence I obtained was due perhaps chiefly to
the enthusiasm with which I was able to dwell on the beauty
of the physical clouds,° and of their colors in the sky ; so all
the influence I now desire to retain must be due to the earnestness with which I am endeavoring to trace the form and beauty
of another kind of cloud than those ; the bright cloud of which
it is written — "What is your life ? It is even as a vapor° that
appeareth for a little time, and then vanisheth away."

98. I suppose few people reach the middle or latter period
of their age, without having, at some moment of change or disappointment, felt the truth of those bitter words ; and been
startled by the fading of the sunshine from the cloud of their
life into the sudden agony of the knowledge that the fabric of
it was as fragile° as a dream, and the endurance of it as
transient as the dew.   But it is not always that, even at such
times of melancholy surprise, we can enter into any true perception that this human life shares in the nature of it, not
only the evanescence, but the mystery of the cloud ; that its
avenues are wreathed in darkness, and its forms and courses
no less fantastic, than spectral and obscure ; so that not only
in the vanity which we cannot grasp, but in the shadow which

we cannot pierce, it is true of this cloudy life of ours, that "man walketh in a vain shadow, and disquieteth himself in vain."°

99. And least of all, whatever may have been the eagerness of our passions, or the height of our pride, are we able to understand in its depths the third and most solemn character in which our life is like those clouds of heaven; that to it belongs not only their transience, not only their mystery, but also their power; that in the cloud of the human soul there is a fire stronger than the lightning, and a grace more precious than the rain; and that though of the good and evil it shall one day be said alike, that the place that knew them° knows them no more, there is an infinite separation between those whose brief presence had there been a blessing, like the mist of Eden° that went up from the earth to water the garden, and those whose place knew them only as a drifting and changeful shade, of whom the Heavenly sentence is, that they are "wells without water;° clouds that are carried with a tempest, to whom the mist of darkness is reserved forever."

100. To those among us, however, who have lived long enough to form some just estimate of the rate of the changes which are, hour by hour in accelerating catastrophe, manifesting themselves in the laws, the arts, and the creeds of men, it seems to me, that now at least, if never at any former time, the thoughts of the true nature of our life, and of its powers and responsibilities, should present themselves with absolute sadness and sternness. And although I know that this feeling is much deepened in my own mind by disappointment, which, by chance, has attended the greater number of my cherished purposes, I do not for that reason distrust the feeling itself, though I am on my guard against an exaggerated degree of it: nay, I rather believe that in periods of new effort and violent change, disappointment is a wholesome medicine; and that in the secret of it, as in the twilight so beloved by Titian,° we

may see the colors of things with deeper truth than in the most dazzling sunshine. And because these truths about the works of men, which I want to bring to-day before you, are most of them sad ones, though at the same time helpful; and because also I believe that your kind Irish hearts ° will answer more gladly to the truthful expression of a personal feeling, than to the exposition of an abstract principle, I will permit myself so much unreserved speaking of my own causes of regret, as may enable you to make just allowance for what, according to your sympathies, you will call either the bitterness, or the insight, of a mind which has surrendered its best hopes, and been foiled in its favorite aims.

101. I spent the ten strongest years of my life (from twenty to thirty), in endeavoring to show the excellence of the work of the man ° whom I believed, and rightly believed, to be the greatest painter of the schools of England since Reynolds.° I had then perfect faith in the power of every great truth of beauty to prevail ultimately, and take its right place in usefulness and honor; and I strove to bring the painter's work into this due place, while the painter was yet alive. But he knew, better than I, the uselessness of talking about what people could not see for themselves. He always discouraged me scornfully, even when he thanked me — and he died before even the superficial effect of my work was visible. I went on, however, thinking I could at least be of use to the public, if not to him, in proving his power. My books got talked about a little. The prices of modern pictures, generally, rose, and I was beginning to take some pleasure in a sense of gradual victory, when, fortunately or unfortunately, an opportunity of perfect trial undeceived me at once, and forever. The trustees of the National Gallery commissioned me to arrange the Turner drawings there, and permitted me to prepare three hundred examples of his studies from nature, for exhibition at Kensington.° At Kensington they were, and are, placed for

exhibition; but they are not exhibited, for the room in which they hang is always empty.

102. Well — this showed me at once, that those ten years of my life had been, in their chief purpose, lost. For that, I did not so much care; I had, at least, learned my own business thoroughly, and should be able, as I fondly supposed, after such a lesson, now to use my knowledge with better effect. But what I did care for was the — to me frightful — discovery, that the most splendid genius in the arts might be permitted by Providence to labor and perish uselessly; that in the very fineness of it there might be something rendering it invisible to ordinary eyes; but that, with this strange excellence, faults might be mingled which would be as deadly as its virtues were vain; that the glory of it was perishable, as well as invisible, and the gift and grace of it might be to us as snow in summer ° and as rain in harvest.

103. That was the first mystery of life to me. But, while my best energy was given to the study of painting, I had put collateral effort, more prudent if less enthusiastic, into that of architecture; and in this I could not complain of meeting with no sympathy. Among several personal reasons which caused me to desire that I might give this, my closing lecture on the subject of art here, in Ireland, one of the chief was, that in reading it, I should stand near the beautiful building, — the engineers' school of your college, — which was the first realization I had the joy to see, of the principles I had, until then, been endeavoring to teach! but which, alas, is now, to me, no more than the richly canopied monument of one of the most earnest souls that ever gave itself to the arts, and one of my truest and most loving friends, Benjamin Woodward.° Nor was it here in Ireland only that I received the help of Irish sympathy and genius. When, to another friend, Sir Thomas Deane,° with Mr. Woodward, was intrusted the building of the museum at Oxford,° the best details of the work were executed

by sculptors who had been born and trained here; and the first window of the façade ° of the building, in which was inaugurated the study of natural science in England, in true fellowship with literature, was carved from my design by an Irish sculptor.

104. You may perhaps think that no man ought to speak of disappointment, to whom, even in one branch of labor, so much success was granted. Had Mr. Woodward now been beside me, I had not so spoken; but his gentle and passionate spirit was cut off from the fulfilment of its purposes, and the work we did together is now become vain. It may not be so in future; but the architecture we endeavored to introduce is inconsistent alike with the reckless luxury, the deforming mechanism, and the squalid misery of modern cities; ° among the formative fashions of the day, aided, especially in England, by ecclesiastical sentiment, it indeed obtained notoriety; ° and sometimes behind an engine furnace, or a railroad bank, you may detect the pathetic discord of its momentary grace, and, with toil, decipher its floral carvings choked with soot. I felt answerable to the schools I loved, only for their injury. I perceived that this new portion of my strength had also been spent in vain; and from amidst ° streets of iron, and palaces of crystal, shrunk back at last to the carving of the mountain and color of the flower.

105. And still I could tell of failure, and failure repeated, as years went on; but I have trespassed enough on your patience to show you, in part, the causes of my discouragement. Now let me more deliberately tell you its results. You know there is a tendency in the minds of many men, when they are heavily disappointed in the main purposes of their life, to feel, and perhaps in warning, perhaps in mockery, to declare, that life itself is a vanity. Because it has disappointed them, they think its nature is of disappointment ° always, or at best, of pleasure that can be grasped by imagination only; that the cloud of it has

no strength nor fire within; but is a painted cloud only, to be delighted in, yet despised. You know how beautifully Pope° has expressed this particular phase of thought : —

> "Meanwhile opinion gilds, with varying rays,
>   These painted clouds that beautify our days;
>   Each want of happiness by hope supplied,
>   And each vacuity of sense, by pride.
>   Hope builds as fast as Knowledge can destroy;
>   In Folly's cup, still laughs the bubble joy.
>   One pleasure past, another still we gain;
>   And not a vanity is given in vain."

But the effect of failure upon my own mind has been just the reverse of this. The more that my life disappointed me, the more solemn and wonderful it became to me. It seemed, contrarily to Pope's saying, that the vanity of it *was* indeed given in vain; but that there was something behind the veil of it, which was not vanity. It became to me not a painted cloud, but a terrible and impenetrable one; not a mirage, which vanished as I drew near, but a pillar of darkness,° to which I was forbidden to draw near. For I saw that both my own failure, and such success in petty things as in its poor triumph seemed to me worse than failure, came from the want of sufficiently earnest effort to understand the whole law and meaning of existence, and to bring it to noble and due end; as, on the other hand, I saw more and more clearly that all enduring success in the arts, or in any other occupation, had come from the ruling of lower purposes, not by a conviction of their nothingness, but by a solemn faith in the advancing power of human nature, or in the promise, however dimly apprehended, that the mortal part of it would one day be swallowed up in immortality; and that, indeed, the arts° themselves never had reached any vital strength or honor, but in the effort to proclaim this immortality, and in the service either of great and

just religion, or of some unselfish patriotism, and law of such
national life as must be the foundation of religion.

106. Nothing that I have ever said is more true or necessary — nothing has been more misunderstood or misapplied —
than my strong assertion that the arts can never be right
themselves unless their motive is right. It is misunderstood
this way: weak painters, who have never learned their business, and cannot lay a true line, continually come to me, cry-
ing out, — "Look at this picture of mine; it *must* be good, I
had such a lovely motive. I have put my whole heart into it,
and taken years to think over its treatment." Well, the only
answer ° for these people is — if one had the cruelty to make
it — "Sir, you cannot think over *any*thing in any number of
years, — you haven't the head to do it; and though you had
fine motives, strong enough to make you burn yourself in a
slow fire, if only first you could paint a picture, you can't paint
one, nor half an inch of one; you haven't the hand to do it."

But, far more decisively we have to say to men who *do*
know their business, or may know it if they choose — "Sir,
you have this gift, and a mighty one; see that you serve your
nation faithfully with it. It is a greater trust than ships and
armies: you might cast *them* away, if you were their captain,
with less treason to your people than in casting your own glorious power away, and serving the devil with it instead of men.
Ships and armies you may replace if they are lost, but a great
intellect, once abused, is a curse to the earth forever."

107. This, then, I meant by saying that the arts must have
noble motive. This also I said respecting them, that they
never had prospered, nor could prosper, but when they had
such true purpose, and were devoted to the proclamation of
divine truth or law. And yet I saw also that they had always
failed in this proclamation — that poetry, and sculpture, and
painting, though only great when they strove to teach us something about the gods, never had taught us anything trust-

worthy about the gods, but had always betrayed their trust in the crisis of it, and, with their powers at the full reach, became ministers to pride and to lust. And I felt also, with increasing amazement, the unconquerable apathy in ourselves the hearers, no less than in these the teachers ; and that while the wisdom and rightness of every act and art of life could only be consistent with a right understanding of the ends of life, we were all plunged as in a languid dream — our hearts fat,° and our eyes heavy, and our ears closed, lest the inspiration of hand or voice should reach us — lest we should see with our eyes,° and understand with our hearts, and be healed.

108. This intense apathy in all of us is the first great mystery of life ; it stands in the way of every perception, every virtue. There is no making ourselves feel enough astonishment at it. That the occupations or pastimes of life should have no motive, is understandable ; but — That life itself should have no motive — that we neither care to find out what it may lead to, nor to guard against its being forever taken away from us — here is a mystery indeed. For just suppose I were able to call at this moment to any one in this audience by name, and to tell him positively that I knew a large estate had been lately left to him on some curious conditions ; but that, though I knew it was large, I did not know how large, nor even where it was — whether in the East Indies or the West, or in England, or at the Antipodes. I only knew it was a vast estate, and there was a chance of his losing it altogether if he did not soon find out on what terms it had been left to him. Suppose I were able to say this positively to any single man in this audience, and he knew that I did not speak without warrant, do you think that he would rest content with that vague knowledge, if it were anywise possible to obtain more ? Would he not give every energy to find some trace of the facts, and never rest until he had ascertained where this place was, and what it was like ? And suppose he were a young man, and all he could

discover by his best endeavor was that the estate was never
to be his at all, unless he persevered, during certain years of
probation, in an orderly and industrious life; but that, according to the rightness of his conduct, the portion of the estate
assigned to him would be greater or less, so that it literally
depended on his behavior from day to day whether he got ten
thousand a year, or thirty thousand a year, or nothing whatever — would you not think it strange if the youth never
troubled himself to satisfy the conditions in any way, nor even
to know what was required of him, but lived exactly as he
chose, and never inquired whether his chances of the estate
were increasing or passing away? Well, you know that this
is actually and literally so with the greater number of the educated persons now living in Christian countries. Nearly every
man and woman, in any company such as this, outwardly professes to believe — and a large number unquestionably think
they believe — much more than this; not only that a quite
unlimited estate is in prospect for them if they please the
Holder of it, but that the infinite contrary of such a possession
— an estate of perpetual misery — is in store for them if they
displease this great Land-Holder, this great Heaven-Holder.
And yet there is not one in a thousand of these human souls
that cares to think,° for ten minutes of the day, where this
estate is, or how beautiful it is, or what kind of life they are to
lead in it, or what kind of life they must lead to obtain it.

109. You fancy that you care to know this: so little do you
care that, probably, at this moment many of you are displeased
with me for talking of the matter! You came to hear about
the Art of this world, not about the Life of the next, and you
are provoked with me for talking of what you can hear any
Sunday in church. But do not be afraid. I will tell you some-
thing° before you go about pictures, and carvings, and pottery,
and what else you would like better to hear of than the other
world. Nay, perhaps you say, "We want you to talk of pic

tures and pottery, because we are sure that you know something of them, and you know nothing of the other world." Well — I don't. That is quite true. But the very strangeness and mystery of which I urge you to take notice, is in this — that I do not ; — nor you either. Can you answer a single bold question unflinchingly about that other world ? — Are you sure ° there is a heaven ? Sure there is a hell ? Sure that men are dropping before your faces through the pavements of these streets into eternal fire, or sure that they are not ? Sure that at your own death you are going to be delivered from all sorrow, to be endowed with all virtue, to be gifted with all felicity, and raised into perpetual companionship with a King, compared to whom the kings of the earth ° are as grasshoppers, and the nations as the dust of His feet ? Are you sure of this ? or, if not sure, do any of us so much as care to make it sure ? and, if not, how can anything that we do be right — how can anything we think be wise ? what honor can there be in the arts that amuse us, or what profit in the possessions that please ?

Is not this ° a mystery of life ?

110. But further, you may, perhaps, think it a beneficent ordinance for the generality of men that they do not, with earnestness or anxiety, dwell on such questions of the future because the business of the day could not be done if this kind of thought ° were taken by all of us for the morrow. Be it so : but at least we might anticipate that the greatest and wisest of us, who were evidently the appointed teachers of the rest, would set themselves apart to seek out whatever could be surely known of the future destinies of their race : and to teach this in no rhetorical or ambiguous manner, but in the plainest and most severely earnest words.

Now, the highest representatives of men who have thus endeavored, during the Christian era, to search out these deep things, and relate them, are Dante and Milton.° There are none who for earnestness of thought, for mastery of word, can be classed with these. I am not at present, mind you, speaking of persons set apart in any priestly or pastoral office, to deliver creeds to us, or doctrines ; but of men who try to discover and set forth, as far as by human intellect is possible, the facts of the other world. Divines may perhaps teach us how to arrive there, but only these two poets have in any powerful manner striven to discover, or in any definite words professed to tell, what we shall see and become there ; or how those upper and nether worlds are, and have been, inhabited.

111. And what have they told us? Milton's account of the most important event in his whole system of the universe, the fall of the angels, is evidently unbelievable to himself ;° and the more so, that it is wholly founded on, and in a great part spoiled and degraded from, Hesiod's ° account of the decisive war of the younger gods with the Titans. The rest of this poem is a picturesque drama, in which every artifice of invention is visibly and consciously employed ; not a single fact being, for an instant, conceived as tenable by any living faith. Dante's conception is far more intense, and, by himself, for the time, not to be escaped from ; it is indeed a vision, but a vision only, and that one of the wildest that ever entranced a soul — a dream in which every grotesque type or fantasy of heathen tradition is renewed, and adorned ; and the destinies of the Christian Church, under their most sacred symbols, become literally subordinate to the praise, and are only to be understood by the aid, of one dear Florentine maiden.°

112. I tell you truly that, as I strive more with this strange lethargy ° and trance in myself, and awake to the meaning and power of life, it seems daily more amazing to me that men such as these should dare to play with the most precious truths, (or the most deadly untruths,) by which the whole human race listening to them could be informed, or deceived ; — all the world their audiences forever, with pleased ear and passionate heart : — and yet, to this submissive infinitude of souls, and evermore

succeeding and succeeding multitude, hungry for bread of life, they do but play upon sweetly modulated pipes; with pompous nomenclature adorn the councils of hell; touch a troubadour's guitar° to the courses of the suns; and fill the openings of eternity, before which prophets have veiled their faces, and which angels desire to look into, with idle puppets of their scholastic imagination,° and melancholy lights of frantic faith in their lost mortal love.°

Is not this a mystery of life?

113. But more. We have to remember that these two great teachers were both of them warped in their temper, and thwarted in their search for truth. They were men of intellectual war, unable, through darkness of controversy, or stress of personal grief,° to discern where their own ambition modified their utterances of the moral law; or their own agony mingled with their anger at its violation. But greater men than these have been — innocent-hearted — too great for contest. Men, like Homer° and Shakespeare, of so unrecognized personality, that it disappears in future ages, and becomes ghostly, like the tradition of a lost heathen god. Men, therefore, to whose unoffended, uncondemning sight, the whole of human nature reveals itself in a pathetic weakness, with which they will not strive; or in mournful and transitory strength, which they dare not praise. And all Pagan and Christian Civilization thus becomes subject to them. It does not matter how little, or how much, any of us have read, either of Homer or Shakespeare; everything round us, in substance or in thought, has been moulded by them. All Greek gentlemen° were educated under Homer. All Roman gentlemen, by Greek literature. All Italian, and French, and English gentlemen, by Roman literature, and by its principles. Of the scope of Shakespeare, I will say only, that the intellectual measure of every man since born, in the domains of creative thought, may be assigned to him, according to the degree in which he has been taught by Shakespeare. Well, what do these

two men, centres of mortal intelligence, deliver to us of conviction respecting what it most behooves that intelligence to grasp? What is their hope — their crown of rejoicing? what manner of exhortation have they for us, or of rebuke? what lies next their own hearts, and dictates their undying words? Have they any peace to promise to our unrest — any redemption to our misery?

114. Take Homer first, and think if there is any sadder image of human fate than the great Homeric story. The main features in the character of Achilles are its intense desire of justice, and its tenderness of affection. And in that bitter song of the Iliad, this man, though aided continually by the wisest of the gods, and burning with the desire of justice in his heart, becomes yet, through ill-governed passion, the most unjust of men : and, full of the deepest tenderness in his heart, becomes yet, through ill-governed passion, the most cruel of men. Intense alike in love and in friendship, he loses, first his mistress, and then his friend ; for the sake of the one, he surrenders to death the armies of his own land ; for the sake of the other he surrenders all. Will a man lay down his life for his friend? Yea — even for his *dead* friend,° this Achilles, though goddess-born and goddess-taught, gives up his kingdom, his country, and his life — casts alike the innocent and guilty, with himself, into one gulf of slaughter, and dies at last by the hand of the basest of his adversaries°.

Is not this a mystery of life?

115. But what, then, is the message to us of our own poet, and searcher of hearts, after fifteen hundred years of Christian faith have been numbered over the graves of men? Are his words more cheerful than the Heathen's — is his hope more near — his trust more sure — his reading of fate more happy? Ah, no! He differs from the heathen poet chiefly in this — that he recognizes, for deliverance, no gods nigh at hand ; and that, by petty chance — by momentary folly — by broken message — by fool's tyranny — or traitor's snare, the strongest and

most righteous are brought to their ruin, and perish without word of hope. He indeed, as part of his rendering of character, ascribes the power and modesty of habitual devotion to the gentle and the just. The death-bed of Katharine° is bright with vision of angels; and the great soldier-king,° standing by his few dead, acknowledges the presence of the hand that can save alike by many or by few. But observe that from those who with deepest spirit, meditate, and with deepest passion, mourn, there are no such words as these; nor in their hearts are any such consolations. Instead of the perpetual sense of the helpful presence of the Deity, which through all heathen tradition is the source of heroic strength, in battle, in exile, and in the valley of the shadow of death, we find only in the great Christian poet, the consciousness of a moral law, through which "the gods are just,° and of our pleasant vices make instruments to scourge us;" and of the resolved arbitration of the destinies, that conclude into precision of doom what we feebly and blindly began; and force us, when our indiscretion serves us, and our deepest plots do pall, to the confession that "there's a divinity that shapes our ends,° rough-hew them how we will."

Is not this a mystery of life?

116. Be it so, then. About this human life that is to be, or that is, the wise religious men tell us nothing that we can trust; and the wise contemplative men, nothing that can give us peace. But there is yet a third class, to whom we may turn — the wise practical men. We have sat at the feet of poets who sang of heaven, and they have told us their dreams. We have listened to the poets who sang of earth, and they have chanted to us dirges and words of despair. But there is one class of men or more: — men, not capable of vision, nor sensitive to sorrow, but firm of purpose — practised in business; learned in all that can be, (by handling,) known. Men, whose hearts and hopes are wholly in this present world, from whom, therefore, we may surely learn, at least, how, at present, conven-

iently to live in it. What will *they* say to us, or show us by
example? These kings — these councillors — these statesmen
and builders of kingdoms — these capitalists and men of business, who weigh the earth,° and the dust of it, in a balance.
They know the world, surely; and what is the mystery of life
to us, is none to them. They can surely show us how to live,
while we live, and to gather out of the present world what is best.

117. I think I can best tell you their answer by telling you
a dream I had once. For though I am no poet, I have dreams
sometimes: — I dreamed° I was at a child's May-day party,
in which every means of entertainment had been provided for
them by a wise and kind host.° It was in a stately house, with
beautiful gardens attached to it; and the children had been set
free in the rooms and gardens, with no care whatever but how
to pass their afternoon rejoicingly. They did not, indeed, know
much about what was to happen next day; and some of them,
I thought, were a little frightened, because there was a chance
of their being sent° to a new school where there were examina-
tions; but they kept the thoughts of that out of their heads as
well as they could, and resolved to enjoy themselves. The
house, I said, was in a beautiful garden, and in the garden
were all kinds of flowers; sweet, grassy banks for rest; and
smooth lawns for play; and pleasant streams and woods; and
rocky places for climbing. And the children were happy for a
little while; but presently they separated themselves into parties; and then each party declared, it would have a piece of the
garden° for its own, and that none of the others should have
anything to do with that piece. Next, they quarrelled vio-
lently which pieces they would have; and at last the boys
took up the thing, as boys should do, "practically," and
fought in the flower-beds till there was hardly a flower left
standing; then they trampled down each other's bits of the
garden out of spite; and the girls cried till they could cry no
more; and so they all lay down at last breathless in the ruin,

and waited for the time when they were to be taken home in the evening.[1]

118. Meanwhile, the children in the house had been making themselves happy also in their manner. For them, there had been provided every kind of in-door pleasure : there was music for them to dance to ; and the library was open, with all manner of amusing books ; and there was a museum, full of the most curious shells, and animals, and birds ; and there was a work-shop, with lathes and carpenter's tools, for the ingenious boys ; and there were pretty fantastic dresses, for the girls to dress in ; and there were microscopes, and kaleidoscopes ; and whatever toys a child could fancy ; and a table, in the dining-room, loaded with everything nice to eat.

But, in the midst of all this, it struck two or three of the more " practical " children, that they would like some of the brass-headed nails ° that studded the chairs ; and so they set to work to pull them out. Presently, the others, who were reading, or looking at shells, took a fancy to do the like ; and, in a little while, all the children, nearly, were spraining their fingers, in pulling out brass-headed nails. With all that they could pull out, they were not satisfied ; and then, everybody wanted some of somebody else's. And at last, the really practical and sensible ones declared, that nothing was of any real consequence, that afternoon, except to get plenty of brass-headed nails ; and that the books, and the cakes, and the microscopes were of no use at all in themselves, but only, if they could be exchanged for nail-heads. And at last they began to fight for nail-heads, as the others fought for the bits of garden. Only here and there, a despised one shrunk away into a corner, and tried to get a little quiet ° with a book, in the midst of the noise ; but

---

[1] I have sometimes been asked what this means. I intended it to set forth the wisdom of men in war contending for kingdoms, and what follows, to set forth their wisdom in peace, contending for wealth.

all the practical ones thought of nothing else but counting nail-
heads all the afternoon — even though they knew they would not
be allowed to carry so much as one brass knob away with them.
But no — it was — "Who has most nails? I have a hundred,
and you have fifty;" or, "I have a thousand, and you have two.
I must have as many as you before I leave the house, or I cannot possibly go home in peace." At last, they made so much
noise that I awoke, and thought to myself, "What a false dream
that is, of *children!*" The child is the father of the man;°
and wiser. Children never do such foolish things. Only men do.

119. But there is yet one last class of persons to be interro-
gated. The wise religious men we have asked in vain; the
wise contemplative men, in vain; the wise worldly men, in
vain. But there is another group yet. In the midst of this
vanity of empty religion — of tragic contemplation — of wrath-
ful and wretched ambition, and dispute for dust, there is yet
one great group of persons, by whom all these disputers live —
the persons who have determined, or have had it by a beneficent Providence determined for them, that they will do something useful; that whatever may be prepared for them hereafter,
or happen to them here, they will, at least, deserve the food
that God gives them by winning it honorably; and that, however fallen from the purity, or far from the peace, of Eden,
they will carry out the duty of human dominion though they
have lost its felicity; and dress and keep° the wilderness,
though they no more can dress or keep the garden.

These, — hewers of wood and drawers of water,° — these, bent
under burdens, or torn of scourges — these, that dig and weave —
that plant and build; workers in wood, and in marble, and in
iron — by whom all food, clothing, habitation, furniture, and
means of delight are produced, for themselves, and for all men
beside; men, whose deeds are good, though their words may be
few; men, whose lives are serviceable, be they never so short,
and worthy of honor, be they never so humble; — from these,

surely, at least, we may receive some clear message of teaching ; and pierce, for an instant, into the mystery of life, and of its arts.

120. Yes ; from these, at last, we do receive a lesson. But I grieve to say, or rather — for that is the deeper truth of the matter — I rejoice to say, this message of theirs can only be received by joining them, — not by thinking about them.

You sent for me to talk to you of art ; and I have obeyed you in coming. But the main thing I have to tell you is, — that art must not be talked about.° The fact that there is talk about it at all, signifies that it is ill-done, or cannot be done. No true painter° ever speaks, or ever has spoken, much of his art. The greatest speak nothing. Even Reynolds° is no exception, for he wrote of all that he could not himself do, and was utterly silent respecting all that he himself did.

The moment a man can really do his work he becomes speechless about it. All words become idle to him — all theories.

121. Does a bird need to theorize about building its nest, or boast of it when built? All good work is essentially done that way — without hesitation, without difficulty, without boasting ; and in the doers of the best, there is an inner and involuntary power which approximates literally to the instinct of an animal — nay, I am certain that in the most perfect human artists, reason does *not* supersede instinct, but is added to an instinct as much more divine than that of the lower animals as the human body is more beautiful than theirs ; that a great singer sings not with less instinct than the nightingale, but with more — only more various, applicable, and governable ; that a great architect does not build with less instinct than the beaver or the bee, but with more — with an innate cunning of proportion that embraces all beauty, and a divine ingenuity of skill that improvises all construction. But be that as it may — be the instinct less or more than that of inferior animals — like or unlike theirs, still the human art is dependent on that first, and then upon an

amount of practice, of science, and of imagination disciplined by
thought, which the true possessor of it knows to be incommuni-
cable, and the true critic of it, inexplicable, except through
long process of laborious years.   That journey of life's conquest,
in which hills over hills, and Alps on Alps arose, and sank, —
do you think you can make another trace it painlessly, by talking?   Why, you cannot even carry us up an Alp, by talking.
You can guide us up it, step by step, no otherwise — even so, best
silently.   You girls, who have been among the hills, know how
the bad guide chatters and gesticulates, and it is "put your foot
here," and "mind how you balance yourself there ;" but the
good guide walks on quietly without a word, only with his eyes
on you when need is, and his arm like an iron bar, if need be.°

122.   In that slow way, also, art can be taught — if you have
faith in your guide, and will let his arm be to you as an iron bar
when need is.   But in what teacher of art have you such faith?
Certainly not in me ; for, as I told you at first, I know well
enough it is only because you think I can talk, not because you
think I know my business, that you let me speak to you at all.
If I were to tell you anything that seemed to you strange you
would not believe it ; and yet it would only be in telling you
strange things that I could be of use to you.   I could be of great
use to you — infinite use — with brief saying, if you would believe it ; but you would not, just because the thing that would
be of real use would displease you.   You are all wild, for instance,
with admiration of Gustave Doré.°   Well, suppose I were to tell
you, in the strongest terms I could use, that Gustave Doré's art
was bad — bad, not in weakness, — not in failure, — but bad
with dreadful power — the power of the Furies and the Harpies °
mingled — enraging and polluting ; that so long as you looked
at it, no perception of pure or beautiful art was possible for
you.   Suppose I were to tell you that !   What would be the
use ?   Would you look at Gustave Doré less ?   Rather, more, I
fancy.   On the other hand, I could soon put you into good

humor with me, if I chose. I know well enough what you like, and how to praise it to your better liking. I could talk to you about moonlight, and twilight, and spring flowers, and autumn leaves, and the Madonnas of Raphæl ° — how motherly ! and the Sibyls of Michel Angelo ° — how majestic ! and the Saints of Angelico ° — how pious ! and the Cherubs of Correggio ° — how delicious ! Old as I am, I could play you a tune on the harp yet, that you would dance to. But neither you nor I should be a bit the better or wiser ; or, if we were, our increased wisdom could be of no practical effect. For, indeed, the arts, as regards teachableness, differ from the sciences also in this, that their power is founded not merely on facts which can be communicated, but on dispositions which require to be created. Art is neither to be achieved ° by effort of thinking, nor explained by accuracy of speaking. It is the instinctive and necessary result of powers which can only be developed through the mind of successive generations, and which finally burst into life under social conditions as slow of growth as the faculties they regulate. Whole eras of mighty history are summed, and the passions of dead myriads are concentrated, in the existence of a noble art ; and if that noble art were among us, we should feel it and rejoice ; not caring in the least to hear lectures on it ; and since it is not among us, be assured we have to go back to the root of it, or, at least, to the place where the stock of it is yet alive, and the branches began to die.

123. And now, may I have your pardon for pointing out, partly with reference to matters which are at this time of greater moment than the arts — that if we undertook such recession to the vital germs of national arts that have decayed, we should find a more singular arrest of their power in Ireland° than in any other European country. For in the eighth century Ireland possessed a school of art in her manuscripts and sculpture, which in many of its qualities — apparently in all essential qualities of decorative invention — was quite without rival ; seeming as

if it might have advanced to the highest triumphs in architecture and in painting. But there was one fatal flaw in its nature,
by which it was stayed, and stayed with a conspicuousness of
pause to which there is no parallel: so that, long ago, in tracing the progress of European schools from infancy to strength,
I chose for the students of Kensington, in a lecture since published,° two characteristic examples of early art, of equal skill;
but in the one case, skill which was progressive — in the other,
skill which was at pause. In the one case, it was work recep-
tive of correction — hungry for correction; and in the other,
work which inherently rejected correction. I chose for them a
corrigible ° Eve, and an incorrigible Angel; and I grieve to say
that the incorrigible Angel was also an Irish Angel![1]

124. And the fatal difference lay wholly in this. In both
pieces of art there was an equal falling short of the needs of
fact; but the Lombardic Eve knew she was in the wrong, and
the Irish Angel thought himself all right. The eager Lombardic ° sculptor, though firmly insisting on his childish idea, yet
showed in the irregular broken touches of the features, and the
imperfect struggle for softer lines in the form, a perception of
beauty and law that he could not render; there was the strain
of effort, under conscious imperfection, in every line. But the
Irish missal-painter ° had drawn his angel with no sense of failure, in happy complacency, and put red dots into the palms of
each hand, and rounded the eyes into perfect circles, and, I
regret to say, left the mouth out altogether, with perfect satis-
faction to himself.

125. May I without offence ask you to consider whether
this mode of arrest in ancient Irish art may not be indicative
of points of character which even yet, in some measure, arrest
your national power? I have seen much of Irish character,°
and have watched it closely, for I have also much loved it. And

---

[1] See "The Two Paths," p. 27.

I think the form of failure to which it is most liable is this, — that being generous-hearted, and wholly intending always to do right, it does not attend to the external laws of right, but thinks it must necessarily do right because it means to do so, and therefore does wrong without finding it out; and then, when the consequences of its wrong come upon it, or upon others connected with it, it cannot conceive that the wrong is in anywise of its causing or of its doing, but flies into wrath, and a strange agony of desire for justice, as feeling itself wholly innocent, which leads it farther astray, until there is nothing that it is not capable of doing with a good conscience.

126. But mind, I do not mean to say that, in past or present relations between Ireland and England, you have been wrong, and we right. Far from that, I believe that in all great questions of principle, and in all details of administration of law, you have been usually right, and we wrong; sometimes in misunderstanding you, sometimes in resolute iniquity to you. Nevertheless, in all disputes between states, though the stronger is nearly always mainly in the wrong, the weaker is often so in a minor degree; and I think we sometimes admit the possibility of our being in error, and you never do.

127. And now, returning to the broader question, what these arts and labors of life have to teach us of its mystery, this is the first of their lessons — that the more beautiful the art, the more it is essentially the work of a people who *feel themselves wrong*; ° — who are striving for the fulfilment of a law, and the grasp of a loveliness, which they have not yet attained, which they feel even farther and farther from attaining the more they strive for it. And yet, in still deeper sense, it is the work of people who know also that they are right. The very sense of inevitable error from their purpose marks the perfectness of that purpose, and the continued sense of failure arises from the continued opening of the eyes more clearly to all the sacredest laws of truth.

I

128. This is one lesson. The second is a very plain, and greatly precious one : namely — that whenever the arts and labors of life are fulfilled in this spirit of striving against misrule, and doing whatever we have to do, honorably and perfectly, they invariably bring happiness, as much as seems possible to the nature of man.   In all other paths, by which that happiness is pursued there is disappointment, or destruction ; for ambition and for passion there is no rest — no fruition ; the fairest pleasures of youth perish in a darkness greater than their past light : and the loftiest and purest love too often does but inflame the cloud of life with endless fire of pain.   But, ascending from lowest to highest, through every scale of human industry, that industry, worthily followed, gives peace.°   Ask the laborer in the field, at the forge, or in the mine ; ask the patient, delicate-fingered artisan, or the strong-armed, fiery-hearted worker in bronze, and in marble, and with the colors of light ; and none of these, who are true workmen, will ever tell you, that they have found the law of heaven° an unkind one — that in the sweat of their face they should eat bread, till they return to the ground ; nor that they ever found it an unrewarded obedience, if, indeed, it was rendered faithfully to the command, " Whatsoever thy hand findeth to do — do it with thy might." °

129. These are the two great and constant lessons which our laborers teach us of the mystery of life.   But there is another, and a sadder one, which they cannot teach us, which we must read on their tombstones.

" Do it with thy might."   There have been myriads upon myriads of human creatures who have obeyed this law — who have put every breath and nerve of their being into its toil — who have devoted every hour, and exhausted every faculty — who have bequeathed their unaccomplished thoughts at death — who, being dead, have yet spoken, by majesty of memory, and strength of example.   And, at last, what has all this

" Might" of humanity accomplished, in six thousand years° of labor and sorrow? What has it *done?* Take the three chief occupations and arts of men, one by one, and count their achievements. Begin with the first — the lord of them all — Agriculture. Six thousand years have passed since we were set to till the ground,° from which we were taken. How much of it is tilled? How much of that which is, wisely or well? In the very centre and chief garden° of Europe — where the two forms° of parent Christianity have had their fortresses — where the noble Catholics of the Forest Cantons,° and the noble Protestants of the Vaudois valleys, have maintained, for dateless ages, their faiths and liberties — there the unchecked Alpine rivers yet run wild in devastation; and the marshes, which a few hundred men could redeem with a year's labor, still blast their helpless inhabitants into fevered idiotism.° That is so, in the centre of Europe! While, on the near coast of Africa, once the Garden of the Hesperides,° an Arab woman, but a few sunsets since, ate her child, for famine. And, with all the treasures of the East at our feet, we, in our own dominion, could not find a few grains of rice, for a people that asked of us no more; but stood by, and saw five hundred thousand° of them perish of hunger.

130. Then after agriculture, the art of kings, take the next head of human arts — Weaving; the art of queens, honored of all noble Heathen women, in the person of their virgin goddess — honored of all Hebrew women, by the word of their wisest king — " She layeth her hands° to the spindle, and her hands hold the distaff; she stretcheth out her hand to the poor. She is not afraid of the snow for her household, for all her household are clothed with scarlet. She maketh herself covering of tapestry; her clothing is silk and purple. She maketh fine linen, and selleth it, and delivereth girdles to the merchant." What have we done in all these thousands of years with this bright art of Greek maid and Christian matron? Six

thousand years of weaving, and have we learned to weave?
Might not every naked wall have been purple with tapestry,
and every feeble breast fenced with sweet colors from the cold?
What have we done? Our fingers are too few, it seems, to
twist together some poor covering for our bodies. We set our
streams to work for us, and choke the air with fire, to turn
our spinning-wheels — and, — *are we yet clothed?* Are not
the streets of the capitals of Europe foul with sale of cast
clouts and rotten rags? Is not the beauty of your sweet children left in wretchedness of disgrace, while, with better honor,
nature clothes the brood of the bird in its nest, and the suck-
ling of the wolf in her den? And does not every winter's snow
robe what you have not robed, and shroud what you have not
shrouded; and every winter's wind bear up to heaven its wasted
souls, to witness against you hereafter, by the voice of their
Christ, — "I was naked,° and ye clothed me not"?

131. Lastly — take the Art of Building — the strongest —
proudest — most orderly — most enduring of the arts of man;
that of which the produce is in the surest manner accumulative,
and need not perish, or be replaced; but if once well done, will
stand more strongly than the unbalanced rocks — more preva-
lently than the crumbling hills. The art which is associated
with all civic pride° and sacred principle; with which men
record their power — satisfy their enthusiasm — make sure
their defence — define and make dear their habitation.
And in six thousand years of building, what have we done?
Of the greater part of all that skill and strength, *no* vestige
is left, but fallen stones, that encumber the field and impede
the streams. But, from this waste of disorder, and of time,
and of rage, what *is* left to us? Constructive and progressive
creatures, that we are, with ruling brains, and forming hands,
capable of fellowship, and thirsting for fame, can we not contend,
in comfort, with the insects of the forest, or, in achievement,
with the worm of the sea? The white surf rages in vain

against the ramparts built by poor atoms of scarcely nascent life; but only ridges of formless ruin mark the places where once dwelt our noblest multitudes. The ant and the moth have cells for each of their young, but our little ones lie in festering heaps, in homes that consume them like graves; and night by night, from the corners of our streets, rises up the cry of the homeless — "I was a stranger, and ye took me not in."

132. Must it be always thus? Is our life forever to be without profit — without possession? Shall the strength of its generations be as barren as death; or cast away their labor, as the wild fig-tree ° casts her untimely figs? Is it all a dream then — the desire of the eyes ° and the pride of life — or, if it be, might we not live in nobler dream than this? The poets and prophets, the wise men, and the scribes, though they have told us nothing about a life to come, have told us much about the life that is now. They have had — they also, — their dreams, and we have laughed at them. They have dreamed of mercy, and of justice; they have dreamed of peace and good-will; they have dreamed of labor undisappointed, and of rest undisturbed; they have dreamed of fulness in harvest, and overflowing in store; they have dreamed of wisdom in council, and of providence in law; of gladness of parents, and strength of children, and glory of grey hairs. And at these visions of theirs we have mocked, and held them for idle and vain, unreal and unaccomplishable.° What have we accomplished with our realities? Is this what has come of our worldly wisdom, tried against their folly? this, our mightiest possible, against their impotent ideal? or, have we only wandered among the spectra ° of a baser felicity, and chased phantoms of the tombs, instead of visions of the Almighty; and walked after the imaginations of our evil hearts,° instead of after the counsels of Eternity, until our lives — not in the likeness of the cloud of heaven, but of the smoke of hell — have become "as a vapor,° that appeareth for a little time, and then vanisheth away"?

133. *Does* it vanish, then? Are you sure of that?—
sure, that the nothingness of the grave will be a rest from this
troubled nothingness; and that the coiling shadow, which
disquiets itself in vain,° cannot change into the smoke of the
torment° that ascends forever? Will any answer that they *are*
sure of it, and that there is no fear, nor hope, nor desire, nor
labor, whither they go? Be it so: will you not, then, make
as sure of the Life that now is, as you are of the Death that
is to come? Your hearts are wholly in this world — will you
not give them to it wisely, as well as perfectly? And see, first
of all, that you *have* hearts, and sound hearts, too, to give.
Because you have no heaven to look for, is that any reason that
you should remain ignorant of this wonderful and infinite earth,
which is firmly and instantly° given you in possession? Although your days are numbered,° and the following darkness
sure, is it necessary that you should share the degradation of the
brute, because you are condemned to its mortality; or live the
life of the moth, and of the worm, because you are to companion them in the dust? Not so; we may have but a few thousands
of days to spend, perhaps hundreds only — perhaps tens; nay,
the longest of our time and best, looked back on, will be but as
a moment, as the twinkling of an eye;° still we are men, not
insects; we are living spirits, not passing clouds. "He maketh the winds° His messengers; the momentary fire, His minister;" and shall we do less than *these?* Let us do the work of
men while we bear the form of them; and, as we snatch our
narrow portion of time out of Eternity, snatch also our narrow
inheritance of passion out of Immortality — even though our
lives *be* as a vapor, that appeareth for a little time, and then
vanisheth away.

134. But there are some of you who believe not this — who
think this cloud of life has no such close — that it is to float,
revealed and illumined, upon the floor of heaven, in the day
when° He cometh with clouds, and every eye shall see Him

Some day, you believe, within these five, or ten, or twenty years, for every one of us the judgment will be set, and the books opened. If that be true, far more than that must be true. Is there but one day of judgment? Why, for us every day is a day of judgment, — every day is a Dies Iræ,° and writes its irrevocable verdict in the flame of its west.° Think you that judgment waits till the doors of the grave° are opened? It waits at the doors of your houses — it waits at the corners of your streets; we are in the midst of judgment° — the insects that we crush are our judges — the moments we fret away are our judges — the elements that feed us, judge, as they minister — and the pleasures that deceive us, judge, as they indulge. Let us, for our lives, do the work of Men while we bear the form of them, if indeed those lives art *Not* as a vapor, and do *Not* vanish away.

135. " The work of men " — and what is that? Well, we may any of us know very quickly, on the condition of being wholly ready to do it. But many of us are for the most part thinking, not of what we are to do, but of what we are to get ; and the best of us are sunk into the sin of Ananias,° and it is a mortal one — we want to keep back part of the price ; and we continually talk of taking up our cross,° as if the only harm in a cross was the *weight* of it — as if it was only a thing to be carried, instead of to be — crucified upon. " They that are His ° have crucified the flesh, with the affections and lusts." Does that mean, think you, that in time of national distress, of religious trial, of crisis for every interest and hope of humanity — none of us will cease jesting, none cease idling, none put themselves to any wholesome work, none take so much as a tag of lace off their footman's coats, to save the world? Or does it rather mean, that they are ready to leave ° houses, lands, and kindreds — yes, and life, if need be? Life! — some of us are ready enough to throw that away, joyless as we have made it. But " *station* in Life," ° — how many of us are ready to quit *that* ?

Is it not always the great objection, where there is question of finding something useful to do — "We cannot leave our stations in Life"?

Those of us who really cannot — that is to say, who can only maintain themselves by continuing in some business or salaried office, have already something to do; and all that they have to see to is, that they do it honestly and with all their might. But with most people who use that apology, "remaining in the station of life to which Providence has called them" means keeping all the carriages, and all the footmen and large houses they can possibly pay for; and, once for all, I say that if ever Providence *did* put them into stations of that sort — which is not at all a matter of certainty — Providence is just now very distinctly calling them out again. Levi's station° in life was the receipt of custom; and Peter's, the shore of Galilee; and Paul's, the ante-chambers of the High Priest, — which "station in life" each had to leave, with brief notice.

And whatever our station in life may be, at this crisis, those of us who mean to fulfil our duty ought, first, to live on as little as we can; and, secondly, to do all the wholesome work for it we can, and to spend all we can spare in doing all the sure good we can.

And sure good is, first in feeding people, then in dressing people, then in lodging people, and lastly in rightly pleasing people, with arts, or sciences, or any other subject of thought.

136.° I say first in feeding; and, once for all, do not let yourselves be deceived by any of the common talk of "indiscriminate charity." The order to us is not to feed the deserving hungry, nor the industrious hungry, nor the amiable and well-intentioned hungry, but simply to feed the hungry.° It is quite true, infallibly true, that if any man will not work,° neither should he eat — think of that, and every time you sit down to your dinner, ladies and gentlemen, say solemnly, before you ask a blessing, "How much work have I done to-day for my dinner ?" But the proper way to enforce that order on those below you, as well as on yourselves, is not to leave vagabonds and honest people to starve together, but very distinctly to discern and seize your vagabond ; and shut your vagabond up out of honest people's way, and very sternly then see that, until he has worked, he does *not* eat. But the first thing is to be sure you have the food to give ; and, therefore, to enforce the organization of vast activities in agriculture and in commerce, for the production of the wholesomest food, and proper storing and distribution of it, so that no famine shall any more be possible among civilized beings. There is plenty of work in this business alone, and at once, for any number of people who like to engage in it.

137. Secondly, dressing people — that is to say, urging every one within reach of your influence to be always neat and clean, and giving them means of being so. In so far as they absolutely refuse, you must give up the effort with respect to them, only taking care that no children within your sphere of influence shall any more be brought up with such habits ; and that every person who is willing to dress with propriety shall have encouragement to do so. And the first absolutely necessary step toward this is the gradual adoption of a consistent dress for different ranks ° of persons, so that their rank shall be known by their dress ; and the restriction of the changes of fashion within certain limits. All which appears for the present quite impossible ; but it is only so far as even difficult as it is difficult to conquer our vanity, frivolity, and desire to appear what we are not. And it is not, nor ever shall be, creed of mine, that these mean and shallow vices are unconquerable by Christian women.

138. And then, thirdly, lodging people, which you may think should have been put first, but I put it third, because we must feed and clothe people where we find them, and lodge them afterwards. And providing lodgement for them means a

great deal of vigorous legislature, and cutting down of vested
interests that stand in the way, and after that, or before that,
so far as we can get it, thorough sanitary and remedial action
in the houses that we have; and then the building of more,
strongly, beautifully, and in groups of limited extent, kept in
proportion to their streams, and walled round, so that there
may be no festering and wretched suburb anywhere, but clean
and busy street within, and the open country without, with a
belt of beautiful garden and orchard round the walls, so that
from any part of the city perfectly fresh air and grass, and
sight of far horizon, might be reachable in a few minutes' walk.
This is the final aim; but in immediate action every minor and
possible good to be instantly done, when, and as, we can; roofs
mended that have holes in them — fences patched that have
gaps in them — walls buttressed° that totter — and floors propped
that shake; cleanliness and order enforced with our own hands
and eyes, till we are breathless, every day. And all the fine
arts will healthily follow. I myself have washed a flight° of
stone stairs all down, with bucket and broom, in a Savoy inn,
where they hadn't washed their stairs since they first went up
them; and I never made a better sketch than that afternoon.

139. These, then, are the three first needs of civilized life;
and the law for every Christian man and woman is, that they
shall be in direct service toward one of these three needs, as far
as is consistent with their own special occupation, and if they
have no special business, then wholly in one of these services.
And out of such exertion in plain duty all other good will come;
for in this direct contention with material evil, you will find out
the real nature of all evil; you will discern by the various
kinds of resistance, what is really the fault and main antago-
nism to good; also you will find the most unexpected helps and
profound lessons given, and truths will come thus down to us
which the speculation of all our lives would never have raised
us up to. You will find nearly every educational problem solved,

as soon as you truly want to do something; everybody will become of use in their own fittest way, and will learn what is best for them to know in that use. Competitive examination° will then, and not till then, be wholesome, because it will be daily, and calm, and in practice; and on these familiar arts, and minute, but certain and serviceable knowledges, will be surely edified and sustained the greater arts and splendid theoretical° sciences.

140. But much more than this. On such holy and simple practice will be founded, indeed, at last, an infallible religion. The greatest of all the mysteries of life, and the most terrible, is the corruption of even the sincerest religion which is not daily founded on rational, effective, humble, and helpful action. Helpful action, observe! for there is just one law, which, obeyed, keeps all religions pure — forgotten, makes them all false. Whenever in any religious faith, dark or bright, we allow our minds to dwell upon the points in which we differ from other people, we are wrong, and in the devil's power. That is the essence of the Pharisee's thanksgiving° — "Lord, I thank thee that I am not as other men are." At every moment of our lives we should be trying to find out, not in what we differ from other people, but in what we agree with them; and the moment we find we can agree as to anything that should be done, kind or good, (and who but fools couldn't?) then do it; push at it together: you can't quarrel in a side-by-side push; but the moment that even the best men stop pushing, and begin talking, they mistake their pugnacity for piety,° and it's all over. I will not speak of the crimes which in past times have been committed in the name of Christ, nor of the follies which are at this hour held to be consistent with obedience to Him; but I *will* speak of the morbid corruption and waste of vital power in religious sentiment, by which the pure strength of that which should be the guiding soul of every nation, the splendor of its youthful manhood, and spotless light

of its maidenhood, is averted or cast away. You may see continually girls who have never been taught to do a single useful
thing thoroughly ; who cannot sew, who cannot cook, who cannot cast an account, nor prepare a medicine, whose whole life
has been passed either in play or in pride ; you will find girls
like these, when they are earnest-hearted, cast all their innate
passion of religious spirit, which was meant by God to support
them through the irksomeness of daily toil, into grievous and
vain meditation over the meaning of the great Book,° of which
no syllable was ever yet to be understood but through a deed ;
all the instinctive wisdom and mercy of their womanhood made
vain, and the glory of their pure conscience warped into fruitless
agony concerning questions which the laws of common serviceable life would have either solved for them in an instant, or
kept out of their way. Give such a girl any true work that
will make her active in the dawn, and weary at night, with the
consciousness that her fellow-creatures have indeed been the
better for her day, and the powerless sorrow of her enthusiasm
will transform itself into a majesty of radiant and beneficent
peace.

So with our youths. We once taught them to make Latin
verses,° and called them educated ; now we teach them to leap
and to row, to hit a ball with a bat, and call them educated.
Can they plough, can they sow, can they plant at the right time,
or build with a steady hand ? Is it the effort of their lives to
be chaste, knightly, faithful, holy in thought, lovely in word
and deed ? Indeed it is, with some, nay, with many, and the
strength of England is in them, and the hope ; but we have
to turn their courage from the toil of war to the toil of mercy ;
and their intellect from dispute of words to discernment of
things ; and their knighthood from the errantry of adventure
to the state and fidelity of a kingly power. And then, indeed,
shall abide, for them and for us, an incorruptible felicity, and
an infallible religion ; shall abide for us Faith, no more to be

assailed by temptation, no more to be defended by wrath and by fear ;— shall abide with us Hope, no more to be quenched by the years that overwhelm, or made ashamed by the shadows that betray :— shall abide for us, and with us, the greatest of these ; the abiding will, the abiding name of our Father.   For the greatest of these is Charity.°

THE

KING OF THE GOLDEN RIVER

THE

KING OF THE GOLDEN RIVER;

OR,

THE BLACK BROTHERS

CHAPTER I

HOW THE AGRICULTURAL SYSTEM OF THE BLACK BROTHERS WAS INTERFERED WITH BY SOUTH-WEST WIND, ESQUIRE

IN a secluded and mountainous part of Stiria° there was, in old time, a valley of the most surprising and luxuriant fertility. It was surrounded, on all sides, by steep and rocky mountains, rising into peaks, which were always covered with snow, and from which a number of torrents descended in constant cataracts. One of these fell westward, over the face of a crag so high, that, when the sun had set to everything else, and all below was darkness, his beams still shone full upon this waterfall, so that it looked like a shower of gold. It was, therefore, called by the people of the neighborhood, the Golden River.° It was strange that none of these streams fell into the valley itself. They all descended on the other side of the mountains, and wound away through broad plains and by populous cities. But the clouds were drawn so constantly to the snowy hills, and rested so softly in the circular hollow, that in time of drought and heat, when all the country round was burnt up, there was still rain in the little valley ; and its crops were so heavy, and its hay so high, and its apples so red, and its grapes so blue, and its wine so rich, and its honey so sweet, that it was a marvel to every one who beheld it, and was commonly called the Treasure Valley.°

The whole of this little valley belonged to three brothers, called Schwartz, Hans, and Gluck.° Schwartz and Hans, the two elder brothers, were very ugly men, with overhanging eyebrows and small dull eyes, which were always half shut, so that you couldn't see into *them*, and always fancied they saw very far into *you*. They lived by farming the Treasure Valley, and very good farmers they were.° They killed everything that did not pay for its eating. They shot the blackbirds, because they pecked the fruit ; and killed the hedgehogs, lest they should suck the cows ; they poisoned the crickets for eating the crumbs in the kitchen ; and smothered the cicadas, which used to sing all summer in the lime trees. They worked their servants without any wages, till they would not work any more, and then quarrelled with them, and turned them out of doors without paying them. It would have been very odd, if with such a farm, and such a system of farming, they hadn't got very rich ;° and very rich they *did* get. They generally contrived to keep their corn ° by them till it was very dear, and then sell it for twice its value ; they had heaps of gold lying about on their floors, yet it was never known that they had given so much as a penny ° or a crust in charity ; they never went to mass ; grumbled perpetually at paying tithes ; and were, in a word, of so cruel and grinding a temper, as to receive from all those with whom they had any dealings, the nick-name of the " Black Brothers."

The youngest brother, Gluck, was as completely opposed, in both appearance and character, to his seniors as could possibly be imagined or desired. He was not above twelve years old, fair, blue-eyed, and kind in temper to every living thing. He did not, of course, agree particularly well with his brothers, or rather, they did not agree with *him*. He was usually appointed the honorable office of turnspit,° when there was anything to roast, which was not often ; for, to do the brothers justice, they were hardly less sparing upon themselves ° than upon other people. At other times he used to clean the shoes, floors, and sometimes the plates, occasionally getting what was left on them, by way of encouragement, and a wholesome quantity of dry blows, by way of education.

Things went on in this manner for a long time. At last came a very wet summer, and everything went wrong in the country around. The hay had hardly been got in, when the haystacks were floated bodily down to the sea by an inundation ; the vines were cut to pieces with the hail ; the corn was all killed by a black blight ; only in the Treasure Valley, as usual, all was safe. As it had rain when there was rain no-where else, so it had sun when there was sun nowhere else. Everybody came to buy corn at the farm, and went away pour-ing maledictions on the Black Brothers. They asked what they liked,° and got it, except from the poor people, who could only beg, and several of whom were starved at their very door, without the slightest regard or notice.

It was drawing toward winter, and very cold weather, when one day the two elder brothers had gone out, with their usual warning to little Gluck, who was left to mind the roast, that he was to let nobody in, and give nothing out. Gluck sat down quite close to the fire, for it was raining very hard, and the kitchen walls were by no means dry or comfortable looking. He turned and turned, and the roast got nice and brown. "What a pity," thought Gluck, "my brothers never ask anybody to dinner. I'm sure, when they've got such a nice piece of mutton as this, and nobody else has got so much as a piece of dry bread, it would do their hearts good to have somebody to eat it with them."

Just as he spoke, there came a double knock at the house

door, yet heavy and dull, as though the knocker had been tied up — more like a puff than a knock.

"It must be the wind," said Gluck; "nobody else would venture to knock double knocks at our door." °

No; it wasn't the wind: there it came again very hard, and what was particularly astounding, the knocker seemed to be in a hurry, and not to be in the least afraid of the consequences. Gluck went to the window, opened it, and put his head out to see who it was.

It was the most extraordinary looking little gentleman ° he had ever seen in his life. He had a very large nose, slightly brass-colored; his cheeks were very round, and very red, and might have warranted a supposition that he had been blowing a refractory fire for the last eight-and-forty hours; his eyes twinkled merrily through long silky eyelashes, his moustaches curled twice round like a corkscrew on each side of his mouth, and his hair, of a curious mixed pepper-and-salt color, descended far over his shoulders. He was about four feet six in height, and wore a conical pointed cap of nearly the same altitude, decorated with a black feather some three feet long. His doublet was prolonged behind into something resembling a violent exaggeration of what is now termed a "swallow-tail," but was much obscured by the swelling folds of an enormous black, glossy-looking cloak, which must have been very much too long in calm weather, as the wind, whistling round the old house, carried it clear out from the wearer's shoulders to about four times his own length.

Gluck was so perfectly paralyzed by the singular appearance of his visitor, that he remained fixed without uttering a word, until the old gentleman, having performed another, and a more energetic concerto on the knocker, turned round to look after his fly-away cloak. In so doing he caught sight of Gluck's little yellow head jammed in the window, with its mouth and eyes very wide open indeed.

"Hollo!" said the little gentleman, "that's not the way to answer the door: I'm wet, let me in."

To do the little gentleman justice, he *was* wet. His feather hung down between his legs like a beaten puppy's tail, dripping like an umbrella; and from the ends of his moustaches the water was running into his waistcoat pockets, and out again like a mill stream.

"I beg pardon, sir," said Gluck, "I'm very sorry, but I really can't."

"Can't what!" said the old gentleman.

"I can't let you in, sir — I can't, indeed; my brothers would beat me to death, sir, if I thought of such a thing. What do you want, sir?"

"Want?" said the old gentleman, petulantly. "I want fire, and shelter; and there's your great fire there blazing, crackling, and dancing on the walls, with nobody to feel it. Let me in, I say; I only want to warm myself."

Gluck had had his head, by this time, so long out of the window, that he began to feel it was really unpleasantly cold, and when he turned, and saw the beautiful fire rustling and roaring, and throwing long bright tongues up the chimney, as if it were licking its chops at the savory smell of the leg of mutton, his heart melted within him that it should be burning away for nothing. "He does look *very* wet," said little Gluck; "I'll just let him in for a quarter of an hour." Round he went to the door, and opened it; and as the little gentleman walked in, there came a gust of wind through the house, that made the old chimneys totter.

"That's a good boy," said the little gentleman. "Never mind your brothers. I'll talk to them."

"Pray, sir, don't do any such thing," said Gluck. "I can't let you stay till they come; they'd be the death of me."

"Dear me," said the old gentleman, "I'm very sorry to hear that. How long may I stay?"

"Only till the mutton's done, sir," replied Gluck, "and it's very brown."

Then the old gentleman walked into the kitchen, and sat himself down on the hob,° with the top of his cap accommodated up the chimney, for it was a great deal too high for the roof.

"You'll soon dry there, sir," said Gluck, and sat down again to turn the mutton.   But the old gentleman did *not* dry there, but went on drip, drip, dripping among the cinders, and the fire fizzed, and sputtered, and began to look very black, and uncomfortable : never was such a cloak ; every fold in it ran like a gutter.

"I beg pardon, sir," said Gluck at length, after watching the water spreading in long, quicksilverlike streams over the floor for a quarter of an hour ; "mayn't I take your cloak?"

"No, thank you," said the old gentleman.

"Your cap, sir?"

"I am all right, thank you," said the old gentleman, rather gruffly.

"But, — sir, — I'm very sorry," said Gluck, hesitatingly ; "but — really, sir, — you're — putting the fire out."

"It'll take longer to do the mutton, then," replied his visitor, drily.

Gluck was very much puzzled by the behavior of his guest ; it was such a strange mixture of coolness and humility.   He turned away at the string meditatively for another five minutes.

"That mutton looks very nice," said the old gentleman at length.   "Can't you give me a little bit?"

"Impossible, sir," said Gluck.

"I'm very hungry," continued the old gentleman : "I've had nothing to eat yesterday, nor to-day.   They surely couldn't miss a bit from the knuckle !"

He spoke in so very melancholy a tone, that it quite melted Gluck's heart.   "They promised me one slice to-day, sir," said he ; "I can give you that, but not a bit more."

"That's a good boy," said the old gentleman again.

Then Gluck warmed a plate, and sharpened a knife. "I don't care if I do get beaten for it," thought he. Just as he had cut a large slice out of the mutton, there came a tremendous rap at the door. The old gentleman jumped off the hob, as if it had suddenly become inconveniently warm. Gluck fitted the slice into the mutton again, with desperate efforts at exactitude, and ran to open the door.

"What did you keep us waiting in the rain for?" said Schwartz, as he walked in, throwing his umbrella in Gluck's face. "Ay! what for, indeed, you little vagabond?" said Hans, administering an educational box on the ear, as he followed his brother into the kitchen.

"Bless my soul!" said Schwartz when he opened the door.

"Amen," said the little gentleman, who had taken his cap off, and was standing in the middle of the kitchen, bowing with the utmost possible velocity.

"Who's that?" said Schwartz, catching up a rolling-pin, and turning to Gluck with a fierce frown.

"I don't know, indeed, brother," said Gluck in great terror.

"How did he get in?" roared Schwartz.

"My dear brother," said Gluck, deprecatingly, "he was so *very* wet!"

The rolling-pin was descending on Gluck's head; but, at the instant, the old gentleman interposed his conical cap, on which it crashed with a shock that shook the water out of it all over the room. What was very odd, the rolling-pin no sooner touched the cap,° than it flew out of Schwartz's hand, spinning like a straw in a high wind, and fell into the corner at the further end of the room.

"Who are you, sir?" demanded Schwartz, turning upon him.

"What's your business?" snarled Hans.

"I'm a poor old man, sir," the little gentleman began very

modestly, "and I saw your fire through the window, and begged shelter for a quarter of an hour."

"Have the goodness to walk out again, then," said Schwartz. "We've quite enough water in our kitchen, without making it a drying-house."

"It is a cold day to turn an old man out in, sir; look at my grey hairs." They hung down to his shoulders, as I told you before.

"Ay!" said Hans, "there are enough of them to keep you warm. Walk!"

"I'm very, very hungry, sir; couldn't you spare me a bit of bread before I go?"

"Bread, indeed!" said Schwartz; "do you suppose we've nothing to do with our bread, but to give it to such red-nosed fellows as you?"

"Why don't you sell your feather?" said Hans, sneeringly. "Out with you."

"A little bit," said the old gentleman.

"Be off!" said Schwartz.

"Pray, gentlemen."

"Off, and be hanged!" cried Hans, seizing him by the collar. But he had no sooner touched the old gentleman's collar, than away he went after the rolling-pin, spinning round and round, till he fell into the corner on the top of it. Then Schwartz was very angry, and ran at the old gentleman to turn him out; but he also had hardly touched him, when away he went after Hans° and the rolling-pin, and hit his head against the wall as he tumbled into the corner. And so there they lay, all three.

Then the old gentleman spun himself round with velocity in the opposite direction; continued to spin until his long cloak was all wound neatly about him; clapped his cap on his head, very much on one side (for it could not stand upright without going through the ceiling), gave an additional twist to his cork-screw moustaches, and replied with perfect coolness: "Gentlemen, I wish you a very good morning. At twelve o'clock to-night I'll call again;° after such a refusal of hospitality as I have just experienced, you will not be surprised if that visit is the last I ever pay you."

"If ever I catch you here again," muttered Schwartz, coming, half frightened, out of the corner — but, before he could finish his sentence, the old gentleman had shut the house door behind him with a great bang: and there drove past the window at the same instant, a wreath of ragged cloud, that whirled and rolled away down the valley in all manner of shapes; turning over and over in the air; and melting away at last in a gush of rain.

"A very pretty business, indeed, Mr. Gluck!" said Schwartz. "Dish the mutton, sir. If ever I catch you at such a trick again — bless me, why the mutton's been cut!"

"You promised me one slice, brother, you know," said Gluck.

"Oh! and you were cutting it hot, I suppose, and going to catch all the gravy. It'll be long before I promise you such a thing again. Leave the room, sir; and have the kindness to wait in the coal-cellar till I call you."

Gluck left the room melancholy enough. The brothers ate as much mutton as they could, locked the rest in the cupboard, and proceeded to get very drunk after dinner.

Such a night as it was! Howling wind, and rushing rain, without intermission. The brothers had just sense enough left to put up all the shutters, and double bar the door, before they went to bed. They usually slept in the same room. As the clock struck twelve, they were both awakened by a tremendous crash. Their door burst open with a violence that shook the house from top to bottom.

"What's that?" cried Schwartz, starting up in his bed.

"Only I," said the little gentleman.

The two brothers sat up on their bolster, and stared into the darkness. The room was full of water, and by a misty moon-beam, which found its way through a hole in the shutter, they could see in the midst of it, an enormous foam globe,° spinning round, and bobbing up and down like a cork, on which, as on a most luxurious cushion, reclined the little old gentleman, cap and all. There was plenty of room for it now, for the roof was off.

"Sorry to incommode you," said their visitor, ironically. "I'm afraid your beds are dampish; perhaps you had better go to your brother's room: I've left the ceiling on, there."

They required no second admonition, but rushed into Gluck's room, wet through, and in an agony of terror.

"You'll find my card on the kitchen table," the old gentleman called after them. "Remember, the *last* visit."

"Pray Heaven it may !" said Schwartz, shuddering. And the foam globe disappeared.

Dawn came at last, and the two brothers looked out of Gluck's little window in the morning. The Treasure Valley was one mass of ruin and desolation. The inundation had swept away trees, crops, and cattle, and left in their stead, a waste of red sand, and grey mud. The two brothers crept shivering and horror-stricken into the kitchen. The water had gutted the whole first floor; corn, money, almost every mov-able thing had been swept away, and there was left only a small white card on the kitchen table. On it, in large, breezy, long-legged letters, were engraved the words : —

South-west Wind, Esquire.

CHAPTER II

OF THE PROCEEDINGS OF THE THREE BROTHERS AFTER THE
VISIT OF THE SOUTH-WEST WIND, ESQUIRE; AND HOW LIT-
TLE GLUCK HAD AN INTERVIEW WITH THE KING OF THE
GOLDEN RIVER

SOUTH-WEST WIND, Esquire, was as good as his word. After
the momentous visit above related, he entered the Treasure
Valley no more; and, what was worse, he had so much influence with his relations, the West Winds in general, and used it
so effectually, that they all adopted a similar line of conduct.
So no rain fell in the valley from one year's end to another.
Though everything remained green and flourishing in the plains
below, the inheritance of the Three Brothers was a desert. What
had once been the richest soil in the kingdom, became a shifting heap of red sand; and the brothers, unable longer to contend with the adverse skies, abandoned their valueless patrimony
in despair, to seek some means of gaining a livelihood among
the cities and people of the plains. All their money was gone.
and they had nothing left but some curious old-fashioned pieces
of gold plate, the last remnants of their ill-gotten wealth.

"Suppose we turn goldsmiths?" said Schwartz to Hans,
as they entered the large city. "It is a good knave's trade;
we can put a great deal of copper into the gold, without any
one's finding it out."

The thought was agreed to be a very good one; they hired a
furnace, and turned goldsmiths. But two slight circumstances
affected their trade: the first, that people did not approve of

the coppered gold; the second, that the two elder brothers, whenever they had sold anything, used to leave little Gluck to mind the furnace, and go and drink out the money in the ale-house next door. So they melted all their gold, without making money enough to buy more, and were at last reduced to one large drinking mug, which an uncle of his had given to little Gluck, and which he was very fond of, and would not have parted with for the world; though he never drank anything out of it but milk and water. The mug was a very odd mug to look at. The handle was formed of two wreaths of flowing golden hair, so finely spun that it looked more like silk than metal, and these wreaths descended into, and mixed with, a beard and whiskers of the same exquisite workmanship, which surrounded and decorated a very fierce little face, of the reddest gold imaginable, right in the front of the mug, with a pair of eyes in it which seemed to command its whole circumference. It was impossible to drink out of the mug without being subjected to an intense gaze of the side of these eyes; and Schwartz positively averred, that once, after emptying it, full of Rhenish, seventeen times, he had seen them wink ! When it came to the mug's turn to be made into spoons, it half broke poor little Gluck's heart; but the brothers only laughed at him, tossed the mug into the melting-pot, and staggered out to the ale-house; leaving him, as usual, to pour the gold into bars, when it was all ready.

When they were gone, Gluck took a farewell look at his old friend in the melting-pot. The flowing hair was all gone; nothing remained but the red nose, and the sparkling eyes, which looked more malicious than ever. "And no wonder," thought Gluck, "after being treated in that way." He sauntered disconsolately to the window, and sat himself down to catch the fresh evening air, and escape the hot breath of the furnace. Now this window commanded a direct view of the range of mountains, which, as I told you before, overhung the

Treasure Valley, and more especially of the peak from which fell the Golden River. It was just at the close of the day, and, when Gluck sat down at the window, he saw the rocks of the mountain tops, all crimson, and purple with the sunset; and there were bright tongues of fiery cloud burning and quivering about them; and the river, brighter than all, fell, in a waving column of pure gold, from precipice to precipice, with the double arch of a broad purple rainbow stretched across it, flushing and fading alternately in the wreaths of spray.

"Ah!" said Gluck, aloud, after he had looked at it for a while, "if that river were really all gold, what a nice thing it would be."

"No, it wouldn't, Gluck," said a clear metallic voice, close at his ear.

"Bless me, what's that?" exclaimed Gluck, jumping up. There was nobody there. He looked round the room, and under the table, and a great many times behind him, but there was certainly nobody there, and he sat down again at the window. This time he didn't speak, but he couldn't help thinking again that it would be very convenient if the river were really all gold.

"Not at all, my boy," said the same voice, louder than before.

"Bless me!" said Gluck again, "what *is* that?" He looked again into all the corners, and cupboards, and then began turning round, and round, as fast as he could in the middle of the room, thinking there was somebody behind him, when the same voice struck again on his ear. It was singing now very merrily, "Lala-lira-la"; no words, only a soft running effervescent melody, something like that of a kettle on the boil. Gluck looked out of the window. No, it was certainly in the house. Up stairs, and down stairs. No, it was certainly in that very room, coming in quicker time, and clearer notes, every moment. "Lala-lira-la." All at once it struck Gluck, that it sounded louder near the furnace. He ran to the opening, and looked in : yes, he saw right, it seemed to be coming, not only out of the furnace, but out of the pot.   He uncovered it, and ran back in a great fright, for the pot was certainly singing ! He stood in the far-thest corner of the room, with his hands up, and his mouth open, for a minute or two, when the singing stopped, and the voice became clear, and pronunciative.

"Hollo !" said the voice.

Gluck made no answer.

"Hollo ! Gluck, my boy," said the pot again.

Gluck summoned all his energies, walked straight up to the crucible, drew it out of the furnace, and looked in.   The gold was all melted, and its surface as smooth and polished as a river ; but instead of reflecting little Gluck's head, as he looked in, he saw meeting his glance from beneath the gold, the red nose, and sharp eyes of his old friend of the mug, a thousand times redder, and sharper than ever he had seen them in his life.

"Come, Gluck, my boy," said the voice out of the pot again, " I'm all right ; pour me out."

But Gluck was too much astonished to do anything of the kind.

"Pour me out, I say," said the voice, rather gruffly.

Still Gluck couldn't move.

" *Will* you pour me out?" said the voice, passionately, " I'm too hot."

By a violent effort, Gluck recovered the use of his limbs, took hold of the crucible, and sloped it, so as to pour out the gold.   But instead of a liquid stream, there came out, first, a pair of pretty little yellow legs, then some coat-tails, then a pair of arms stuck a-kimbo, and, finally, the well-known head of his friend the mug ; all which articles, uniting as they rolled out, stood up energetically on the floor, in the shape of a little golden dwarf, about a foot and a half high.

"That's right !" said the dwarf, stretching out first his legs, and then his arms, and then shaking his head up and down, and as far around as it would go, for five minutes, without stopping; apparently with the view of ascertaining if he were quite correctly put together, while Gluck stood contemplating him in speechless amazement. He was dressed in a slashed doublet of spun gold, so fine in its texture, that the prismatic colors gleamed over it, as if on a surface of mother of pearl; and, over this brilliant doublet, his hair and beard fell full half way to the ground, in waving curls, so exquisitely delicate, that Gluck could hardly tell where they ended; they seemed to melt into air. The features of the face, however, were by no means finished with the same delicacy; they were rather coarse, slightly inclining to coppery in complexion, and indicative, in expression, of a very pertinacious and intractable disposition in their small proprietor. When the dwarf had finished his self-examination, he turned his small sharp eyes full on Gluck, and stared at him deliberately for a minute or two. "No, it wouldn't, Gluck, my boy," said the little man.

This was certainly rather an abrupt, and unconnected mode of commencing conversation. It might indeed be supposed to refer to the course of Gluck's thoughts, which had first produced the dwarf's observations out of the pot; but whatever it referred to, Gluck had no inclination to dispute the dictum.

"Wouldn't it, sir?" said Gluck, very mildly, and submissively indeed.

"No," said the dwarf, conclusively, "no, it wouldn't." And with that, the dwarf pulled his cap hard over his brows, and took two turns, of three feet long, up and down the room, lifting his legs up very high, and setting them down very hard. This pause gave time for Gluck to collect his thoughts a little, and, seeing no great reason to view his diminutive visitor with dread, and feeling his curiosity overcome his amazement, he ventured on a question of peculiar delicacy.

"Pray, sir," said Gluck, rather hesitatingly, "were you my mug?"

On which the little man turned sharp round, walked straight

up to Gluck, and drew himself up to his full height. "I," said the little man, "am the King of the Golden River." Whereupon he turned about again, and took two more turns, some six feet long, in order to allow time for the consternation which this announcement produced in his auditor to evaporate. After which, he again walked up to Gluck, and stood still, as if expecting some comment on his communication.

Gluck determined to say something at all events. "I hope your Majesty is very well," said Gluck.

"Listen !" said the little man, deigning no reply to this polite inquiry. "I am the King of what you mortals call the Golden River. The shape you saw me in, was owing to the malice of a stronger king, from whose enchantments you have this instant freed me. What I have seen of you, and your conduct to your wicked brothers, renders me willing to serve you ; therefore, attend to what I tell you. Whoever shall climb to the top of that mountain from which you see the Golden River issue, and shall cast into the stream at its source, three drops of holy water, for him, and for him only, the river shall turn to gold. But no one failing in his first, can succeed in a second attempt ; and if any one shall cast unholy water into the river, it will overwhelm him, and he will become a black stone." So saying, the King of the Golden River turned away and deliberately walked into the centre of the hottest flame of the furnace. His figure became red, white, transparent, dazzling — a blaze of intense light — rose, trembled, and disappeared. The King of the Golden River had evaporated.

"Oh !" cried poor Gluck, running to look up the chimney after him ; "oh, dear, dear, dear me ! My mug ! my mug ! my mug !"

CHAPTER III

HOW MR. HANS SET OFF ON AN EXPEDITION TO THE GOLDEN RIVER, AND HOW HE PROSPERED THEREIN

THE King of the Golden River had hardly made the extraordinary exit related in the last chapter, before Hans and Schwartz came roaring into the house, very savagely drunk. The discovery of the total loss of their last piece of plate had the effect of sobering them just enough to enable them to stand over Gluck, beating him very steadily for a quarter of an hour; at the expiration of which period they dropped into a couple of chairs, and requested to know what he had got to say for himself. Gluck told them his story, of which, of course, they did not believe a word. They beat him again, till their arms were tired, and staggered to bed. In the morning, however, the steadiness with which he adhered to his story obtained him some degree of credence; the immediate consequence of which was, that the two brothers, after wrangling a long time on the knotty question, which of them should try his fortune first, drew their swords and began fighting.° The noise of the fray alarmed the neighbors, who, finding they could not pacify the combatants, sent for the constable.

Hans, on hearing of this, contrived to escape, and hid himself; but Schwartz was taken before the magistrate, fined for breaking the peace, and, having drunk out his last penny the evening before, was thrown into prison till he should pay.

When Hans heard this, he was much delighted, and determined to set out immediately for the Golden River. How to

L

get the holy water, was the question. He went to the priest, but the priest could not give any holy water to so abandoned a character. So Hans went to vespers in the evening for the first time in his life, and, under pretence of crossing himself, stole a cupful, and returned home in triumph.

Next morning he got up before the sun rose, put the holy water into a strong flask, and two bottles of wine and some meat in a basket, slung them over his back, took his alpine staff in his hand, and set off for the mountains.

On his way out of the town he had to pass the prison, and as he looked in at the windows, whom should he see but Schwartz himself peeping out of the bars, and looking very disconsolate.

"Good morning, brother," said Hans; "have you any message for the King of the Golden River?"

Schwartz gnashed his teeth with rage, and shook the bars with all his strength; but Hans only laughed at him, and advising him to make himself comfortable till he came back again, shouldered his basket, shook the bottle of holy water in Schwartz's face till it frothed again, and marched off in the highest spirits in the world.

It was, indeed, a morning that might have made any one happy, even with no Golden River to seek for. Level lines of dewy mist lay stretched along the valley, out of which rose the massy mountains — their lower cliffs in pale grey shadow, hardly distinguishable from the floating vapor, but gradually ascending till they caught the sunlight, which ran in sharp touches of ruddy color, along the angular crags, and pierced, in long level rays, through their fringes of spear-like pine. Far above, shot up red splintered masses of castellated rock, jagged and shivered into myriads of fantastic forms, with here and there a streak of sunlit snow, traced down their chasms like a line of forked lightning; and, far beyond, and far above all these, fainter than the morning cloud, but purer and changeless, slept, in the blue sky, the utmost peaks of the eternal snow.

The Golden River, which sprang from one of the lower and snowless elevations, was now nearly in shadow; all but the uppermost jets of spray, which rose like slow smoke above the undulating line of the cataract, and floated away in feeble wreaths upon the morning wind.

On this object, and on this alone, Hans' eyes and thoughts were fixed; forgetting the distance he had to traverse, he set off at an imprudent rate of walking, which greatly exhausted him before he had scaled the first range of the green and low hills. He was, moreover, surprised, on surmounting them, to find that a large glacier,° of whose existence, notwithstanding his previous knowledge of the mountains, he had been absolutely ignorant, lay between him and the source of the Golden River. He entered on it with the boldness of a practised mountaineer; yet he thought he had never traversed so strange or so dangerous a glacier in his life. The ice was excessively slippery, and out of all its chasms came wild sounds of gushing water; not monotonous or low, but changeful and loud, rising occasionally into drifting passages of wild melody, then breaking off into short melancholy tones, or sudden shrieks, resembling those of human voices in distress or pain. The ice was broken into thousands of confused shapes, but none, Hans thought, like the ordinary forms of splintered ice. There seemed a curious *expression* about all their outlines — a perpetual resemblance to living features, distorted and scornful. Myriads of deceitful shadows, and lurid lights, played and floated about and through the pale blue pinnacles, dazzling and confusing the sight of the traveller; while his ears grew dull and his head giddy with the constant gush and roar of the concealed waters. These painful circumstances increased upon him as he advanced; the ice crashed and yawned into fresh chasms at his feet, tottering spires nodded around him, and fell thundering across his path ; and though he had repeatedly faced these dangers on the most terrific glaciers, and in the wildest weather, it was with a new and oppressive feeling of panic terror that he leaped the last chasm, and flung himself, exhausted and shuddering, on the firm turf of the mountain.

He had been compelled to abandon his basket of food, which became a perilous incumbrance on the glacier, and had now no means of refreshing himself but by breaking off and eating some of the pieces of ice. This, however, relieved his thirst ; an hour's repose recruited his hardy frame, and with the indomitable spirit of avarice, he resumed his laborious journey.

His way now lay straight up a ridge of bare red rocks, without a blade of grass to ease the foot, or a projecting angle to afford an inch of shade from the south sun. It was past noon, and the rays beat intensely upon the steep path, while the whole atmosphere was motionless, and penetrated with heat. Intense thirst was soon added to the bodily fatigue with which Hans was now afflicted ; glance after glance he cast on the flask of water which hung at his belt. "Three drops are enough," at last thought he ; "I may, at least, cool my lips with it."

He opened the flask, and was raising it to his lips, when his eye fell on an object lying on the rock beside him ; he thought it moved. It was a small dog, apparently in the last agony of death from thirst. Its tongue was out, its jaws dry, its limbs extended lifelessly, and a swarm of black ants were crawling about its lips and throat. Its eye moved to the bottle which Hans held in his hand. He raised it, drank, spurned the animal with his foot, and passed on. And he did not know how it was, but he thought that a strange shadow had suddenly come across the blue sky.

The path became steeper and more rugged every moment ; and the high hill air, instead of refreshing him, seemed to throw his blood into a fever. The noise of the hill cataracts sounded like mockery in his ears; they were all distant, and his thirst increased every moment. Another hour passed, and he again looked down to the flask at his side; it was half empty; but there was much more than three drops in it. He stopped to open it, and again, as he did so, something moved in the path above him. It was a fair child, stretched nearly lifeless on the rock, its breast heaving with thirst, its eyes closed, and its lips parched and burning. Hans eyed it deliberately, drank, and passed on. And a dark grey cloud came over the sun, and long, snake-like shadows crept up along the mountain sides. Hans struggled on. The sun was sinking, but its descent seemed to bring no coolness; the leaden weight of the dead air pressed upon his brow and heart, but the goal was near. He saw the cataract of the Golden River springing from the hillside, scarcely five hundred feet above him. He paused for a moment to breathe, and sprang on to complete his task.

At this instant a faint cry fell on his ear. He turned, and saw a grey-haired old man extended on the rocks. His eyes were sunk, his features deadly pale, and gathered into an expression of despair. "Water!" he stretched his arms to Hans, and cried feebly, "Water! I am dying."

"I have none," replied Hans; "thou hast had thy share of life." He strode over the prostrate body, and darted on. And a flash of blue lightning rose out of the East, shaped like a sword; it shook thrice over the whole heaven, and left it dark with one heavy, impenetrable shade. The sun was setting; it plunged toward the horizon like a red-hot ball.

The roar of the Golden River rose on Hans' ear. He stood at the brink of the chasm through which it ran. Its waves were filled with the red glory of the sunset: they shook their crests like tongues of fire, and flashes of bloody light gleamed along their foam. Their sound came mightier and mightier on his senses; his brain grew giddy with the prolonged thunder. Shuddering, he drew the flask from his girdle, and hurled it into the centre of the torrent. As he did so, an icy chill shot through his limbs: he staggered, shrieked, and fell. The waters closed over his cry. And the moaning of the river rose wildly into the night, as it gushed over

THE BLACK STONE.°

CHAPTER IV

HOW MR. SCHWARTZ SET OFF ON AN EXPEDITION TO THE
GOLDEN RIVER, AND HOW HE PROSPERED THEREIN

POOR little Gluck waited very anxiously alone in the house,
for Hans' return. Finding he did not come back, he was terri-
bly frightened, and went and told Schwartz in the prison, all
that had happened. Then Schwartz was very much pleased,
and said that Hans must certainly have been turned into a black
stone, and he should have all the gold to himself. But Gluck
was very sorry, and cried all night. When he got up in the
morning, there was no bread in the house, nor any money; so
Gluck went, and hired himself to another goldsmith, and he
worked so hard, and so neatly, and so long every day, that he
soon got money enough together, to pay his brother's fine, and
he went, and gave it all to Schwartz, and Schwartz got out of
prison. Then Schwartz was quite pleased, and said he should
have some of the gold of the river. But Gluck only begged he
would go and see what had become of Hans.

Now when Schwartz had heard that Hans had stolen the
holy water, he thought to himself that such a proceeding might
not be considered altogether correct by the King of the Golden
River, and determined to manage matters better. So he took
some more of Gluck's money, and went to a bad priest, who
gave him some holy water very readily for it. Then Schwartz
was sure it was all quite right. So Schwartz got up early in
the morning, before the sun rose, and took some bread and wine,
in a basket, and put his holy water in a flask, and set off foi

the mountains.   Like his brother he was much surprised at the sight of the glacier, and had great difficulty in crossing it, even after leaving his basket behind him.   The day was cloudless, but not bright : there was a heavy purple haze hanging over the sky, and the hills looked lowering and gloomy.   And as Schwartz climbed the steep rock path, the thirst came upon him, as it had upon his brother, until he lifted his flask to his lips to drink. Then he saw the fair child lying near him on the rocks, and it cried to him, and moaned for water.   "Water, indeed," said Schwartz ; "I haven't half enough for myself," and passed on. And as he went he thought the sunbeams grew more dim, and he saw a low bank of black cloud rising out of the West ; and, when he had climbed for another hour the thirst overcame him again, and he would have drunk.   Then he saw the old man lying before him on the path, and heard him cry out for water. "Water, indeed," said Schwartz, "I haven't half enough for myself," and on he went.

Then again the light seemed to fade from before his eyes, and he looked up, and, behold, a mist, of the color of blood, had come over the sun ; and the bank of black cloud had risen very high, and its edges were tossing and tumbling like the waves of the angry sea.   And they cast long shadows, which flickered over Schwartz's path.

Then Schwartz climbed for another hour, and again his thirst returned ; and as he lifted his flask to his lips, he thought he saw his brother Hans lying exhausted on the path before him, and, as he gazed, the figure stretched its arms to him, and cried for water.   "Ha, ha," laughed Schwartz, "are you there? remember the prison bars, my boy.   Water, indeed ! do you suppose I carried it all the way up here for *you* ?"   And he strode over the figure ; yet, as he passed, he thought he saw a strange expression of mockery about its lips.   And, when he had gone a few yards farther, he looked back ; but the figure was not there.

And a sudden horror came over Schwartz, he knew not why; but the thirst for gold prevailed over his fear, and he rushed on. And the bank of black cloud rose to the zenith, and out of it came bursts of spiry lightning, and waves of darkness seemed to heave and float between their flashes, over the whole heavens. And the sky where the sun was setting was all level, and like a lake of blood; and a strong wind came out of that sky, tearing its crimson clouds into fragments, and scattering them far into the darkness. And when Schwartz stood by the brink of the Golden River, its waves were black, like thunder clouds, but their foam was like fire; and the roar of the waters below, and the thunder above met, as he cast the flask into the stream. And, as he did so, the lightning glared in his eyes, and the earth gave way beneath him, and the waters closed over his cry. And the moaning of the river rose wildly into the night, as it gushed over the

TWO BLACK STONES.

CHAPTER V

HOW LITTLE GLUCK SET OFF ON AN EXPEDITION TO THE
GOLDEN RIVER, AND HOW HE PROSPERED THEREIN; WITH
OTHER MATTERS OF INTEREST

WHEN Gluck found that Schwartz did not come back, he
was very sorry, and did not know what to do. He had no
money, and was obliged to go and hire himself again to the
goldsmith, who worked him very hard, and gave him very
little money. So, after a month or two, Gluck grew tired,
and made up his mind to go and try his fortune with the
Golden River. "The little king looked very kind," thought
he. "I don't think he will turn me into a black stone." So
he went to the priest, and the priest gave him some holy
water° as soon as he asked for it. Then Gluck took some
bread in his basket, and the bottle of water, and set off very
early for the mountains.

If the glacier had occasioned a great deal of fatigue to his
brothers, it was twenty times worse for him, who was neither
so strong nor so practised on the mountains. He had several
very bad falls, lost his basket and bread, and was very much
frightened at the strange noises under the ice. He lay a long
time to rest on the grass, after he had got over, and began to
climb the hill just in the hottest part of the day. When he
had climbed for an hour, he got dreadfully thirsty, and was
going to drink like his brothers, when he saw an old man coming down the path above him, looking very feeble, and leaning
on a staff. "My son," said the old man, "I am faint with

thirst, give me some of that water." Then Gluck looked at him, and when he saw that he was pale and weary, he gave him the water; "Only pray don't drink it all," said Gluck. But the old man drank a great deal, and gave him back the bottle two-thirds empty. Then he bade him good speed, and Gluck went on again merrily. And the path became easier to his feet, and two or three blades of grass appeared upon it, and some grasshoppers began singing on the bank beside it; and Gluck thought he had never heard such merry singing.

Then he went on for another hour, and the thirst increased on him so that he thought he should be forced to drink. But, as he raised the flask, he saw a little child lying panting by the roadside, and it cried out piteously for water. Then Gluck struggled with himself, and determined to bear the thirst a little longer; and he put the bottle to the child's lips, and it drank it all but a few drops. Then it smiled on him, and got up, and ran down the hill; and Gluck looked after it, till it became as small as a little star, and then turned and began climbing again. And then there were all kinds of sweet flowers growing on the rocks, bright green moss, with pale pink starry flowers, and soft belled gentians, more blue than the sky at its deepest, and pure white transparent lilies. And crimson and purple butterflies darted hither and thither, and the sky sent down such pure light, that Gluck had never felt so happy in his life.

Yet, when he had climbed for another hour, his thirst became intolerable again; and, when he looked at his bottle, he saw that there were only five or six drops left in it, and he could not venture to drink. And, as he was hanging the flask to his belt again, he saw a little dog lying on the rocks, gasping for breath — just as Hans had seen it on the day of his ascent. And Gluck stopped and looked at it, and then at the Golden River, not five hundred yards above him; and he thought of the dwarf's words, "that no one could succeed, except in his first attempt ;" and he tried to pass the dog, but it whined piteously, and Gluck stopped again. "Poor beastie," said Gluck, "it'll be dead when I come down again, if I don't help it." Then he looked closer and closer at it, and its eye turned on him so mournfully that he could not stand it. "Confound the King, and his gold too," said Gluck ; and he opened the flask, and poured all the water into the dog's mouth.

The dog sprang up and stood on its hind legs. Its tail disappeared, its ears become long, longer, silky, golden ; its nose became very red, its eyes became very twinkling ; in three seconds the dog was gone, and before Gluck stood his old acquaintance, the King of the Golden River.

"Thank you," said the monarch ; "but don't be frightened, it's all right ;" for Gluck showed manifest symptoms of consternation at this unlooked-for reply to his last observation. "Why didn't you come before," continued the dwarf, "instead of sending me those rascally brothers of yours, for me to have the trouble of turning into stones ? Very hard stones they make too."

"Oh, dear me !" said Gluck, "have you really been so cruel ?"

"Cruel !" said the dwarf, "they poured unholy water into my stream : do you suppose I'm going to allow that ?"

"Why," said Gluck, "I am sure, sir — your Majesty, I mean — they got the water out of the church-font."

"Very probably," replied the dwarf ; "but," and his countenance grew stern as he spoke, "the water which has been refused° to the cry of the weary and dying is unholy, though it had been blessed by every saint in heaven ; and the water which is found in the vessel of mercy is holy, though it had been defiled with corpses."

So saying, the dwarf stooped and plucked a lily that grew at his feet. On its white leaves there hung three drops of clear dew. And the dwarf shook them into the flask which Gluck held in his hand. "Cast these into the river," he said, "and descend on the other side of the mountains into the Treasure Valley. And so good speed."

As he spoke, the figure of the dwarf became indistinct. The playing colors of his robe formed themselves into a prismatic mist of dewy light: he stood for an instant veiled with them as with the belt of a broad rainbow. The colors grew faint, the mist rose into the air; the monarch had evaporated.

And Gluck climbed to the brink of the Golden River, and its waves were as clear as crystal, and as brilliant as the sun. And, when he cast the three drops of dew into the stream, there opened where they fell, a small circular whirlpool, into which the waters descended with a musical noise.

Gluck stood watching it for some time, very much disappointed, because not only the river was not turned into gold, but its waters seemed much diminished in quantity. Yet he obeyed his friend the dwarf, and descended the other side of the mountains, towards the Treasure Valley; and, as he went, he thought he heard the noise of water working its way under the ground. And, when he came in sight of the Treasure Valley, behold, a river, like the Golden River, was springing from a new cleft of the rocks above it, and was flowing in innumerable streams among the dry heaps of red sand.

And as Gluck gazed,° fresh grass sprang beside the new streams, and creeping plants grew, and climbed among the moistening soil. Young flowers opened suddenly along the river-sides, as stars leap out when twilight is deepening, and thickets of myrtle, and tendrils of vine, cast lengthening shadows over the valley as they grew. And thus the Treasure Valley became a garden again, and the inheritance, which had been lost by cruelty, was regained by love.

And Gluck went, and dwelt in the valley, and the poor were never driven from his door: so that his barns became full of corn, and his house of treasure. And, for him, the river had, according to the dwarf's promise, become a River of Gold.

And, to this day, the inhabitants of the valley point out the place where the three drops of holy dew were cast into the stream, and trace the course of the Golden River under the ground, until it emerges in the Treasure Valley. And at the top of the cataract of the Golden River, are still to be seen two BLACK STONES, round which the waters howl mournfully every day at sunset; and these stones are still called by the people of the valley

THE BLACK BROTHERS.

NOTES TO SESAME AND LILIES

PREFACE OF 1882

This preface was prefixed to an edition containing only the first two lectures.

Page 1., § 1. **The irrelevant Preface.** The original preface on Alpine climbing, suggested by the disaster on the Matterhorn (see note on p. 187). This and the "gossiping introduction" are both, observe, sternly cut out, Ruskin, from the vantage-point of comparative old age, seeing their fault clearly, yet very characteristically unable to prevent himself from indulging in several pages of comment hardly less "gossiping" and "irrelevant." What he does not apparently realize is that he is read mainly for what he says, without any regard to its relevancy to anything in especial. See Introduction, p. xxiii.

Good books, good women. Treated, respectively, in Lectures I. and II.

§ 2. **Pet.** Ill temper.

P. 11., § 2. **Orpheus, Camilla.** Noted, one for music, the other for graceful swiftness. See Classical Dictionary.

§ 3. **Untried instruments.** Bicycle and steam whistle.

Out-of-college education. University extension or, perhaps, merely a reference to unattached students, sharing privileges without membership in one of the colleges.

Positivism. A religion based, not on revelation, but on love of humanity. Le Comte (1798–1857) was the founder of the system.

Negativism. Not the name of any distinct school, perhaps applied here to agnosticism, with its belief in the impossibility of certain knowledge of ultimate truth.   (Yet Ruskin, in the third lecture, comes rather near agnostic doctrine.)

Realistic, materialistic.   Inclined to esteem the real and material above the ideal and spiritual.

Dissolutely.   Apparently in its derivative signification, — without regard to bonds, dissolvingly, in endeavor to overturn and break up all.

P. III., § 4. **Mammoth and Dodo.**   Extinct creatures, — the first, a species of elephant, the second, a bird.

§ 7. **Monthly parcels.**   See note on *library*, on p. 205.

PREFACE OF 1871

P. v., § I. **Truism.**   Truth so obvious as to make statement unnecessary.

Affected language.   See Introduction, pp. xxiv to xxvii.

P. VI., § I. **Modern Painters.**   See Introduction, p. xxxi.

Richard Hooker (1554–1600).   An early theological writer. His chief work is his *Laws of Ecclesiastical Polity*, upholding the government of the Church of England.   His style is somewhat involved and inclined to long sentences.

§ III. **Into the language of books.**   One cannot read the lectures that follow without being struck by their oral character.   This is one consideration that makes it especially desirable that they be read aloud.

P. VII., § IV. **The first lecture says.**   It is rather characteristic that Ruskin, setting out to define sharply what he has said, or meant to say, goes branching off upon the matter of honest binding.   See Introduction, p. xxiii.

P. VIII., § VI. **The entire gist and conclusion.**   Such a direction from the author himself is worth heeding.   In these paragraphs one will find stated Ruskin's ideal of man's work in the world. See how far it is your own.

The famine of Orissa. Orissa, an ancient kingdom of India, now forms the southwestern district of Bengal.

P. IX., § VII. **You have not been singled out.** Compare the treatment of this subject in Lecture I., §§ 25–26, Lecture II., § 73, and Lecture III., § 140. It is a topic on which Ruskin held strong opinions.

Luminous. Blessed with light.

Immaculate and final verity. Spotless and conclusive truth.

P. X., § VII. **The most abstruse of all possible subjects.** Theology.

§ VIII. **"Work while you have light."** A variation, probably, of John ix. 4, "I must work . . . while it is day: the night cometh, when no man can work."

Be merciful, etc. Compare Matthew v. 7. "Blessed are the merciful, for they shall obtain mercy."

The light of morning. Of the morning of life.

P. XI., § VIII. **Solennis.** Literally *annual;* then, *established,* as a regular custom. Ruskin would remind us that repeated deeds establish habit. The turn by which he reaches this subject through the double use of the word "solemn" is characteristic, paralleling Lecture I., § 42, and Lecture II., § 95, as well as other passages.

Two mirrors. The physical and the mental. Inspect the dress, that is, of mind as well as of body.

Smooth-braided. Have your mind "smoothed down."

P. XII., § IX. **A clear-voiced little instrument . . .** which other people can depend upon. Typical advice. It is what we find Ruskin advising of every activity in life, — sincerity, accuracy, honesty, devotion to the good of others.

Vulgar. Here in the sense of *useful.*

P. XIV., § X. **Proverbs xxxi.** In which, 10–31, is described the virtuous woman, whose price is above rubies.

P. XV., § XI. **Gates of Pearl.** The gates of heaven. See the description in Revelation xxi. 21.

M

P. xvi., § xii. **Neither need you expect.** Compare Emerson, *Compensation*.

§ xiii. **Lord, I thank thee**, etc. See the prayer of the Pharisee, Luke xviii. 11 and 12, "The Pharisee stood and prayed thus with himself, God, I thank thee, that I am not as other men are, extortioners, unjust, adulterers, or even as this publican: I fast twice in the week, I give tithes of all that I possess." A very ironical imitation of the same mood is found in Burns's poem, "Holy Willie's Prayer."

P. xvii., § xiii. **Which clergymen so much dislike preaching on.** Why? What does Ruskin imply?

How hardly, etc. Mark x. 23.

Joy in a jest, etc. Hardly in accord with the grim ideal of the Puritan.

P. xviii., § xv. **Ménagères.** Housekeepers. **Monde and demi-monde**, respectable and disreputable society. **Premières représentations**, first views (of exhibits of paintings, etc.). **Mobiliers**, furniture. **Vaudevilles**, light comedies, not, as the word denotes in English, variety shows. **Anonymas**, persons whose names one doesn't care to mention.

P. xix., § xv. **Émeutes.** Outbreaks. For a lively definition of the *émeute* as opposed to other varieties of uprising, see Victor Hugo's *Les Misérables*.

Vous êtes, etc. "You are an English woman, we believe you; English women always tell the truth."

Sic (Latin for thus). It calls attention to some peculiarity, generally some error, in the words quoted. Here "pretty" should, in strict grammar, be "prettily." "Better," perhaps, in that it expresses, though at the expense of grammar, the main thought, — that the houses are made "pretty."

P. xx., § xvi. **Ellesmere.** Probably Francis Egerton, Earl of Ellesmere (1800–1857). The reference to the intervention and Gretchen is obscure. Ellesmere had published, in 1823 (Warren's notes), a translation of Goethe's *Faust*, in which Margaret, contractible to "Gretchen," is the heroine. But this accounts for nothing in Ruskin's statement.

Φίλη, *philē*. The Greek adjective for dear, or friendly. Here in the feminine form. The masculine would be φίλος, *philos*. (Found in combination in *philosopher*, lover of wisdom, *Philadelphia*, brotherly love.)

P. XXI., § XVII. **Greek and Syrian tragedy.** In which women appear in vengeful rôles, and as perpetrators of violent crimes. Medea is an example from Greece, as would be also Clytemnestra. In Syrian tragedy (Ruskin seems to be referring to the Old Testament), we have Herodias, below, and such other evil characters as Jezebel, Delilah, etc.

As dutiful as Medea. As the daughter of Herodias. Ironical. Medea showed her dutifulness to her children by murdering them to punish her husband for his desertion of her. The daughter of Herodias was "dutiful," in a way, by carrying out faithfully her mother's evil commands. She danced as bidden before King Herod, gained his sworn promise to give her whatever she might ask, and then asked for the head of John the Baptist, whom he esteemed, but whom Herodias hated. See Matthew xiv. 1–11.

§ XVIII. **Not an unjust person,** etc. A description of Ruskin as he saw himself. Is his opinion true? He may have been, at times, unintentionally unjust, unknowingly unkind. He had, no one who knows his work can fail to perceive, a deep desire for both justice and kindliness. The three good things that he loves, order, labor, and peace, are typical of the tendency of his whole teaching.

Guido Guinicelli. An early Italian poet of Bologna. Dante speaks of him in his *Purgatory*, in Canto xi., where he speaks of one Guido (Cavalcanti) snatching the prize of letters from the other (Guinicelli), and in Canto xxvi., where Guinicelli himself is introduced, suffering his purgation of earthly sin. In Dante Gabriel Rossetti's *Dante and his Circle* will be found transla-

tions from his poems. See also Cary's notes to the *Purgatory*,
Canto xi. His work is marked by a high, pure idealism, and a
deep sense of the refining power of womanly love. It is in this
tenderness, this adoration of pure beauty, this directing idealism,
that Ruskin resembles him.

Marmontel. A French writer and reformer (1723–1799).
Approximately contemporary with Rousseau and Voltaire. Like
Rousseau he is distinguished for his love for nature, and affection-
ate observation of beauty in nature. Like Rousseau he suggested
reforms in education, and urged the value of spiritual development
as opposed to worldly success. In these respects, and in his toleration of religious opinion, his views of society, his desire for minute
faithful accuracy in all study, he has also much in common with
Ruskin.

P. XXII., § XVII. **Dean Swift.** The "great and terrible" Jonathan
Swift (1667–1745). He is chiefly known as a satirist. His greatest work of satire is his *Gulliver's Travels* — which very young
readers read without the least suspicion that it is anything more
than a pleasant fairy story. In reality, it is an attack on the pride
of mankind. To a larger being, the author points out, all that we
regard as great would appear minute and trivial, our royal state-
liness mere strutting of dwarfs. To a minute being, our refinement
would appear ridiculous, every detail of our life being revolting.
To beings of another species — the idealized horse, for example —
the very idea of humanity would be loathsome. Ruskin means,
evidently, in stating the resemblance, — one not very easily perceived, — that he is forced by the meannesses and hypocrisies of the
world into a bitterness of spirit akin to that of Swift. Observe,
however, in these essays, that while Ruskin's attacks on shams
are violent, are in a way bitter, they have always a basis of kindliness. His hate is, as Carlyle puts it, "an inverted love" springing from a desire to see things better. He is not without hope and
endeavor. Swift, on the other hand, seems to have given mankind

up for lost, and to be railing, bitterly and hopelessly, at their vain ideals and empty pretences.   Swift depresses, Ruskin inspires. Swift leaves you feeling that there is nothing to be done; Ruskin, that there is everything to do.

SESAME

OF KINGS' TREASURIES

THIS lecture "Of Kings' Treasuries," was given December 6, 1864, at Rusholme Town Hall, Manchester, in aid of a library fund for the Rusholme Institute.   The second was given a little over a week later, December 14, at the Town Hall, King Street, Manchester, now the Free Reference Library, in aid of schools for Ancoats. The third was delivered almost four years later, in the Theatre of the Royal College of Science, Dublin.   This last was not, then, originally closely associated with the other two, which were intentionally linked, one supplementing the other.   These are to be regarded consequently almost as a unit and studied with their relationship in mind.   The year in which the first two were written was important in Ruskin's life.   It was the year of his father's death, an event that led to his passing much time in the stately house at Richmond Hill, amid its seven acres of ground.   Here he had lived in the company of his mother and of his cousin, Miss Joanna Ruskin Agnew, afterward Mrs. Severn, who remained his close and devoted friend to his death.   Perhaps, one of his biographers suggests, these two may have turned his thoughts toward questions of woman's work and influence.

The first lecture, aimed to aid a library, discusses the worth of books.   The second, in aid of a school, discusses the ideal education of women.   The first resembles, in some respects, some other essays that should be read.   There is Lowell's *Books and Libraries* and Emerson's *Books*, the latter being especially similar to parts of this in both spirit and substance. The student will find it interesting to compare the thoughts of the three writers upon this subject.

The first two lectures were first published in 1865. In 1869, in the tenth edition, was added *The Mystery of Life.* This was withdrawn again in the edition of 1882, though editions since show that a demand necessitated its reinsertion. There have been material changes in the text, mainly in the direction of cutting out sentences which, though well enough suited for offhand delivery, yet lacked the dignity expected in written form.

The motto is from Lucian, a Greek writer of the second century A.D. His writings consist in great part of dialogues, mostly satirical, inclined to attacks upon religion. The extract cited has no reference to the subject of the lecture beyond its use of the keyword Sesame.

P. 3, § 1. **Sesame.** The best explanation of this, as Ruskin uses it, is found in his own words on p. 49, "bread made of that old enchanted Arabian grain, the Sesame, which opens doors;— doors, not of robbers', but of Kings' Treasuries." For the reference to Arabian story, see the note, p. 194. The sesame is used figuratively here for the magic grain of education, the grain that opens the doors of the treasuries of wisdom (see p. 195 for Lilies). As for the *treasuries,* Ruskin perhaps has in mind Ezra v. 17, "Let there be search made in the king's treasure house."

One observes, at the outset, a marked wordiness. The opening paragraph is diffuse. Why may this, ordinarily a defect, be almost a merit under the circumstances that governed this lecture? Consider the effect upon the hearers, the mood that the lecturer aimed to establish, the kind of advice that was to follow.

Not . . . of kings, known as regnant. Of what kind of kings is he, then, going to talk? See paragraph 42, pp. 44–45, and the first paragraph of Lecture II. The kingship he means is the "power over the ill-guided and illiterate," a power springing from "well-directed moral training and well-chosen reading."

To hide what I wanted most to show. This is rather characteristic of Ruskin. His titles seldom, if ever, give much clew to the subject.

I will take the slight mask off. Does he take it off entirely? We are still left rather uncertain as to the exact nature of the kings. A sharper definition here would have helped the reader.

P. 4, § 1. **The compass.** The whole circuit, all that it encompasses.

Irrigation of literature. Observe how this figure accords with the word "levels."

§ 2. **Some connection with schools**, etc. Ruskin taught for years in the Workingman's College and took more or less active interest in the work for a long time after. His father's position at the head of various charities had left him in responsible relations to several institutions, among them Christ's Hospital and the Bluecoat School (see Charles Lamb's *Recollections of Christ's Hospital*). Ruskin's connection with the Oxford classes came some years later.

Letters. One of these is quoted in *Time and Tide*, Letter xx.

Double-belled doors, one bell for visitors, one for "inferiors."

An education. The keynote of the essay, which advocates culture for development, not for material ends.

Advancement in life. See p. xl on the plan and construction of this lecture. This is the first step in the logical progress of the argument. Observe how clearly the author's intention is announced.

Advancement in death. In spiritual death. Does Ruskin refer to sin or to mere failure to live, in the highest sense of the word?

P. 5, § 3. **"The last infirmity."** Milton, *Lycidas*, l. 71.

> " Fame is the spur that the clear spirit doth **raise**
>   (That last infirmity of noble mind)
> To scorn delights and live laborious days."

Ruskin writes *minds* for Milton's *mind*, but the misquotation has become, in popular use, almost the accepted form.

As its greatest catastrophes. What are some examples?

§ 4. **Mortal.** Literally *deadly*, from the Latin *mortalis*, for *mors*, death. Mortification, used figuratively for shame and humiliation, is here used in its derivative meaning of gangrenous corruption.

Effect . . . upon health and energy. There are certainly many cases where men have sickened or have even died of shame.

The captain, etc. How far is this true? Examine your own ambitions. Are they wholly free from selfish hopes?

P. 6, § 4. **My Lord.** Bishops of the Church of England are peers of the realm and members of the House of Lords.

§ 5. **Not that we may have it.** The right longing for good society, that is for ennobling fellowship, is not condemned.

The motives . . . too low. There is a peculiar condescension of manner in the following passage, as if the speaker were talking to children. This taking so little for granted, either in moral standard or intellect, has at times an effect rather ironical. He is less anxious to find out what they think than to make them ashamed, secretly, of what they do think.

My writings on Political Economy. *Unto this Last* and *Munera Pulveris.* See Introduction, p. xxxiv. *Fors Clavigera*, etc., were of later date than this lecture.

What used to be called virtue. Implying that this has gone out of fashion.

"Not in human nature." The objection most commonly raised now to the theories of Ruskin and other reformers. In his insistence that political economy failed to take into account the humane, disinterested motives in human action lies the chief object of all his attacks on the science. Read his works and see what conclusion you reach. The objection referred to has been raised against all social reformers from Plato to Morris and Bellamy.

P. **7,** § 5. **Hold up their hands.** This is a good place for the reader — in secret — to cast his own vote.

In this paragraph there is a slight shifting of ground. The main idea is, we should choose wise and noble friends. The desire to be praised and the desire to do one's duty are, however, made disproportionately prominent. One knows that the writer was aiming at this idea of companionship, and one sees that it is associated with the ideas that precede it, but one cannot help feeling that the connection is not made along clearly defined lines. For discussion of similar cases, see Introduction, pp. xxiii–xxiv and xl *seq.*

P. 8, § 6. **Princess and queen.** What kind of benefit (for there is benefit) is derived from the sight of these ? How far is it in the person, how far in the human ideals they represent ? Would Emerson or Lowell have included them in a similar list ? Compare with this whole passage the third paragraph of Emerson's essay on *Books.*

§ 7. **Folded in two.** Fanciful, almost fantastic, elaborating rather than explaining. Ruskin seems to be playing a game, trivial but charming, with his rather perplexed hearers. Yet, for all this intricate adornment, one feels not the slightest doubt of his sincerity.

P. 9, § 7. **Privy Council.** As a king summons a privy council of the wisest of his people to advise him, you summon a council of the wisest of all time, to counsel you in your narrower kingship.

§ 8. **Ephemeral.** Literally, for the day, of the day, passing away with it.

The books of the hour. You can easily think of several instances.

P. 10, § 9. **The newspaper may be proper.** Compare Emerson in *Books,* "If you should transfer the amount of your reading day by day from the newspaper to the standard authors — But who dare speak of such a thing ?" and "Never read a book that is not a year old."

Though bound up in a volume. The *Voyage of the Yacht Sunbeam*, for example.

That is a "book." It is perhaps worth one's while to reflect how many books really worthy of the title one has read during the year.

P. 11, § 10. That bit is his book, or his piece of art. In applying the terms to works other than printed books, Ruskin, while pointing a valuable moral, is departing from his immediate subject. The suggestion is inspiring, but not in place here. He is anticipating what he says in Lecture III. The footnote, by Ruskin, directs the reader to compare this with *Queen of the Air*, § 106. In this section he maintains that the "foundation of art is in moral character," and that "great art is the expression, by an art-gift, of a pure soul."

§ 11. Housemaid or stable-boy. Have you not read, in a newspaper or in light fiction, writing that imparts no more than such gossip? The reporters too often chronicle mere servant gossip of the dress and doings of rich people, or stable-boy gossip of their new carriages and swift and costly horses.

With queens and kings. Note that the contrast between queen and housemaid is meant to represent not mere social station, but, symbolically, far more. In actual life, some housemaids may excel some queens. In type, in theory at least, the queen has higher ideals, wider culture, profounder wisdom. The kings and queens thought of here are kings and queens worthy of their state and responsibility.

Entrée. Right of entrance.

Your own inherent aristocracy. Aristocracy means by derivation "rule of the best" (ἄριστος, *aristos*, best, and κρατεῖν, *kratein*, be strong, or govern). Too often now by the "best" we mean those possessed of the most money, or descended from the "oldest family." Such aristocracy as Ruskin speaks of here is the true preëminence of those that are really the best, whose excellence is inherent, rooted, in themselves. Lack of money or of wealth cannot deprive one of such fitness, nor can the possession of these obtain it.

P. 12, § 12. **Those Elysian gates.** The gates of those Elysian fields where, according to ancient belief, the souls of the virtuous dead lived in bliss after death, — the gates, then, that admit one into companionship with the great and wise of past time.

Portières. Gates.

Faubourg St. Germain. Once a suburb, the aristocratic district of Paris. Why *silent?* Would the real Faubourg be marked by silence?

§ 13. **This, then, is what you have to do.** Here is taken up a new section of the subject. Granted that we desired to enter this fellowship, how shall we become worthy of it and attain admission? Ruskin here outlines his plan. There are two ways of showing true love of great writers. (*a*) By a true desire to enter into their thoughts. (*b*) [See § 27.] By endeavor to enter into their hearts. (*a*) deals mainly with the intellect, how to understand their message; (*b*) mainly with the sympathies, how to fit one's self to feel it.

P. 13, § 13. **Reticence.** Be sure that you get the meaning and derivation of this word.

P. 14, § 15. **Syllable by syllable, letter by letter.** Newspaper and light novel are getting people out of this habit of thoroughness. It is well, in reading this essay, for instance, to discipline one's self by a deliberate application.

Literature. Derived from the Latin word *literatus*, skilled in letters, derived in turn from *litera*, a letter.

British Museum. Containing, besides vast art collections, the famous Reading Room, a circular apartment one hundred and forty feet in diameter, and one hundred and six feet high. The total number of printed books is estimated at almost two million. Obviously Ruskin's supposition is a large one.

Whatever language he knows, he knows precisely. Ruskin, in all his writings as in his life, is an advocate of scrupulous accuracy in work of whatever kind one may undertake. Observe other instances in these lectures.

The peerage of words. Compared, by implication, to the peerage of persons, that is, their relative rank, as determined by ancestry. Observe in what it differs from "pedigree," which denotes rather the line of descent itself.

Canaille. The French term for the vulgar multitude, the "great unwashed."

Noblesse. Nobility of rank.

An ordinarily clever . . . seaman, etc., will be known for . . . illiterate. Because the language that he knows, he knows far from precisely, and pronounces words quite regardless of the proper pronunciation.

P. 15, § 15. **A false accent or a mistaken syllable.** There are many cases where a speaker in the English Parliament has been humiliated on account of some slight error in a Latin quotation. In the present day, members of Parliament are less distinguished by Latinity. In our own Congress, quotations in Latin are unlikely, and serious mispronunciations might very possibly be perpetrated without detection.

§ 16. Section 16 diverges from the subject. Ruskin is telling us how to study words in reading the works of great writers. Here he takes up the meaning of words in quite other relations. Observe the hit at information as opposed to true education. See Dickens's *Hard Times* for another attack on the teaching of mere "facts."

Masked words. Words with two faces.

Wear chameleon cloaks. The chameleon is a creature that changes color according to the tint of the surface upon which it lies. The word is derived from the Greek words χαμαί, *chamai*, = on the ground ; and λέων, *leon*, = lion. Hence Ruskin's "ground-lion." The word seems also, however, explicable as *dwarf-lion*, χαμαί often having this signification in combination.   The idea of "lion" is developed in the later figure of "rend him."

Unjust stewards.   Luke xvi. 1–8, though the reference is hardly more than verbal.

§ 17. So mongrel in breed.   The student will do well to look up the history of the origin of the English language. R. C. Trench's *English Past and Present*, while perhaps not strictly modern, is a most readable and suggestive history of our tongue. Very good books also are those of Sweet, Skeat, Emerson, and Lounsbury.

P. 16, § 17. **By which the heavens.**   2 Peter iii. 5–7.

Cannot be made a present . . . in morocco binding.   Ruskin wishes to distinguish between the word of God, his sacred revelation and speech to man, and the mere material book, the volume in which some part of that speech and revelation finds utterance.

Sown on any wayside.   A reference to the Parable of the Sower, Matthew xiii. 4, 7.   The seed sown by the wayside is devoured by the birds. That sown among thorns is choked.   "Steam plough" carries out the figure of sowing; "steam press" applies it to the actual conditions.

P. 17, § 18. **"Damno," and condemn.**   These are derived from one source, *condemn* being from the Latin *condemnare*, which is simply *damnare* strengthened by the prefix *con*, altogether.   Derivatively, then, condemn should be the more vigorous word; damn, the weaker form.   But the ways of language are not governed by logic.

Divisions in the mind of Europe.   The great religious wars in European history.   These were rendered possible, according to Ruskin, by the restricting in meaning of the word *ecclesia* (as seen in our English ecclesiastic) to denote the church as an organization. The word *ecclesia* meant, in Greek, merely a public assembly, but, through being applied to the gathering of all the members of the church, reached very naturally its later sense. *Priest* and *presbyter* (terms over whose relative merit much Scotch and English blood has been shed) are virtually the same word, though *priest,* a form occurring far back in the history of our tongue (Saxon *preóst*) is "vulgar" only as "common." Milton, in his sonnet on *New Forms of Conscience*, writes, "New Presbyter is but Old Priest writ large." Yet does this resemblance in derivation mean that there was no real difference in signification? Would *priest* and *presbyter* have agreed in doctrine, even had they agreed on one name?

§ 19. **Greek first**, etc. Trace out the history of the words in an etymological dictionary. An example would be the Greek προφήτης (*prophētēs*), Latin *propheta*, Old French *prophête*, English *prophet.*

Max Müller. A philologian, of German descent, professor of Sanscrit at Oxford. He wrote many noted works on philology, etc.

P. 18, § 19. **It takes a whole life to learn**, etc. Not as one usually learns a foreign tongue, — Ruskin speaks of a knowledge so perfect that one feels its finest shades as keenly as they may be felt. Do you in this sense as yet "know" the English language?

§ 20. **Lycidas.** Milton's famous elegy on his friend Edward King, who perished while crossing the Irish Channel. The student will do well to review the whole poem. The name Lycidas is taken from that of a shepherd in Virgil's Eclogues. In the passage selected by Ruskin, lines 108–129, St. Peter, last of the imagined mourning train, bewails the young man, and through his mouth Milton utters this mighty denunciation of the corruption that he sees at work in God's temples.

In the extract from Milton, the following notes may be of help: **Pilot of the Galilean lake**, St. Peter, who owned a fishing-boat upon the sea of Galilee. **Twain** = two. **Mitred** = covered by the mitre, the hat of the bishop. **Bespake** = addressed him. **Swain** = shepherd or farmer. **Enow** = enough. **Fold** = sheepfold. **Shove**, not trivial, as now. **What recks it** = what does it matter to? we should now say, "what do they reck (care)?" **Are sped** = have prospered (are in the condition of having pros-

pered). **List,** like. **Lean and flashy,** showy and unsatisfying.
Songs is pastorally figurative for sermons, etc. **Grate** = sound
harsh. **Scrannel** = thin, eager. **Pipes** = pipes cut from oat
or reed, a shepherd's instrument. **Drew** = drew in with their
breath. **Wolf,** Milton, the Protestant, so designates the Church of
Rome. **Privy** = secret, unnoted. **Apace** = swiftly. **And nothing
said** — no voice is raised in protest.

The clergy are spoken of throughout as *shepherds,* a figure in harmony with the pastoral character of the poem. It fits, besides, the
idea of the pastoral duties of the clergy, their care of spiritual flocks.

P. 19, § 20. **Episcopal function.** Performance of the duties
of bishop. *Bishop* and *episcopal* are from one source. Drop the
e and *al* and you will see this. Both are from the Greek word
ἐπίσκοπος = *episcopos,* a bishop or, literally, an overseer (ἐπί = *epi* =
upon, σκοπός = *skopos* = one that watches).

No bishop-lover. Milton is frequently spoken of as the Puritan
poet. What was the attitude of the Puritans toward bishops?
Why might Milton be expected to be unwilling to recognize Peter
as the mitred head of the church? See Macaulay's *Essay on
Milton.*

The power . . . claimed. Fully to understand this passage one
must have looked into the exact nature of one of the doctrines of
the Roman church, — that the Bishop, the Pope of Rome, is, as
spiritually descended from St. Peter, made preëminent in power
over all other bishops, and that what he binds or looses on earth is
"bound or loosed in heaven." **That text.** See Matthew xvi. 17–19.

P. 20, § 21. **Lords over . . . flock.** 1 Peter v. 3.

With Peter's denunciation here, one may well compare that
which he is represented as uttering in Dante's *Paradise,* Canto
xxvii.

> "In shepherd's clothing, greedy wolves below
>   Range wide o'er all the pastures. Arm of God!
>   Why longer sleepest thou?"

P. 20, § 22. **A broken metaphor.** A metaphor not in harmony with itself, inconsistent. Mouths, which can never see, might seem unfittingly described as "deprived of sight." Mixed metaphor is another term applied to such inconsistent constructions.

A "bishop" means. The short paragraphs give the clear-cut logical progress that one finds in a mathematical demonstration. Each step is made distinct.

Pastor. A shepherd; literally, one who feeds (his flock). The derivation of *bishop* has been given above.

P. 21, § 22. **Power rather than light.** Watch carefully the distinction made. In what does the bishop's office, his function, differ from the king's?

Does the bishop know? It does not follow that he ought, in a vast diocese, to watch personally all the dealings of each individual Bill and Nancy. Presumably he might, as overseer, use other eyes in his service.

In the letter referred to, in *Time and Tide*, Ruskin reiterates, more emphatically, what he says here, — that it is a bishop's business to watch over his flock, body and soul.

As high as Salisbury steeple. The steeple of Salisbury cathedral, the loftiest in Great Britain. It is as if we said, in America, "as high as the Washington Monument."

At the helm. Who should properly be there?

P. 22, § 23. **Only a contraction;** from Latin *spiritus*, breath. The Greek word referred to is πνεῦμα, *pneuma*, breath or wind. Compare the familiar word *pneumatic*. **The wind bloweth.** Both extracts are from one sentence. John iii. 8, "The wind bloweth where it listeth, and thou hearest the sound thereof, but canst not tell whence it cometh, and whither it goeth: so is every one that is born of the Spirit." Ruskin would point out that in the original the words *wind* and *Spirit* are the same, though translated differently. (The Revised Version suggests as an alternative reading "The Spirit breatheth where," etc.)

That "puffing up." Ruskin had an almost intolerant distaste for religious intolerance and sectarian conceit. He had been brought up in rather narrow beliefs, from which he resolutely stepped out, recognizing that all sincere worships of men had in them something of the divine. This lecture was written while he was strongly under the impulse of this new perception. See the discussion of this point in the Introduction, p. xxxvi. Compare also the second lecture, § 73.

Cretinous. Cretinism is a form of idiocy, combined with deformity, common in the Alpine region.

High church or low. Referring to the divisions of the Church of England.

P. 23, § 23. Clouds without water. From the description of false teachers in Jude xii.

§ 24. Dante. The great Florentine poet (1265–1321). His greatest work is the *Divine Comedy* (*Commedia*, since not tragedy), his vision of Hell, Purgatory, and Heaven. It stands among the very greatest of poems. There are excellent translations in verse by H. F. Cary and H. W. Longfellow, and a prose version by C. E. Norton.

He supposes both the keys. A reference to *Purgatorio*, Canto ix.

> "I could descry
>   A portal, and three steps beneath, that led
>   For inlet there, of different color each. . . .
>   The lowest stair was marble white, so smooth
>   And polished, that therein my mirrored form
>   Distinct I saw. The next of hue more dark
>   Than sablest grain, a rough and singèd block,
>   Cracked lengthwise and across. The third that lay
>   Massy above, seemed porphyry, that flamed
>   Red as the life-blood spouting from a vein.
>   On this God's angel either foot sustained,
>   Upon the threshold seated, which appeared

N

> A rock of diamond. . . .
> From underneath that vestment forth he drew
> Two keys, of metal twain: the first was gold,
> Its fellow silver. With the pallid first,
> And next the burnished, he so plied the gate,
> As to content me well.   'Whenever one
> Faileth of these, that in the keyhole straight
> It turn not, to this alley then expect
> Access in vain.' Such were the words he spake.
> 'One is more precious; but the other needs
> Skill and sagacity. . . .
>   From Peter these
> I hold, of him instructed, that I err
> Rather in opening than in keeping fast.'"

The first step is explained in Cary's notes as the distinctness with which the conscience of the penitent reflects his offences; the second (burned and cracked), his contrition on account of them; the third (red as blood), the glowing fervor with which he resolves upon the future pursuit of virtue.

In the same notes the two keys are explained, — one, the golden, as denoting the divine authority of absolution; the other, the silver, as typical of the learning and judgment necessary for the discharge of the priest's office.

Have taken away the key. Luke xi. 52. Spoken by Christ of the Jewish lawyers.

"He that watereth." Proverbs xi. 25.

That command. From the parable of the wedding. Matthew xxii. 13, "Then said the king to his servants [the Lord, that is, to his "strong angels"], Bind him hand and foot, and take him away, and cast him forth into outer darkness; there shall be weeping and gnashing of teeth." One may note, in comparison, Revelation xx. 1–3.

The rock-apostle. St. Peter. *Petra* is the Greek word for a rock. See Matthew xvi. 18, " Thou art Peter, and upon this rock I will build my church."

P. 24, § 25.   **Annihilating our own personality.**   Should such annihilation be carried out indefinitely ? Evidently it is valuable only while one is striving to enter into a writer's thought. When this once is mastered, one will, if independent, reflect upon it, and come, so far as one modestly may, to conclusions. What is to be avoided is mere prejudice, mere simulation of knowledge, standing in the way of any right reception of wisdom of others. Ruskin's opposition is not to independent thought, but to "convictions" that refuse to admit further enlightenment. It is the things that we "think we know" that stand in the way of our really learning something.

Serious matters.   Ruskin is both a reformer and a conservative, or, as some would put it, a reactionary — out of harmony with the old, urging a return to the best in the past. See Introduction, where his teaching is analyzed.

A ditch to cleanse.   Ruskin was a sturdy advocate of doing the nearest duty earnestly and with diligence. See Introduction, and notes on p. 220.

P. 25, § 25.   **Roguery and lying.**   Observe the bitterness and intensity of this passage, an intensity that, becoming over-vociferous, often weakens the real power of Ruskin's writings. See Introduction, p. xxxvi.

You can know nothing.   As Carlyle, preaching the doctrine of silence, was one of the most outspoken and clamorous of writers, so Ruskin, preaching the doctrine of ignorance, is one of the most assured and dogmatic. Yet see if the note on § 23 above does not in some measure explain the apparent inconsistency.

The thoughts of the wisest.   Again a minor subject is developed fascinatingly. Observe that this passage anticipates some of the ideas developed in the third lecture, "Of the Mystery of Life."

To mix the music. Quoted, with variation, from Emerson's *To Rhea.* The gift of the god to the mortal is that

> "He mixes music with her thoughts,
> And saddens her with heavenly doubts."

This writer. Milton, not Emerson.

The scene with the bishops. Act III., Scene viii., in *Richard III.*, where Gloster appears between two bishops, who lend themselves to his hypocritical pretence of absorbed devotion and unwillingness to accept the offered crown of England. The subservience of the prelates here is in sharp contrast with the true dignity and firmness displayed by Archbishop Cranmer in *Henry VIII.* (Act V., Scenes i. and ii.).

St. Francis and St. Dominic. Dante, *Paradiso*, Canto xi., ll. 27–39 (Thomas Aquinas, "the Angelic Doctor," is the speaker):

> "The Providence, that governeth the world, . . .
> Hath two ordained, who should on either hand
> In chief escort her: one, seraphic all
> In fervency; for wisdom upon earth,
> The other, splendor of cherubic light.
> I but of one will tell: he tells of both,
> Who one commendeth, which of them soe'er
> Be taken: for their deeds were to one end."

Then follows the story of St. Francis, who, "against his father's will," wedded poverty, his "stripling choice." St. Francis was the founder of the order of the Franciscans, as St. Dominic of the Dominicans.

Who made Virgil wonder. Dante, *Inferno*, Canto xxiii., ll. 126–129:

> "I noted then
> How Virgil gazed with wonder upon him,
> *Thus abjectly extended on the cross*
> *In banishment eternal.*"

[Cary's translation. The italicized words in this and in the passage below translate the Italian in the text.] The sufferer is Caiaphas, the high priest who "gave the Pharisees

> "Counsel, that it were fitting for one man
>   To suffer for the people."

He is fastened to a cross so placed that he is trampled upon by every passer-by. The second is Pope Nicholas the Fifth, plunged, head down, in a pit "of the size of the fonts of St. John the Baptist at Florence." Dante says:

> "*There stood I like the friar, that doth shrive
>   A wretch for murder doomed*, who, e'en when fixed,
>   Calleth him back, whence death a while delays."
>   —*Inferno*, Canto xix., Cary's translation, ll. 51–53.

In these passages, Ruskin points out, Dante treats the great men of the church with stern impartiality. The noble and worthy are praised, while the evildoer, be it the Pope himself, gets his deserts. He fares no better than Caiaphas, whose punishment, indeed, seems the milder of the two.

P. 26, § 25. **Articles**. Definite declarations of faith, like the "thirty-nine Articles" of the Established Church of England.

§ 26. **Mere chance prejudice**. It is this that must be cleared before one can begin the planting of the right seed; the fallow ground, the ground that has lain idle, must be broken up, and the thorns, the prickly prejudices that encumber it, must be rooted out and burned.

Brakes, bushes, thickets.

Break up, etc. Jeremiah iv. 3.

§ 27. In Section 27 we enter on the second division of the subject. We have seen (13–26) how to understand the meaning of the great writers. We are now to learn how to enter into the spirit of their teaching.

Passion or sensation. The two are related in meaning. *Passion* is from the Latin *patior*, I undergo or suffer. *Sensation* from the Latin *sentio*, I feel. Both have the signification of *receiving impression, absorbing experience*. They denote the touch-faculty. What is generally meant by "sensational" is something of a sort to rouse sensation. "Sensational" literature is the crude stimulant necessary to rouse the dull, torpid senses of the "vulgar." Had they more true "sensation," they could appreciate more refined pleasure. The finer the development of sensibilities of eye, ear, touch, taste, spirit, the greater the development of the man.

P. 27, § 28. **The essence of all vulgarity, . . . want of sensation.** Test this derivation. What is it that makes people read "yellow journals," go to vulgar plays, dress in flaring colors, enjoy loud and discordant music, boast themselves in ostentatious language? Is not bluntness of perception, lack of tact, at the root of all? For further treatment of the same idea, see also *Modern Painters*, Vol. V., Part IX., Chapter VII., "Of Vulgarity."

Tact, derived from the Latin *tactus*, touch, from the verb *tangere*, to touch, whence our forms *tangible* and *tangent*.

Mimosa, most familiar in the common sensitive plant, *Mimosa pudica*, a plant which closes its leaves at the touch of a finger, as if resenting an insult to its delicacy.

Passion. See the beginning of the preceding paragraph.

§ 29. **Not only to know, but chiefly to feel.** The keynote of the discussion that follows.

P. 28, § 29. **The golden balls of heaven.** "The stars in their courses."

The River of Life. Revelation xxii. 1, 2.

The angels desire to look into. 1 Peter i. 12.

Catastrophe, the calamity, the overturning, denoting the crisis or culmination of a story or play. It is derived from the Greek καταστροφή (*katastrophē*), from κατά, down, and στρέφειν (*strephein*), turn.

The life of an agonized nation. Referring to the Civil War, then in progress in America. Too many in England gave attention to the effect of the struggle upon trade, rather than to the real merits of the questions involved. (It is possible, of course, that, instead of referring to America, this may have reference to events mentioned in the note following.)

Junketings, "private feastings," generally at public expense.

See noble nations murdered. Referring probably to the Russian suppression of the uprising in Poland. It might, however, refer also to dissensions in Italy, or possibly to Turkish cruelties in Asia Minor.

P. 29, § 30. You can talk a mob. Naturally,—*mob* being a contraction of *mobile*, the Latin adjective signifying easily moved, hence fickle.

Spend its entire national wits . . . a single murder. One does not have to strain one's memory to recall recent instances of such wasted national interest.

Its own children. Evidently another reference to the American Civil War. What was the status of the war in 1864, when this lecture was delivered?

The price of cotton. This was to many Englishmen the chief point of interest in the war. The blockade of the southern ports cut short the supply of cotton, English mills stopped, and men were thrown out of employment. Perhaps some attention to this fact, on the part of those so thrown out, was to be expected. Many Englishmen, however,—and Henry Ward Beecher did much by his eloquence to increase the number of these,—sided, though against their own interest, in the cause of the North.

Stealing six walnuts. The pettiness of the crime selected is grotesque. Probably Ruskin had some recent instance in mind.

Under circumstances, etc. A common excuse in large mercantile failures. Ruskin may have had in mind some particular bank failure. "By your leave" implies that the only amends expected of them was a graceful apology.

Made their money. A reference to recent war in China. The real root of the trouble lay in China's opposition to the opium trade with India, a trade in which England had a lively interest.

P. 30, § 30. **Sixpence a life.** Such landlords refuse improvements, and allow unsanitary conditions to remain unremedied in order to make a minute profit in rent, which is virtually murder at the rate stated.

Piously save . . . lives of its murderers. Rather an unfair reference to attempts to abolish capital punishment.

Unhappy crazed boy and **gray-haired clodpate Othello.** Reference to some trial fresh in the minds of his hearers. For Othello, see note, p. 197. This Othello is evidently aged and a "clodpate"; that is, a country fellow. Ruskin (see Section 36) was in the habit of collecting significant clippings from the daily papers.

"Perplexed i' the extreme." *Othello*, Act V., Scene ii.

Sending a Minister of the Crown. To Russia, presumably, where horrible cruelties were being perpetrated.

A revelation which asserts. "Love of money," etc., is to be found in 1 Timothy vi. 10.

Declaring at the same time. A reference to the political economy of the day. Read *Unto This Last*, where Ruskin discusses this fully.

§ 31. **Ring true still.** Like a good coin when tested on the counter.

P. 31, § 31. **Good Samaritan . . . twopence.** A reference to the well-known story found in Luke x. 35, the parable of "a certain man" who "fell among thieves." "And . . . when he departed he took out two pence, and gave them to the host, and said unto him, Take care of him, and whatsoever thou spendest more, when I come again I will repay thee."

There is a capacity for noble passion. Observe that Ruskin, while attacking what his countrymen do, has a high opinion of what they might, perhaps may, do. It is this positive hope that keeps his writings from becoming mere cynical complaints. For *passion*, see note on § 27.

Rock-eagles. Eagles of the rocky heights, in contrast to the monsters of the sea. Note the picturing power of the compound.

Scorpion whips. See 1 Kings xii. 11 and 14. "My father hath chastised you with whips, but I will chastise you with scorpions."

As a money-making mob. A keynote in Ruskin's denunciations. Were his reproaches deserved in England then? Do they apply in America now?

§ 32. **Bibliomaniac.** One mad with love of collecting rare books. The latter part of the word is plain enough. For the first part, see what Ruskin says of *biblion*, § 18.

P. 32, § 32. **Munching.** As at "public dinners."

Sparkling. As do the foolish women with their bracelets.

Multipliable barley loaves. A reference to the miracle of the loaves and fishes — the five barley loaves and two small fishes that fed five thousand. (See Matt. xiv.) Is it not true that a book though read is not diminished, but still keeps its food of thought for the new reader, or for the former reader if he consent to return?

Circulating libraries. Are they wholly an evil? They prevent, perhaps, individual ownership of books and close intimacy with them, yet, on the other hand, consider the enlarged range of literature opened to each reader. But do they offer the *best* books?

§ 33. **We have despised,** etc. Observe the formal regularity in the series that follows. See analysis in the Introduction.

P. 33, § 33. **For the safety of our ships.** It is the absolute determination of the time as determined in such observatories as Greenwich that makes accurate navigation possible. This practical reason relating to the accumulation of dollars is, according to Ruskin, all that induces the British public to support an astronomical observatory.

British Museum. See note, § 15.

Resolve another nebula. Break up star-mist (such as we see in the Milky Way) into its component stars.

Portion for foxes. Psalm lxiii. 10.

Negation of such discovery. The neglect to make.

Fossil of Solenhof. Solenhof (or Solnhof) is in Bavaria, and is noted for quarries of lithographic stone. It was here that in 1861 was discovered one fossil of the archæopteryx, "a genus notable as the oldest avian type, and as combining some characteristics of a lizard with some of a bird" (Century Dictionary).

P. 34, § 33. **Professor Owen.** Sir Richard Owen (1804–1892), a distinguished naturalist, author of *Anatomy and Physiology of Vertebrates*.

P. 35, § 34. **Free trade.** Ruskin is not discussing the relative merits of free trade and protection; he merely attacks the selfishness that is brought out in the average discussion.

Ludgate apprentices. These used to stand at the doors of the shops near the "Ludgate," which gave its name to the modern street "Ludgate Hill."

Bronzed vines, volcanic cliffs, etc. This seems to say that the Englishman with his damp, fat fields of clay, cannot equal in art-feeling the Frenchman or Italian. The actual meaning is more likely that the fault is not geographical so much as spiritual, — the Englishman cares only for his fields of clay, not for his nobler surroundings. There is, besides, a hint that the English genius, when aroused, is of a different type from the French or Italian.

Venice, Austrian guns. War had recently (1848) been in progress between Austria and Venice. Ruskin mentions elsewhere the sight of precious paintings tattered by shot.

P. 36, § 35. **Made stables.** In the general overturn of the French Revolution, reverence for what had been sacred was laid aside with respect for kings and nobles. Nothing was sacred but "Liberty, Equality, and Fraternity."

Falls of Schaffhausen. A cataract of the Rhine in Switzerland.

Cliffs of Lucerne. Lucerne, a lake of Switzerland; it is the largest and most romantic lake in the interior of Switzerland.

Tell's chapel. Erected in memory of William Tell, a great Swiss patriot — in legend at least. Some modern historians question whether he ever lived.

Clarens shore. Clarens, a village of Switzerland, in the Canton of Vaud.

Bellowing fire. The usual protest against railway and factory. See Introduction for Ruskin's attitude toward these.

Soaped poles. In a later lecture, 1884, Ruskin again refers to the Alps — as viewed by Alpine clubs — in the same terms, "soaped poles they want to get to the top of."

The preface to the first edition, hardly worth reproduction in full (see reference to it in Preface of 1882), takes up this matter of the Alps at some length. An accident on the Matterhorn, resulting in the death of a tourist and a guide, made Ruskin feel that he should somewhat soften the asperity of his language here. He acknowledges that the meeting of peril on the Alps is a discipline in manly courage, and defends the hiring guides to go into danger. "We need not, it seems to me, loudly blame any one for paying a guide to take a brave walk with him." He objects, however, to the personal ambition that is the incentive of the greater number of climbers.

"Many an otherwise sensible person will risk his life for the sake of a line in future guide-books, to the fact that '——horn was first ascended by Mr. X, in the year ——,' — never reflecting that of all the lines in the page, the one that he has thus wrought for will be precisely the least interesting to the reader. . . . While no good soldier talks of the charge he has led, nor any good sailor of the helm he held, — every man among the Alps seems to lose his senses and modesty with the fall of the barometer,[1] and returns from his Nephelo-coccygia,[2] flourishing his ice-axe in everybody's face."

[1] The barometer falls as one ascends a mountain.

[2] Cloud-cuckoo-land, a comic name from a play of Aristophanes.

Cutaneous eruptions of conceit. Their conceit breaks out, like a red "eruption" on their faces.

Hiccough of self-satisfaction apparently means that the speakers are too well pleased with themselves to speak smoothly.

English mobs. Tourists.

Chamouni is a village near Mont Blanc.

Firing rusty howitzers. In order to listen to the echoes among the mountains. What would he have said to the American fashion of expressing patriotic devotion by the explosion of fire-crackers?

Towers of the vineyards. 2 Chronicles xxvi. 10; Isaiah v. 2; Matthew xxi. 23, and other passages. The towers were for watchers who guarded the vineyards. They are still in use in Palestine.

P. 37, § 36. **My store-drawer.** Referring to his habit of collecting clippings.

This year (1864). In most copies this stands 1867, an obvious error. (See date of lecture, p. 165.)

Translator. Explained in the text.

P. 38, § 36. **10s.** About $2.50.

The stones. Presumably work at stone-breaking. The passage suggested by the appeal for bread and the threat of the "stone" is Matthew vii. 9, "What man is there of you, whom if his son ask bread, will he give him a stone?"

Salons. Reception halls.

Princess Metternich and Madame Drouyn de Lhuys. Prominent members of French society.

P. 39, § 36. **Chaîne diabolique.** Devil's chain.

Cancan d'enfer. Cancan (a cancan is a loose dance) of hell. Ruskin wants to make the "diabolical" element emphatic.

Morning service. This hints a comparison, "such was their morning worship." The quotation, from Milton's *Lycidas*, seems to let in on their indecent revel the white, pure daylight of the dawn.

P. 40, § 37. **A pension.** Not in the modern military sense. Here it means rather a government allowance to distinguished people.

Peculation means appropriation or theft. (It is possible that *speculation* was the word intended. *Peculation* is seldom followed by *with*.)

The bread of affliction and the water of affliction. 1 Kings xxii. 27. Isaiah, etc. See Isaiah lviii. 1, 4, and 7.

P. 41, § 37. **Satanellas, Roberts, Fausts.** The operas dealing with the devil, — rather as a myth, however, than as an actual Power of Evil. *Satanella* by Balfe, *Robert le Diable* by Meyerbeer, and *Faust* by Gounod. In such works occur passages representing congregations kneeling in prayer in cathedrals, and this simulated prayer, with its theatrical setting, Ruskin regards as more truly a violation of the Third Commandment than swearing, which "slips off the tongue unawares." Do you agree with him?

Dio. Italian for God, used in the "mimicked prayer."

Draw back the hem. To avoid contamination. Compare the same term in Matthew ix. 20, 21.

Incense smoke. Incense is used in the extreme "high church" wing of the Church of England as well as in the Catholic church.

P. 42, § 37. **Property man.** The functionary who looks after the properties, lamps, pistols, papier-mâché eatables, tin armor, etc., in the theatres. All this Christianity of mere showy externals should be left to him.

Carburetted hydrogen ghost. Carburetted hydrogen is the scientific name for illuminating gas. Ghostly apparitions produced by such illumination were attracting attention in 1864. "Give up the ghost" seems intended for a pun.

Lazarus. The beggar who lay at the rich man's door. Luke xvi. 20.

For there is a true church wherever, etc. Compare the moral of Lowell's *Sir Launfal.*

P. 42, § 38. **All these pleasures and all these virtues.** Literature, art, science, nature, and compassion for one's fellow-man.

P. 43, § 39. **Their amusement grows out of their work.** In this lies the core of Ruskin's theory of art and true craftsmanship. Work is to be done lovingly for the sake of the doing. Compare William Morris's *News from Nowhere.*

Idolatrous Jews. Ezekiel viii. 7–12.

P. 43, § 40. **Chalmers.** Thomas Chalmers (1780–1847). A distinguished Scottish divine.

P. 44, § 41. **Last of our great painters. Turner.** Joseph Mallord William Turner (1775–1851). A famous landscape painter, raised from humble surroundings in youth by his genius. He was noted especially for his painting in water colors, in which medium he achieved wonderful effects. His drawings in illustration of poems of travel and of books of description of places are also widely known. Critics disagree regarding the merit of his work. The student should examine it impartially for himself, remembering that later work which surpasses it may owe much merit to Turner's perhaps erring experiment. His work is notable for striking brilliancy of color, and peculiarly elaborate detail, especially in cloud and sea. His "Slave Ship," praised highly by Ruskin, is splendidly daring in color, and his "Fighting Téméraire," fairly familiar in reproductions, shows his love for intricate minglings of light and shade. Whatever error may be in his work, it is certain that he saw much new truth, opening, as did few of his time, his eyes to the real forms of nature. The tendency in the eighteenth century, in painting as in writing, had been rather the imitation of a previous representation of nature than an original attempt to represent frankly what the eye saw. Turner realized the need of observation and sincere study. But, first in the movement, pioneer in a new trail, he found his task far harder than do those who now follow where he led and wonder at the awkwardness of his progress. He relapses into the artificial, he exaggerates without regard to what he sees, he overdoes color and contrast. And yet, doing all these, he came nearer nature than the other men of his time, and, influenced by his obstinate aggression, others who followed Ruskin were won over by the fearless honesty of his work, and admired it perhaps unduly. It was Ruskin, at any rate, that gave Turner's work its fame — a fame that, when an impartial verdict is given, when the undulations of extravagant praise and unmerited censure have subsided, may be found to be well deserved.

Kirkby Lonsdale. In Westmoreland.

Incantation. Spell, charm.

The fallen kings of Hades. Isaiah xiv. 9, 10: "Hell from beneath is moved for thee to meet thee at thy coming : . . . it hath raised up from their thrones all the kings of the nations. All they shall speak, and say unto thee, Art thou also become weak as we ? Art thou become like unto us ?" *Hades,* "the world of the dead," the "unseen world," is a better translation than the *hell* of the King James version.

P. 45, § 42. That old Scythian custom. See Herodotus, Book IV. (Melpomene), Chapter 74: "As for the people, when any one dies, his nearest of kin lay him upon a wagon and take him round to all his friends in succession : each receives them in turn, and entertains them with a banquet, whereat the dead man is served with a portion of all that is set before the others; this is done for forty days, at the end of which time the burial takes place." Scythia denotes what is now the southern part of Russia. Ruskin had become much impressed, in reading Herodotus, with his account of Scythian customs, and some of these — that mentioned here included — he had treated in his own early poems. See the poem entitled *The Scythian Guest.*

The ice of Caina. That circle, in Dante's hell (Canto xxxii.), in which traitors and murderers receive their punishment. They stand neck-deep in a lake of ice, each raising his head "as peeps the frog croaking above the wave."

Living Peace. Romans viii. 6: "But to be spiritually minded is life and peace." The revised version translates more literally

" For the mind of the flesh is death ; *but the mind of the spirit is life and peace.*"

P. 46, § 42. **Elsewhere.** *Munera Pulveris*, Section 122.

With regard to the end of Section 42, where the subject is shifted from personal, private kingship to the responsibilities of literal kings, see the Introduction, p. xli.

P. 46, § 43. **Achilles.** *Iliad*, Book I., l. 231. He describes Agamemnon, the commander-in-chief of the Greeks, as δημοβόρος, *dēmo-boros, i.e.* people-eating.

Il gran rifiúto. The great refusal, denial, abdication. A reference to Dante's *Inferno*, Canto iii., l. 56, where he speaks of one " who, to base fear yielding, abjured his high estate."

§ 44. **Trent cuts you a cantel out.** Shakespeare, *King Henry IV.*, Part I., Act III., Scene i. Hotspur is objecting to the partition of territory :

> " See how this river comes me cranking in,
>   And cuts me from the best of all my land,
>   A huge half moon, a monstrous cantle out."

A *cantel* is a piece or fragment broken off.

Can say to this man. Matthew viii. 9.

P. 47, § 45. **Do and teach.** Matthew v. 19 : " Whosoever therefore shall break one of these least commandments, and shall teach men so, he shall be called the least in the kingdom of heaven : but whosoever shall do and teach them, the same shall be called great in the kingdom of heaven."

Moth-kings, Rust-kings, Robber-kings. Indirect reference to Matthew vi. 19, 20.

Broidered robe, etc. To which king does each of these wasted treasures belong ?

A fourth kind of treasure. Wisdom. For the description, see Job xxviii. 12–19. See also Proverbs iii. 13–18.

Delphian cliffs. Delphi was renowned as the oracle of Apollo, the Sun-god.

Deep-pictured tissue, etc. See just what this treasure is. First, a web, deep-pictured (the work of Athena, angel of conduct) ; second, armor (the work of Vulcan, angel of toil) ; and, third, potable gold (the gift of Apollo, the angel of thought). These deities are called angels or messengers ; or, rather, the great angels that Ruskin images as proffering these gifts are identified with the great powers that the Greeks worshipped as their deities. For development of the symbolism of the Greek Athena, read Ruskin's *Queen of the Air.*

Potable gold. Literally, gold that can be drunk, — gold dissolved in acid, constituting, so old alchemists fancied, a magic draught, an elixir of life. (Now, however, under the name of chloride of gold, it is a regular article of commerce.)

P. 48, § 46. **Instead of armies of stabbers.** Many writers and philosophers insist on this reduction of war to first principles. See Lowell's *Biglow Papers:*

> "Ef you take a sword an' dror it,
>   An' go stick a feller thru,
> Guv'ment ain't to answer for it,
>   God'll send the bill to you."

Or read Carlyle's celebrated description of war in his *Sartor Resartus,* Book II., Chapter VIII. See also Ruskin's *Modern Painters,* Part IV., Chapter XVIII., near the end.

P. 48, § 47. **The only book.** *Unto This Last.* *Modern Painters,* Ruskin had by this time ceased to regard with enthusiasm, finding it immature in the light of later thought and experience.

Half thorns, half aspen leaves. Composed, that is, half of irritation, half of fear.

P. 49, § 48. **France and England.** During the reign of Napoleon Third there was continual distrust between the two countries, and there were frequent rumors of an intended invasion of England.

P. 49, § 49. **A royal series.** Apparently a pun. The description of the books anticipates some of the ideals of Morris and the Kelmscott press.

P. 49, § 50. **Constitution.** A national constitution is its system of government. Great Britain has no constitution formulated by articles like that of the United States, but merely a collected body of custom and precedent. Here, by a pun, the constitution of the country is compared to the constitution — bodily condition — of a person who is "run down," dropsical perhaps, and needs a tonic.

Corn laws. Laws that restricted the importation of corn till the price attained a certain level. These kept the price of food high, and led indirectly to much suffering. They were repealed, after a good deal of lively agitation, in 1846. The new corn laws to be established are to be of a different sort, spiritual, supplying a finer bread, not for the body.

Not of robbers. See, in the *Arabian Nights*, the story of Ali Baba and the Forty Thieves. For comment on *Sesame*, see note on p. 166.

P. 50, § 30. **Section 30.** This is a statement of Ruskin's position on the question of private ownership, or, to put it differently, on the matter of socialism. He makes it quite clear that he is no socialist. He advances, in fact, no solution, contenting himself with making it clear that there is a problem to be solved. Mere division of land and wealth would be of no use, he tells us, until we can overcome the present selfish view of life as competition. Indeed, he has doubts about democracy, questioning frankly whether a noble aristocracy is not worth some price in loss of equality.

P. 51, § 30. **A bye one.** A mere side issue, not the main question, which is not of land, but of labor.

Inexorable. Not to be prayed off, that is, not to be begged off, disposed of.

Azure-blooded. Blue-blooded, an epithet commonly applied to the upper classes. It seems to be a fact that in people delicately reared, and not exposed to rough weather or rude manual labor, the blue of the veins is more visible, from the greater delicacy of the skin, — not because the blood is really bluer.

P. 52, § 30. **Weasels.** Who suck the blood of their victims.

Clowns. Ignorant rustics.

Gratis. For nothing.

Sacrifice. But is the sacrifice worth while? A grave question.

Of which presently. In the lecture that follows.

LILIES

OF QUEENS' GARDENS

P. 55, § 51. **The motto** is from the Septuagint, the Greek translation of the Old Testament, here retranslated into English. The name Septuagint comes from the fact that the translation (made at Alexandria about 280 B.C.) was the work of seventy, or about seventy, translators, the Latin for seventy being *septuaginta*. It is interesting to observe the differences from the more familiar King James version, where the lily has become the rose. It is, perhaps, characteristic of Ruskin that he explains in the second lecture the precise object of the first. The first dealt, or was intended mainly to deal, with the topic " How and What to Read." This second takes as its theme " Why to Read," or, more definitely, " Why Women should Read," aiming to bring out clearly just what nobility of nature a woman may hope to develop from the inspiration of the great masters of literature. It is her function to be Queen of her Garden, and, lily-like in beauty, to tend the lilies that languish in the lack of her care. The lily, that is, stands at once as a symbol of the maidenly purity of ideal womanhood, and as a symbol of the garden of beauty that should flourish under the kindly fingers of a proper queen.

I want you to feel, etc. This sentence gives us the object of the lecture, and teaches, if rightly understood, a valuable lesson. Be sure to understand the exact significance of this whole sentence.

Insignia. See dictionary.

Likeness of a kingly crown. *Paradise Lost*, Book II., l. 673. It occurs in Milton's famous description of Death.

P. 56, § 52. Only one pure kind of kingship. See if you can state what this is. On this depends the whole teaching of the previous lecture.

State. From the Latin *stare* (past participle *statum*) to stand. *Statue* is from the same root.

§ 53. Queens' Gardens. Over what territories is each of them to reign? What is the garden?

P. 57, § 54. We cannot determine . . . until we are agreed. Observe this introductory outlining of the subject. See Introduction, page xlii.

Helpmate. A word of accidental origin. For its source, see Genesis ii. 18. "And the Lord said . . . I will make him an help meet for him," a help, that is, appropriate and fitted. The words by mistake became combined into *helpmeet*, and thence, by attempted explanation, came *helpmate*.

P. 58, § 56. Shakespeare has no heroes. No heroes, that is, in the strict sense of the word — men whom his audience can regard with unqualified admiration. Surely, however, *Brutus* comes very near to heroic stature. **Entirely heroic** would mean wholly noble, with no petty or detracting qualities.

Henry the Fifth. The hero of the play so named, and the chief character in the two parts of *King Henry IV*. He appears at first among dissolute companions whom, when need arises, he puts from him, appearing as the ideal prince and general. But he stands rather as the type of a noble king than as a character closely studied and personally presented.

Valentine. This character is but vaguely drawn compared with most of Shakespeare's characters. The play, far from being one of the "labored and perfect" plays, is recognizedly inferior to most of his other productions.

Othello. The Moor of Venice, deceived by the crafty and villanous Iago into jealousy of his beautiful young wife, Desdemona, whom he puts to death — only to discover her real innocence when it is too late. The fault of **Coriolanus** is pride and contempt of the common people. **Cæsar** errs in ambition, **Antony** in sensual love and oriental luxury. **Hamlet.** The spirit of Hamlet's father reveals that he was murdered by Hamlet's uncle. Hamlet, however, takes no action, but hesitates in fatal contemplation. **Romeo** brings on the catastrophe by a series of impetuous acts. Each of the above gives name to the tragedy in which he appears. Antonio, the **Merchant of Venice**, very contentedly leaves his deliverance to others. The story of **Kent** is clearly enough explained in the text. **Orlando**, in *As You Like It*, after his defeat of the wrestler, his flight into the forest, and his demand of food for his perishing companion, becomes a very subordinate character, the heroine, **Rosalind**, doing with him quite what she will.

Cordelia, in *King Lear;* **Desdemona**, in *Othello;* **Isabella** in *Measure for Measure;* **Hermione**, in *The Winter's Tale;* **Imogen**, in *Cymbeline;* **Queen Catherine**, *King Henry VIII.;* **Perdita**, in *The Winter's Tale;* **Sylvia**, in *Two Gentlemen of Verona;* **Viola**, in *Twelfth Night;* **Rosalind**, in *As You Like It;* **Helena**, in *All's Well that Ends Well;* **Virgilia**, in *Coriolanus.*

§ 57. **Catastrophe.** See note on p. 182. In *King Lear* the catastrophe is the king's madness and death.

P. 59, § 57. **King Lear** gives over his kingdom to two of his daughters, **Regan** and **Goneril**, who protest the strongest affection for him. The third, **Cordelia**, who says she loves him but as she

ought, — meaning that she loves him with all her heart, — he dis-
inherits.   The cruelty of the hypocritical two to whom he has given
everything, with its tragic consequences, is the subject of the play.

   Othello.   See preceding page.   The stories of the others would
take far too long to tell in full.   The student should look them up
in Lamb's *Tales from Shakespeare*, or, better still, in the plays
themselves.

   "**O murderous coxcomb.**"   Emilia, the wife of Iago, denounces
Othello in these words just before her death.   Her villanous husband, his treachery exposed by her, puts her to death.   Coxcomb
here means fool.   The professional fool or jester wore a cap shaped
and colored like a cock's comb.

   The impatience.   Juliet pretends death in order to escape to
Romeo.   He, mistaking the false death for real, poisons himself at
the tomb, and so ruins all.

   The Winter's Tale.   Leontes, unjustly suspecting his wife Hermione, orders her put to death, and his child exposed to wild
beasts.   The child is saved by shepherds, and the wife, who turns
out to have been concealed by friends, returns to him when, later
in life, he repents of his folly.

   In **Cymbeline,** Posthumus makes a foolish wager as to his wife's
constancy, and, being deceived as to the result of Iachimo's attempt, orders his servant to kill her.   She escapes after strange
adventures, and is restored to her reconciled husband.

   In **Measure for Measure,** the selfish Claudio, at the dictates of a
tyrant, is willing to sacrifice his sister's honor to save his own life.

   In **Coriolanus,** Volumnia persuades her son rather to die than to
seek vengeance by sending the enemy against his own city, Rome.

   Julia, in *Two Gentlemen of Verona;* **Hero and Beatrice,** in *Much
Ado about Nothing;* **unlessoned girl,** Portia, in *Merchant of Venice* (where she, by native talent and shrewd logic, defeats in court
the designs of the crafty usurer, Shylock).

   P. 60, § 58.   **Ophelia,** in *Hamlet;* **Lady Macbeth** in *Macbeth;*

Regan and Goneril, in *King Lear,* — the old king's unfilial daughters. (Lady Macbeth and they are very remote in kind of wickedness, — theirs is selfish, hers wholly unselfish.)

All these, like those that follow from Scott's novels, were evidently as vividly familiar to Ruskin as his own personal friends. Compare the extent of his acquaintance with these noble people of literature with your own.

P. 60, § 59. **Walter Scott.** Ruskin always estimated Scott highly, placing him, in an early essay, above Goethe. See Mrs. Meynell's comment below.

His merely romantic prose writings. In this case those of his novels that, like *Ivanhoe, The Talisman,* and *Kenilworth,* were based less on human nature than on fancy and imagination of exciting adventure and stirring scenes. These are opposed by Ruskin to his "true works," studied from Scottish life. One critic (Mrs. Alice Meynell) finds even these "true works" unduly romantic. The Shakespeare exemplars she can accept. She cannot but "boggle at a like ascription of honor to the women of Scott." She explains her reason as follows:

"These young creatures Scott made virtuous because convention required a virtuous maid for the hero to love, and made faultless, at a blow, because he could not be at the pains to work upon their characters. It is chilling to hear their intellect and tenderness praised in the noble terms that honor the intellect and tenderness of Imogen, Hermione, or Perdita, of a goddess or of the fairy women of romance."

Dandie Dinmont, a border farmer, in *Guy Mannering;* **Rob Roy,** the outlaw, Rob Roy McGregor, in the novel of that name; **Claverhouse,** John Graham of Claverhouse, prominent in *Old Mortality;* the "Bonnie Dundee" of the well-known song; **Ellen Douglas,** the *Lady of the Lake;* **Flora MacIvor,** in *Waverley;* **Rose Bradwardine,** in *Waverley;* **Catherine Seyton,** in *The Abbot;* **Diana Vernon,** in *Rob Roy;* **Lilias Redgauntlet,** in *Redgauntlet;* **Alice Bridgenorth,**

in *Peveril of the Peak;* **Alice Lee**, in *Woodstock;* **Jeanie Deans**, in *Heart of Midlothian;* **Edward Glendinning**, in *The Monastery;* **Colonel Gardiner** and **Colonel Talbot**, in *Waverley;* **Colonel Mannering**, in *Guy Mannering*.

P. 61, § 60. **Dante.** See note on p. 177.

Dante's great poem. Dante's inspiration in writing his *Divine Comedy* was the thought of Beatrice, whom he had loved in her girlhood upon earth and whom in his vision he saw as watching over him with uplifting love in the world beyond the grave. Had it not been for the impulse of his devotion to her, the poet's great work might forever have remained unwritten.

P. 62, § 60. **A Knight of Pisa.** Pannucio dal Bagno Pasano (1250). The extract is from his *Canzone, of his change through Love*, translated by Rossetti and appearing in his *The Early Italian Poets* (see his collected works). Dante Gabriel Rossetti (1828–1882), an English poet of Italian parentage, combined literary qualities of both nations. His original poems are of great beauty, depth, and sweetness, and his translations from the Italian are, as the extract shows, less like translations than original expression. Be sure you discover the spirit of the passage quoted, the element for which Ruskin selected it.

P. 63, § 61. **A Greek knight.** Were there knights in Greece, knights in the literal sense of the word as used in days of chivalry? If not, what does Ruskin mean by this term? In what sense might an Athenian or Roman be a true knight? See note on "Greek gentleman," p. 214.

Andromache. The wife of Hector. See the *Iliad*, Book VI., the latter part.

Cassandra. A Trojan prophetess, daughter of King Priam. She appears in the *Agamemnon* of Æschylus.

Nausicaa. Daughter of the king of the Phæacians. She conducts the shipwrecked Ulysses to her father's court. See *Odyssey*, Book VI.

Penelope. The wife of Ulysses. She waited his return for nine years, unmarried, putting off by clever expedients the insistent suitors for her hand. See the *Odyssey*, concluding books.

Antigone. The heroine of the *Antigone* of Sophocles. Regardless of the orders of Creon, the tyrannical king of Thebes, she buried by night the body of her brother, Polynices, who had fallen fighting against the city. Creon condemned her to be buried alive, but she, hearing his sentence, committed suicide, and her lover, Hæmon, the king's son, killed himself upon her grave.

Iphigenia. Daughter of Agamemnon, offered as a sacrifice to Artemis (Diana), to induce that goddess to grant the Grecian fleet fair winds to Troy. Some stories represent her as actually put to death, others as miraculously rescued at the last moment. See Classical Dictionary, also Tennyson's *A Dream of Fair Women*.

Alcestis. She volunteered to die in place of her husband, the gods offering him life if any one would voluntarily meet death in his stead. She was saved, according to the story, by Hercules, who forced Death, by main strength, to give up his prey.

P. 63, § 62. **Chaucer.** The first really great English poet. He wrote in the latter part of the fourteenth century. *The Legend of Good Women*, one of his latest works, is intended to atone for his previous unkindly pictures of the female sex by recording the histories of nine ladies of constancy and purity of life. The nine selected are Cleopatra, Thisbe, Dido, Medea, Lucretia, Ariadne, Philomela, Phyllis, and Hypermnestra. The "goodness" of most of these "good women" consisted, apparently, in their willingness to die for love when deserted.

Spenser. Edmund Spenser (1552–1599) author of the *Faerie Queene*, an allegorical poem of great beauty. **Una** and **Britomart** are characters in this poem, the first representing Truth, the second armed Chastity, overcoming all that dare battle with her. For **Una**, see Book I., for **Britomart**, Book III. The story of *Una and the Lion*, Book I., Canto iii., is particularly beautiful.

P. 64, § 62. **The lawgiver of all the earth.** Moses, brought up by Pharaoh's daughter. Exodus ii. 10.

Egyptian people gave. A reference to Neith or Neth, a goddess of the upper heaven, also of wisdom, resembling in many respects the Greek Athena.

Athena of the olive-helm. For a full development of this idea of the symbolism in the worship of *Athena* (Minerva), read Ruskin's *Queen of the Air.* The olive was sacred to Athena.

P. 64, § 64. **In all Christian ages.** Observe that this extreme of obedience and chivalrous devotion has been peculiarly Christian, — has been also, one might almost say, peculiarly modern.

P. 65, § 64. **That chivalry.** Chivalry involves a possible insincerity, a reverence that is mere "mouth-honor." To flatter women to their faces and disparage them when they are out of hearing, is not true chivalry, but is often taken by those who practise it as all that can be expected. True chivalry pays real reverence to woman, present or absent.

Even . . . in caprice. See the poem of *The Glove,* as told by Schiller in German and by Browning in English.

P. 65, § 65. **The buckling on.** The custom in arming a newly dubbed knight. See Scott's *Marmion,* Canto vi., stanza 12 :

> " Then at the altar Wilton kneels,
>   And Clare the spurs bound on his heels ;
>   And think what next he must have felt,
>   At buckling of the falchion belt !
>   And judge how Clara changed her hue,
>   While fastening to her lover's side
>   A friend which, though in danger tried,
>   He once had found untrue ! "

P. 66, § 65. **Ah, wasteful woman !** From Patmore's *Angel in the House.* See Part VII., " The Queen." Patmore's work is perhaps estimated rather too highly in Ruskin's note. The poem referred to, while containing really inspiring and ennobling passages, is full of uncouth attempts at graceful wit, — found in many poets when they try to be unaffectedly domestic.

P. 67, § 67. **What only the other can give.** See Tennyson's *Princess*, Part VII. :

> "Not like to like, but like in difference,
>   Yet in the long years liker must they grow;
> The man be more of woman, she of man;
>   He gain in sweetness and in moral height,
> Nor lose the wrestling thews that throw the world;
>   She mental breadth, nor fail in childward care,
> Nor lose the childlike in the larger mind;
>   Till at the last she set herself to man,
> Like perfect music unto noble words."

P. 67, § 68. **A vestal temple.** Vesta was the Roman goddess of the hearth. The fire in her temple burned perpetually.

Household gods. The "household gods" of the Romans were those whose images stood in the secret innermost parts of the house. They were associated with the sacredness of domestic life and happiness. The *penates* were the domestic images of the greater gods generally worshipped; the *lares*, images of minor deities presiding exclusively over the household.

P. 68, § 68. **Rock in a weary land.** Isaiah xxxii. 2.

Pharos. Lighthouse, from the island Pharos, bearing the great lighthouse at the entrance of the harbor of Alexandria — one of the seven wonders of the world. Compare the French *phare*, lighthouse.

Ceiled . . . vermilion. Jeremiah xxii. 14.

P. 68, § 69. **La donna è mobile.** See the Duke's song in Verdi's opera, *Rigoletto*. The meaning is, "Woman is changeable." "**Qual piúm' al vento,**" the line following, means, "As a feather in the wind."

Variable as the shade. Scott, *Marmion*, Canto vi., l. 30.

Variable as the light, etc.   Is Ruskin's ideal too high for human nature? Is it the mere dream of an idealist? Have there been, or may there be, women that at all accord with his description?

P. 68, § 70. **Section 70** begins a new division of the lecture. The opening sentences of the paragraph make this clear, showing what has been accomplished, and what is to be taken up in the paragraphs following.   The student will do well to note how helpful this is to the reader, and to apply the hint in his own writing.

P. 69, § 70. **That poet.** William Wordsworth (1770–1850). In his collected poems the poem quoted is without title.   In the extract here, three stanzas — three, five, and the concluding stanza — are omitted.   Observe that Nature is represented as speaking throughout the poem, not the poet in his own person.   The two lines in § 71, **in a countenance,** etc., are from another poem by the same poet, beginning, " She was a phantom of delight."

P. 71, § 72. **Bitter valley of humiliation.** What valleys are mentioned in the Bible? What has Ruskin in mind here? See Bunyan's *Pilgrim's Progress.*

It is not the object of education, etc. Is this true only of women? Does Ruskin mean that the boy *is* to be turned into a dictionary?

Hidden equities of divine reward, etc. Read Emerson's essay *Compensation,* where he traces out these " threads of woven fire."

P. 72, § 72. **For all who are desolate and oppressed.** From the litany, in the service of the Church of England, *Book of Common Prayer.*

P. 72, § 73. **There is one dangerous science.** Observe the bitterness shown in this passage.   See Introduction, page xxxvi.

Consecrated myrrh. Religious bitterness.

By crawling up the steps of his judgment-throne, to divide it. A daring figure, characteristic of Ruskin's more excited style of condemnation.

The Spirit of the Comforter. John xv. 26, also xvi. 7.

P. 73, § 74. **Hers, general.** Should a woman's education be less thorough than a man's? Should she know only enough to enable her to sympathize in her husband's pleasures? This paragraph affords a field for a good deal of discussion. Observe its bearing on the problems of coeducation.

P. 73, § 75. **Exquisite.** Why not *perfect* or *exact?* What does *exquisite* here imply? In what is it characteristic of the writer?

P. 74, § 75. **The circulating library.** Ruskin here condemns the habit of reading, as such, all new popular works, regardless of their merit. By *circulating libraries* he refers to the great English concerns, Mudie's, etc., that send regularly to their subscribers packages of the latest popular books.

P. 74, § 77. **Moral anatomy and chemistry.** Scientific study and analysis of character.

Thackeray, William Makepeace (1811–1863). His novels are cynical or kindly, according to the point of view of the reader.

P. 75, § 78. **The Narcissus.** See a picture of the flower, noting the appropriateness of the figure.

Her household motions. Wordsworth, from the poem beginning, "She was a phantom of delight."

P. 77, § 81. **Dean of Christ Church, or Master of Trinity.** Colleges in the great English universities. The officials mentioned would hardly be men to patronize.

P. 77, § 82. **Joan of Arc.** The maid of France who, putting on armor like a man, and leading the French armies, compelled England to raise the siege of Orleans. She was later captured, and burned at the stake. She was canonized (declared a saint) in the year 1894. See any good history of France, Shakespeare's *Henry VI.* (Part I.), also, perhaps, Mark Twain, *Joan of Arc.*

Domrémy. A village in the department of Vosges, near the eastern border of France.

Diets   Legislative assemblies.

P. 78, § 82 (note). **Michelet.** A noted French historian (1798–1874).

De Quincey. English critic and essayist (1785–1859). He wrote *Confessions of an Opium-eater.*

P. 78, § 83. **Sharp arrows of the mighty. Coals of juniper.** Psalm cxx. 3–4 : " What shall be given unto thee ? or what shall be done unto thee, thou false tongue ? Sharp arrows of the mighty, with coals of juniper."

P. 78, § 84. **The Mersey** flows into the Irish Sea to the north of Wales. **Snowdon** is a mountain close by **Menai Straits,** which separates from the mainland the island of **Anglesea,** west of which lies **Holyhead,** a smaller island. The scenery of the whole region is rugged and inspiring.

P. 79, § 84. **Its red light.** The red light of its lighthouse.

P. 79, § 85. **Christian Minerva.** The work of Christian education and culture, Minerva being the goddess of learning and wisdom.

Parnassus. A mountain of Greece, sacred to the muses. Ægina, an island in the Ægean sea, was noted for its temple to Minerva.

Those inch-deep fonts of yours. The little fonts of schoolroom wisdom. Not that these can teach nothing, but they cannot take the place of the greater lessons and inspirations of nature.

Waters which the great Lawgiver. Reference to Exodus xvii. 6 : " Thou shalt smite the rock, and there shall come water out of it, that the people may drink. And Moses did so . . ."

P. 80, § 85. **An Unknown God.** See Acts xvii. 23. Altars were raised in Athens so inscribed.

P. 82, § 88. **Lady.** Not, according to Skeat's Dictionary, "loaf-giver," but "loaf-kneader." Does this latter fit so well with Ruskin's meaning here ? Writers of moral and critical essays are a little given to fanciful and interesting, though inaccurate, etymologies. Carlyle derives king from *canning,* or *able-man,* and bases argument on it, when the real origin of the word is very different.

But does this slight inaccuracy make any difference in the truth of the main idea presented?

Lord, according to Skeat, means not "maintainer of laws," but "loaf-ward," guardian of the loaves. The lady kneaded them, the man kept them from enemies. These functions coincide with the duties that Ruskin has assigned each in paragraph 86.

In breaking of bread. Mark xiv. 22 ; Luke xxiv. 30, 31, 35.

P. 82, § 89. **Dominus and domina.** Master and mistress of the house, derived from the Latin *domus,* house. Compare the modern vulgar "lady of the house."

P. 83, § 90. **Rex,** etc. Is not this derivation also a little fanciful? See etymological dictionary. The words are of course related to the word *right,* but also to *direct,* and many others.

Myrtle crown. The myrtle was sacred to Venus, goddess of beauty.

Prince of Peace. Isaiah ix. 6 : "And his name shall be called Wonderful, Counsellor, The Mighty God, The Everlasting Father, The Prince of Peace."

P. 83, § 91. **Dei gratiâ.** "By the grace of God." See English coins, with their inscription, "*Victoria, dei gratiâ regina,*" "Victoria, by the grace of God, queen." It is part of the formal title of the sovereign.

P. 84, § 91. **Park walls.** In England the grounds of large private estates are called *parks.*

P. 84, § 92. **The shroud wrapped about his feet.** Already near the grave.

Chrysolite. A gem, a yellow topaz. Revelation xxi. 20.

To play at precedence. A brief description of a great part of the business of "social life."

The wild grass . . . torn up. Figurative, of course. Implying what?

P. 85, § 93. **Her feet have touched,** etc. Tennyson, *Maud,* Part XII., stanza 6.

P. 85, § 94. **Even the light harebell.** Scott, *Lady of the Lake*, Canto i., stanza 18.

Hyperbole. A rhetorical term, denoting exaggeration for figurative effect.

Flowers only flourish rightly. (Where should the "only" be placed?) This idea of sympathy between the flowers and the queen of the garden will be found in Shelley's *Sensitive Plant.*

P. 86, § 94. **Bid the black blight**, etc. Even where there is not direct quotation from the Bible, note the biblical turn of the language.

"**Come, thou south.**" From the Song of Solomon iv. 16. Observe how frequently, in this lecture, Ruskin refers to that great song of the garden.

Florets. Botanically, such tiny flowers as make up a cluster; here, hardly more than a tender diminutive for flowers. What in the world of men does Ruskin mean these "feeble florets" to represent?

The English poet's lady. Tennyson's *Maud.* (Maud is, observe, a shortened form of Matilda.)

Dante's great Matilda. See Dante's *Purgatory*, Canto xxviii., l. 41 and following. Dante meets her straying beside the shores of the river Lethe.

> "I beheld
> A lady all alone, who singing went,
> And culling flower from flower."

It is she by whom he is drawn through the waters of Lethe, immersion in which removes all memory of offence, and brings recollection of every good deed done. Commentators differ as to what she represents. Lombardi says she typifies affection toward the holy church.

Come into the garden. From *Maud*, Part XXII., stanza 1. Be sure to understand into what garden Ruskin summons his hearers. It is the great garden of the world, where human hearts are thirsting for waters of comfort.

P. 87, § 94. **The larkspur.** From *Maud*, from the same song as the preceding.

P. 87, § 95. **Who is it, think you?** This turn is ingenious. Is the connection real enough, however? Note that this playful seriousness, this deliberately fantastic earnestness is characteristic of Ruskin.

A Madeleine. (The name is related to Maud.) The faithful Mary Magdalene. Matthew xxviii. 1; Mark xvi. 1; Luke xxiv. 10; John xx. 11–18. The last best explains the passage in the text.

The old garden, . . . the fiery sword. See Genesis iii. 24.

The vine has flourished and the pomegranate budded. Song of Solomon vi. 11.

Sanguine. A reference to the red of the pomegranate seed.

Take us the foxes, the little foxes. Song of Solomon ii. 15.

The foxes have holes, etc. Matthew viii. 20.

THE MYSTERY OF LIFE AND ITS ARTS

ONE might state the real subject of this lecture as the sense of wonder in life, the sense that all is not commonplace and petty and matter-of-fact. Only from such a realization, felt by all the greatest (only little minds claim to understand all mysteries of life and death and heaven and hell), can spring really great art.

For comment on the general plan and design of this essay, see Introduction, pp. xliii–xlvi.

P. 91, § 96. **A restriction.** Explained in the foot-note. Ruskin apparently keeps to the spirit of the rule, while violating its letter. He finds fault with no particular religion, while attacking vigorously the narrowness and self-content shown by the more narrow-minded in every church and sect.

This society. The lecture was delivered (1868) in the theatre of the Royal College of Science, Dublin, Ireland.

The connection, etc. In these words lies the keynote of the

P

lecture. It is just this connection between man's faith and man's craftsmanship that Ruskin is endeavoring to make clear.

P. 92, § 97. **An ingenious or pleasant essayist . . . to set my words . . . prettily together.** We notice in this work that Ruskin is aware of the charges that critics bring against him, filled, too, with a deliberate determination to dispose of any ground for the charge. To what extent is he successful?

With great plainness. Ruskin's later style is simpler than his earlier manner, — less complex and less adorned. See p. v.

Beauty of the physical clouds. See *Modern Painters;* Part VII. is devoted to study of beauty in the clouds.

Even as a vapor, etc. James iv. 14.

P. 92, § 98. **Fabric . . . fragile.** An instance, among others, of Ruskin's use of rhythm (almost metre) and alliteration. That the *fa′bric* of it was as *fr′agile* as a *dr′eam*, and the en*d′urance* of it as tra*′nsient* as the *d′ew*.

P. 93, § 98. **Man walketh.** Psalm xxxix. 6. From the translation used in the English prayer book, a translation earlier than that found in the King James Bible. This version, in many instances less faithful to the original, excels the "authorized" translation in cadence and in poetic suggestion.

P. 93, § 99. **The place that knew them.** Psalm ciii. 16. Also see Job vii. 9.

The mist of Eden. Genesis ii. 6.

Note the three resemblances of life to the clouds of heaven. It is like them in transience, in mystery, in power.

Wells without water. 2 Peter ii. 17.

P. 93, § 100. **Twilight . . . Titian.** Titian was a famous painter of Venice (1477–1576). He is noted as a colorist and painter of landscape. "All landscape grandeur vanishes before that of Titian and Tintoret." His subjects are for the most part religious — "The Assumption of the Virgin," "Death of St. Peter," "Presentation of the Virgin."

Kind Irish hearts. Why Irish hearts? What are the characteristics generally attributed to the Irish people?

P. 94, § 101. **The work of the man.** Turner, whom Ruskin praised in *Modern Painters*. See note, p. 190.

Since Reynolds. Sir Joshua Reynolds (1723–1792). An English portrait painter influenced by Titian and Tintoretto. Among his famous sitters was the actor, Garrick. He ranks as one of the greatest painters of England.

Kensington. Museum at Brompton, south of Hyde Park, containing National Gallery of British Art, and other institutions.

P. 95, § 102. **As snow in summer**, etc. "As snow in summer, and as rain in harvest, so honor is not seemly for a fool." Proverbs xxvi. 1.

P. 95, § 103. **Benjamin Woodward.** An architect of prominence, partner of **Sir Thomas Deane**, a distinguished Irish architect (1792–1871).

Museum at Oxford. An experiment in Gothic revival. The architects, in sympathy with Ruskin's teaching, followed his theories, allowing their workmen to design parts of the detail, as had been done in the days of original Gothic art.

Façade. Front, or chief face of a building.

P. 96, § 104. **Of modern cities.** Ruskin's work is full of this distaste for the modern. See Introduction, pp. xvi and xxxv.

Notoriety. What distinction from fame or celebrity?

From amidst streets. Read the whole sentence aloud, and note the harmony and beauty of sound.

Palaces of crystal. A reference to the famous Crystal Palace, a huge and hideous structure of iron and glass, erected 1851.

P. 96, § 105. **Disappointment.** With what object has Ruskin been telling about the Museum? Why has he dwelt on his discouragement? Observe that he goes on to make use of the material he has presented, telling what effect this disappointment has had upon him. What is this effect? See the page following.

P. 97, § 105. **Pope.** From his *Essay on Man*, Epistle ii., ll. 283–290. (The quotation, as given by Ruskin, is not quite accurate.)

Pillar of darkness. Such a pillar as the cloud that guided Israel from Egypt, and hung over the tabernacle of the Lord. See Exodus.

The arts, etc. In this lies the substance of most of Ruskin's teaching.

P. 98, § 106. **Answer.** The complaint is common enough. Industry without endowment is not, in spite of millions of well-meant assertions, equivalent to genius. The power must be there before it can be developed.

P. 99, § 107. **Our heart fat.** Psalm cxix. 70.

See with our eyes, etc. John xii. 40.

§ 108. **Not one cares to think.** This is the constant cry of all the great prophets, preachers, and reformers. Think, wake, wonder! They feel the vastness and mystery of life, and must rouse others to share the inspiring yet disquieting experience.

P. 100, § 108. **I will tell you something.** Ruskin's lectures are often marked by this "writing down" to his audience, as if they were but children.

P. 101, § 109. **Are you sure.** Determine, that is, Ruskin tells his hearers, whether you really believe these things, or merely subscribe to them without the least thought on the subject. What is your real opinion on these subjects that so vitally concern us?

The kings of the earth, etc. Isaiah lx. 22.

"**Is not this,**" etc. Almost a refrain. See end of 112, 114, and 115. What is Ruskin's object?

§ 110. **This kind of thought . . . the morrow.** Compare Matthew vi. 34, "Take therefore no thought for the morrow," etc.

Dante. See note on p. 177.

P. 102, § 111. **Evidently unbelievable to himself.** Is this your own opinion after reading the poem and studying Milton's biography and Macaulay's essay on his character? Is it not con-

ceivable that Milton may, with his earnestness, have believed in
the pictures he drew? If his story of the revolt of Satan is like
some classic myths, is it not possible that he regarded these classic
myths as mere perversions of the real story of the fall of the angels.

Hesiod was a celebrated poet of Bœotia (eighth century B.C.). He
wrote of the deeds and origin of the gods, telling of the overthrow
of the elder divinities by their children. The Titans, however, as
such, are not treated in his narrative. Ruskin would represent
his rebellious gods as the models of Milton's rebel angels in *Paradise Lost*.

Dante's conception, . . . one dear Florentine maiden. Dante is
guided by the spirit of Beatrice, whom he had loved, in vain, upon
earth. Ruskin hardly does justice, however, to the noble symbolism of the poem. Beatrice stands for far more than "one Florentine maiden"; otherwise the poem would not, as it does, concern
all mankind. Compare what is said here with what is said of
Dante in the lecture preceding. Has not Ruskin, in four years,
slightly shifted his point of view?

§ 112. **This strange lethargy.** This failure to realize life's wonder.

P. 103, § 112. **A troubadour's guitar.** A troubadour was a poet
who sang of love. A reference to Dante's love for Beatrice. But
the impression does not do justice to Dante's stern seriousness.
Ruskin exaggerates unjustly.

Idle puppets of scholastic imagination. Are Moloch, Belial, and
the grand figure of Satan "idle puppets"? Does this fairly
describe the *Paradise Lost?* Is not Ruskin unjust?

Lost mortal love. Beatrice.

§ 113. **Darkness of controversy, personal grief.** See the biography of both Milton and Dante.

Homer, the reputed author of the *Iliad* and *Odyssey.* His name
is hardly more than an algebraic x, representing an unknown quantity. We can know him only through tradition and his great poems.

All Greek gentlemen. Gentlemen in what sense? Could the term, in this significance, be applied to all mature male Greeks?

P. 104, § 114. **Even for his dead friend,** Patroclus, killed by Hector. See the *Iliad*, Book XVI. **The basest of his adversaries** is Paris, son of Priam and the cause of the war.

P. 105, § 115. **Katharine.** See Shakespeare, *King Henry VIII.*, Act IV., Scene ii. **The great soldier king.** See *King Henry V.*, Act IV., Scene viii. (the king reads the list of English dead):

> "But five-and-twenty. O God, thy arm was here,
>   And not to us, but to thy arm alone
>   Ascribe we all. . . . Take it, God,
>   For it is only thine!"

The gods are just, etc. *King Lear*, V., iii., 170.

There's a divinity that shapes our ends. *Hamlet*, V., ii., 10.

P. 106, § 116. **Who weigh the earth,** etc. Isaiah xl. 15.

§ 117. **I dreamed,** — possibly, of course, a real dream, but probably an allegory cast into dream form.

A wise and kind host, God, who placed men in the world, his "stately house."

A chance of being sent, — representing our uncertainty regarding death, and life after death.

A piece of the garden. The quarrel represents the wars for territory.

P. 107, § 118. **Brass-headed nails.** The wealth of the earth, the gold that is scattered here and there in nature to adorn the rocks, and that men dig up to brag about and contend over.

Here and there . . . one . . . tried to get a little quiet. Philosophers and "dreamers" — Ruskin, of course, includes himself among them. How far does this dream misrepresent the tone of much of human life as it is lived in the world about us? How far is it true? Dare we hope that things will grow better?

P. 108, § 118. **The child is father of the man.** From Wordsworth's poem without title, beginning,

> "My heart leaps up when I behold
> 　　A rainbow in the sky."

Eden, . . . dress and keep. Allusion to Genesis ii. 15, "The Lord God took the man, and put him into the garden of Eden to dress it and to keep it."

Hewers of wood, etc. Joshua ix. 21, "Let them be hewers of wood and drawers of water unto the congregation."

P. 109, § 120. **The main thing is that art must not be talked about.** Yet Ruskin is always talking about it. He means, however, evidently to denounce the empty, deedless talk of those that preach but never practise. Men should be too busy doing to discuss what they do. Ruskin's *doing*, observe, is active teaching.

No true painter, etc. Is this true of other arts than painting ?

Reynolds. See note on page 211. Reynolds wrote chiefly of landscape, etc., while his own celebrity was based on his portraits.

P. 110, § 121. **When need is, if need be.** Note the fine distinction between the subjunctive and indicative. The watchful eye *is* needed, the sustaining arm *may be*.

§ 122. **Gustave Doré.** Paul Gustave Doré (1832–1883), a French painter, best known by his illustrations to the Bible, Dante's *Inferno*, Milton's *Paradise Lost*, and other works. His paintings, like his drawings, tend to the depiction of the grand (or grandiose), the terrible, sublime, and horrible, though lacking, many think, true beauty or sublimity. He has, as painter, some characteristics that mark Victor Hugo as novelist.

Furies. The Furies were goddesses (or fiends) of vengeance ; the **Harpies**, or Snatchers, were goddesses of wind and storm, foul creatures with faces of women and bodies and talons of birds of prey.

P. 111, § 122. **Raphael** (1483–1520). An Italian painter, noted for smooth beauty and delicate idealization, painter of the celebrated Madonna di San Sisto.

Michel Angelo (1475–1564). An Italian sculptor and painter, famed for the grandeur and power of his conceptions.

Angelico. Fra Giovanni da Fiesole (1387–1455), a religious painter of Italy, considerably earlier, observe, than the others. Noted for portrayal of religious emotion.

Correggio. Antonio Allegri (1494–1534). Italian painter.

Art is neither to be achieved, etc. The really important idea here. We must, Ruskin says, aim to cultivate art, not by discussing technique, but by seeking to develop in us the true art spirit, the sense of wonder at life and the world, and second, the love of work that impels every true artist in his task.

§ 123. **In Ireland.** Ireland, during the early Saxon occupation of England, was more advanced than England itself in art and in Christian culture.

P. 112, § 123. **In a lecture since published.** *Two Paths*, lectures on art practically applied in decoration and manufactures (published 1854). Ruskin, in the passage referred to, discusses the two examples of barbarism, "one a barbarism that did not get on, and could not get on; the other a barbarism that could get on, and did get on." In the first, he tells us ironically, the artist "applies Aristotelian principles, Order, Symmetry, and the Definite." "Here you have the most pure type possible of the principles of idealism in all ages: whenever people don't look at Nature, they always think they can improve her." "Even the eyes are made symmetrical — entirely round, instead of irregular, oval; and the iris is set properly in the middle, instead of — as Nature has absurdly put it — rather under the upper lid." In the "corrigible" picture, the serpent tempting Eve, "The workman's whole aim is straight at the facts. . . . This man does not care about arms and body, if he can only get at Eve's mind — show that she is pleased at being flattered, and yet in a state of uncomfortable hesitation." "Nothing can be declared impossible to people who could begin thus — the world is open to them and all that is in it; while, on the contrary, nothing is possible to the man who did the symmetrical angel — the world is keyless to him; he has built a cell for himself, in which he must abide, barred up forever — there is no more hope for him than for a sponge or a madrepore."

Corrigible, to be corrected ; incorrigible, beyond correction or help.

§ 124. **Lombardic.** Of the province of Lombardy in Italy, — now subdivided.

Missal-painter. The missal is strictly the mass-book of the Catholic church. In mediæval days mass-books were illuminated or decorated by hand with most elaborate initials and other adornments. The term later came to be applied to other books similarly illuminated.

§ 125. **Irish character.** An interesting study. Do you agree with it? Are not some of the peculiarities described to be detected in Ruskin's own character? Could this be owing to his Celtic descent? How much confidence is to be put into such studies of national character?

P. 113, § 127. **The work of people who feel themselves wrong.** See Browning's poem, *Andrea del Sarto,* "*the Faultless Painter.*" "A man's reach," he tells us, "should exceed his grasp." The man who can execute his ideals, has ideals that need enlargement.

P. 114, § 128. **Industry, worthily followed, gives peace.** A great truth, which, if rightly understood, would put an end to half the discontent with life. But one reform would be needed, one for which Ruskin and Morris and many others have worked strenuously — that is that a man's work should be one that he can take delight in, not mere feeding of bits of iron into a machine, or moving a lever at regular intervals. Work, to bless the worker, must make use of his intellect as well as of his lower faculties.

The law of heaven. See Genesis iii. 19, " In the sweat of thy face shalt thou eat bread, till thou return unto the ground."

Whatsoever thy hand findeth. Ecclesiastes ix. 10.

P. 115, § 129. **In six thousand years**. The world, according to one reckoning, was created some four thousand years before Christ.

To till the ground, etc.   From Genesis iii. 23.

Centre and chief garden.   Switzerland.

Two forms.   See the rest of the sentence.

Forest Cantons.   Lucerne, Schwyz, Uri, and Unterwalden.

The Vaudois valleys are the valleys of the Cottian Alps (Piedmont, Provence, and Dauphine) where the Vaudois (Waldenses) sought refuge from French persecution.

Fevered idiotism.   A reference to the cretinism of Switzerland. Compare Lecture I., § 23.

Hesperides.   The gardens of the Hesperides were fabulous gardens, guarded by the three Hesperides, daughters of Hesperus. They were supposed to be in the West, near Gibraltar, the site of the Pillars of Hercules.   See Classical Dictionary.

Saw five hundred thousand.   A reference to the great famine in Orissa, in India (1860–1861).

§ 130.   **She layeth her hands**, etc.   Proverbs xxxi. 19.

P. 116, § 130.   **I was naked**, etc.   Matthew xxv. 36.   **I was a stranger**, below, is from the same verse.

§ 131.   **The art associated with civic pride and sacred principle**. Architecture, as shown in public buildings and in churches.

P. 117, § 132.   **The wild fig-tree**.   Revelation vi. 13.   This lecture, like the most of Ruskin's writings, turns to the arraignment of modern society.

The desire of the eyes.   Ezekiel xxiv. 21.

Visions . . . unaccomplishable.   This charge has been brought against Ruskin's own visions.   But has he not done something in striving to make the world's reach exceed its grasp, its desires superior to its paltry possessions ?

Spectra.   Spectres ? or does he mean rainbow mists, opposed to realities ?

After the imaginations of our evil hearts. Jeremiah iii. 17 ; vii. 24 ; xi. 8.

As a vapor. See p. 210.

P. 118, § 133. Disquiets itself in vain. Psalm xxxix. 6, " Surely they are disquieted in vain," or, more probably, the prayer-book version, xxxix. 7, " Man walketh in a vain shadow, and disquieteth himself in vain."

The smoke of the torment. Revelation xiv. 11.

Firmly and instantly. What meaning has *instantly* here ?

Your days are numbered. Psalm xc. 12.

In the twinkling of an eye. 1 Corinthians xv. 52.

He maketh the winds, etc. Psalm civ. 4, " Who maketh his angels spirits ; his ministers a flaming fire." Ruskin's translation — it is not that of the prayer book — is, perhaps, his own. *Angels* and *messengers* are identical in derivative meaning. As for *winds* and *spirits*, see note on *Spirit* on p. 176. The revised version, by the way (1886), gives a reading much like Ruskin's. " Who maketh the winds his messengers."

§ 134. In the day when. Revelation i. 7.

P. 119, § 134. Dies Iræ. The day of wrath, the Judgment Day. See the ancient hymn beginning with these words.

In the flame of its west, in the fire of its sunset.

The doors of the grave. Isaiah xxxviii. 10, " I said . . . I shall go to the gates of the grave."

We are in the midst of judgment, etc. A sentence not to be passed over lightly.

§ 135. The sin of Ananias. Acts v. His sin was not mere lying, as it is generally represented. It is explained in the line following.

Taking up our cross. Matthew x. 38 ; xvi. 24 ; xxvii. 32.

They that are his. Galatians v. 24.

Ready to leave. Luke xviii. 28–29. Also Matthew xix. 29.

Station in Life. With reference, perhaps, to the catechism of the Church of England, "to do my duty in that state of life, unto which it shall please God to call me." Cf. Lecture I., § 2.

P. 120, § 135. **Levi's station.** Mark ii. 14; Luke v. 27.

Peter's. John i. 40.

Paul's. Acts ix. 1.

§ 136. A paragraph lacking in unity. Compare the first part with the last and observe the total shift of subject, from feeding the hungry by charity to the need of reform that shall obviate the need of such charity.

To feed the hungry. Isaiah lviii. 7.

If any man will not work, etc. 2 Thessalonians iii. 10.

P. 121, § 137. **A consistent dress for different ranks.** This might do for each occupation, but it would be hard to reconcile us to such indication of rank, if rank means social position as determined by wealth, ancestry, etc. What would you think of the plan?

P. 122, § 138. **Buttressed.** Supported by masonry. See dictionary for illustration.

I myself have washed a flight, etc. See Introduction, p. xxxviii. Of this particular case Ruskin writes, in *Præterita*, Vol. II., Chap. X. :

"But quite the happiest bit of manual work I ever did was for my mother in the old inn at Sixt, where she alleged the stone staircase to have become unpleasantly dirty since last year. Nobody in the inn appearing to think it possible to wash it, I brought the necessary buckets of water from the yard myself, poured them into beautiful image of Versailles waterworks down the fifteen or twenty steps of the great staircase, and with the strongest broom I could find, cleaned every step into its corners. It was quite lovely work to dash the water and drive the mud, from each, with accumulating splash down to the next."

P. 123, § 139. **Competitive examination.** Wholesome when it is practical, to show a man's power to do the work, not to make statements about doing it — or about things quite unrelated to it.

Theoretical sciences. Those that have no immediate practical object.

§ 140. **The Pharisee's thanksgiving.** Luke xviii. 11.

Mistake pugnacity for piety. Observe the bitterness of Ruskin on this subject. See note on p. 177 and the Introduction, p. xxxvi.

P. 124, § 140. **The great Book.** See Lecture I., § 17.

To make Latin verses, . . . to hit a ball. Apparently Ruskin can give unqualified approval to neither means. What, according to this paragraph, would be the true education? Observe the objects set before us, faithfulness and purity of spirit, and skill of hand in work. What relation has this subject of education to art? Would it not be better if this relation were clearly brought out, not left to the reader to discover?

P. 125, § 140. **Charity.** 1 Corinthians xiii. 13. What is meant here by charity? Does it signify merely giving to the poor? Is there not a larger meaning,—love for one's fellow-man, tenderness, and reverence for all that is? It is, Ruskin feels, charity in this sense, — a grand humanity, an inclusive kindliness, which can make art possible and life venerable.

THE KING OF THE GOLDEN RIVER

WRITTEN during convalescence, in the year 1841, at the request of the young girl who was afterward to be his wife. Story as it is, Ruskin has been unable, in it, to refrain from the didactic. The story teaches a lesson; and not a general lesson of kindliness merely, but a lesson regarding true wealth and happiness. In spite of the playful style, one feels the presence of the Ruskin who preached generous helpfulness. The plot is not novel, being based on many old tales. Much of the charm lies in the style, half playful, half serious. There is a hint of the touch that we find in Andersen's *Fairy Tales,* or in Hawthorne's *Tales of the White Hills.* There is, too, a feeling that the writer is not frankly and credulously telling a fairy tale, but that he is only gracefully "pretending." The story is charmingly told, and we feel the deepest interest in the adventures of little Gluck; yet one does not read of him with the conviction with which one reads of the heroes of Andersen, Hoffman, or Hawthorne.

Note the musical delicacy of the style, with its delicate balance between poetry and comedy. Only by trying to write in this tone can one realize how difficult it is not to slip off the narrow ridge to the one side or the other.

P. 129. **Stiria.** It is not advisable to look this up in the atlas.

The Golden River, the Treasure Valley. Here, as in Lecture I., we find Ruskin pointing a moral regarding gold and treasure.

P. 130. **Schwartz and Gluck** are both appropriate, *Schwartz* meaning, in German, *black*, while *Gluck* means *luck* or *good fortune.*

Good farmers they were. Ironical. The things that they did as described in the lines that follow are done by other "good farmers."

With such a system. Ironical again. Ruskin has in mind the merchants and farmers of his own land, many of whom were "getting rich" at the expense of their own better natures.

To keep their corn. A common device of speculators, sometimes called "cornering" the market. Certain "operations" in wheat (*corn* here means wheat, not maize) will readily occur to any reader of the newspapers.

So much as a penny. Meanness is their characteristic defect. See its result.

P. 131. **Turnspit.** The person who turned the spit or rotary piece of iron upon which the meat was revolved before the fire while roasting.

Hardly less sparing upon themselves. Does Ruskin mean us to regard this as creditable to them?

They asked what they liked. Capitalists favored by "natural monopoly " have been known to do this since the day of the Black Brothers.   It is not hard to recall instances.

P. 132. **Nobody else would venture.** Why? What relation between this fact and the character of the brothers?

Extraordinary looking little gentleman. The figure is quaint, but not, observe, in any way horrible or disgusting. Ruskin draws him with the good-natured love of the grotesque that the mediæval workman showed in chiselling out a grotesque gargoyle.

P. 134. **The hob.** A projection at the side of the fireplace.

P. 135. **No sooner touched the cap.** Note that here we get the first clear hint that the old gentleman is something more than an old gentleman, though his dripping, before, and a few similar indications may have appeared a bit significant.

P. 136. **Away he went after Hans.** Here the comedy becomes almost rollicking. Ruskin makes no effort at romantic dignity.

P. 137. **I'll call again.** Do you begin to have any suspicion of what is to come next? Is not the " wreath of ragged cloud " that follows a pretty clear indication?

P. 138. **An enormous foam globe.** Have you ever seen one in disturbed water? Try to imagine precisely the posture of the little old gentleman. Why was the ceiling "left on " in Gluck's room?

P. 139. **Patrimony.** The land that came to them as their inheritance.

P. 145. **Drew their swords and began fighting.** Suggestive of what happens in the party seen in the dream. See p. 107.

P. 147. **A glacier.** Be sure you learn what this is. What, by the way, does the sudden appearance of this glacier denote? Is it quite natural, or is there a bit of magic involved? Note, too, the changes in the sky. Note the uneasy, supernatural impression accumulating in the lines that follow.

P. 150. **The Black Stone.** Was this idea original with Ruskin? What have you read like it in collections of fairy tales, or in the *Arabian Nights?*

P. 154. **The priest gave him some holy water.** Why was he willing to give it to Gluck?

P. 156. **The water that has been refused**, etc. Compare Lowell's *Vision of Sir Launfal*, ll. 322–327.

P. 157. **As Gluck gazed, . . . fresh grass.** Why does this, which could not happen in nature, seem quite natural here?

The wealth is taken from the men that abuse it, and given to him that had shown himself worthy. In that lies the "moral." We see justice done, the good rewarded, the bad punished.

INDEX

Q   225

Macmillan's
Pocket Series of English Classics

Uniform in Size and Binding

Cloth   **25 cents each**

Addison's Sir Roger de Coverley. Edited by ZELMA GRAY, East Side High School, Saginaw, Mich.

Andersen's Fairy Tales. Translated from the Danish by CAROLINE PEACHEY and Dr. H. W. DULCKEN. With biographical notes and introduction by SARAH C. BROOKS, Training School, Baltimore, Md.

Arabian Nights. Edited by CLIFTON JOHNSON.

Arnold's Sohrab and Rustum and other Poems. Edited by JUSTUS COLLINS CASTLEMAN, Bloomington High School, Bloomington, Ind.

Bacon's Essays. Edited by Professor GEORGE HERBERT CLARKE, Mercer University, Macon, Ga.

Blackmore's Lorna Doone. Edited by ALBERT L. BARBOUR, Superintendent of Schools, Natick, Mass.

Browning's Shorter Poems. Edited by FRANKLIN T. BAKER, Teachers College, New York City.

Mrs. Browning's Poems (Selections from). Edited by HELOISE E. HERSHEY.

Bryant's Thanatopsis, Sella, and other Poems. Edited by J. H. CASTLEMAN, Michigan Military Academy, Orchard Lake, Mich.

Bunyan's The Pilgrim's Progress, Part I. Edited by Professor HUGH MOFFATT, Central High School, Philadelphia, Pa.

Burke's Speech on Conciliation. Edited by S. C. NEWSOM, Manual Training High School, Indianapolis, Ind.

Byron's Childe Harold. Edited by A. J. GEORGE, High School, Newton, Mass.

Byron's Shorter Poems. Edited by RALPH HARTT BOWLES, Instructor in English in The Phillips Exeter Academy, Exeter, N.H.

Carlyle's Essay on Burns, with Selections. Edited by WILLARD C. GORE, Armour Institute, Chicago, Ill.

Carlyle's Heroes and Hero Worship. Edited by Mrs. ANNIE RUSSELL MARBLE.

Carroll's Alice in Wonderland. Edited by CHARLES A. McMURRY.

Chaucer's Prologue to the Book of the Tales of Canterbury, the Knight's Tale, and the Nun's Priest's Tale. Edited by ANDREW INGRAHAM, Late Headmaster of the Swain Free School, New Bedford, Mass.

Church's The Story of the Iliad.

Church's The Story of the Odyssey.

Coleridge's The Ancient Mariner. Edited by T. F. HUNTINGTON, Leland Stanford Junior University.

Cooper's Last of the Mohicans. Edited by W. K. WICKES, Principal of the High School, Syracuse, N.Y.

Cooper's The Deerslayer.

Pocket Series of English Classics — CONTINUED

Defoe's Robinson Crusoe. Edited by CLIFTON JOHNSON.

De Quincey's Confessions of an English Opium-Eater. Edited by ARTHUR BEATTY, University of Wisconsin.

De Quincey's Joan of Arc and The English Mail-Coach. Edited by CAROL M. NEWMAN, Virginia Polytechnic Institute, Blacksburg, Va.

Dickens's A Christmas Carol and The Cricket on the Hearth. Edited by JAMES M. SAWIN, with the collaboration of IDA M. THOMAS.

Dickens's A Tale of Two Cities. Edited by H. G. BUEHLER, Hotchkiss School, Lakeville, Conn.

Dryden's Palamon and Arcite. Edited by PERCIVAL CHUBB, Vice-Principal Ethical Culture Schools, New York City.

Early American Orations, 1760-1824. Edited by LOUIE R. HELLER, Instructor in English in the De Witt Clinton High School, New York City.

Edwards's (Jonathan) Sermons (Selections). Edited by H. N. GARDINER, Professor of Philosophy, Smith College.

Emerson's Essays (Selected). Edited by EUGENE D. HOLMES, High School, Albany, N.Y.

Emerson's Representative Men. Edited by PHILO MELVYN BUCK, Jr., William McKinley High School, St. Louis, Mo.

Epoch-making Papers in United States History. Edited by M. S. BROWN, New York University.

Franklin's Autobiography.

Mrs. Gaskell's Cranford. Edited by Professor MARTIN W. SAMPSON, Indiana University.

George Eliot's Silas Marner. Edited by E. L. GULICK, Lawrenceville School, Lawrenceville, N. J.

Goldsmith's The Deserted Village and The Traveller. Edited by ROBERT N. WHITEFORD, High School, Peoria, Ill.

Goldsmith's Vicar of Wakefield. Edited by H. W. BOYNTON, Phillips Academy, Andover, Mass.

Grimm's Fairy Tales. Edited by JAMES H. FASSETT, Superintendent of Schools, Nashua, N.H.

Hawthorne's Grandfather's Chair. Edited by H. H. KINGSLEY, Superintendent of Schools, Evanston, Ill.

Hawthorne's The House of the Seven Gables. Edited by CLYDE FURST. Secretary of Teachers College, Columbia University.

Hawthorne's The Wonder-Book. Edited by L. E. WOLFE, Superintendent of Schools, San Antonio, Texas.

Hawthorne's Twice-Told Tales. Edited by R. C. GASTON, Richmond Hill High School, Borough of Queens, New York City.

Homer's Iliad. Translated by LANG, LEAF, and MYERS.

Homer's Odyssey. Translated by BUTCHER and LANG.

Irving's Alhambra. Edited by ALFRED M. HITCHCOCK, Public High School, Hartford, Conn.

Irving's Life of Goldsmith. Edited by GILBERT SYKES BLAKELY, Teacher of English in the Morris High School, New York City.

Irving's Sketch Book.

Keary's Heroes of Asgard. Edited by CHARLES H. MORSE, Superintendent of Schools, Medford, Mass.

Pocket Series of English Classics — CONTINUED

Kingsley's The Heroes: Greek Fairy Tales. Edited by CHARLES A. McMURRY, Ph.D.

Lamb's Essays of Elia. Edited by HELEN J. ROBINS, Miss Baldwin's School, Bryn Mawr, Pa.

Longfellow's Courtship of Miles Standish. Edited by HOMER P. LEWIS.

Longfellow's Courtship of Miles Standish. Edited by W. D. HOWE, Butler College, Indianapolis, Ind.

Longfellow's Evangeline. Edited by LEWIS B. SEMPLE, Commercial High School, Brooklyn, N.Y.

Longfellow's Tales of a Wayside Inn. Edited by J. H. CASTLEMAN, William McKinley High School, St. Louis, Mo.

Longfellow's The Song of Hiawatha. Edited by ELIZABETH J. FLEMING, Teachers' Training School, Baltimore, Md.

Lowell's Vision of Sir Launfal. Edited by HERBERT E. BATES, Manual Training High School, Brooklyn, N.Y.

Macaulay's Essay on Addison. Edited by C. W. FRENCH, Principal of Hyde Park High School, Chicago, Ill.

Macaulay's Essay on Clive. Edited by J. W. PEARCE, Assistant Professor of English in Tulane University.

Macaulay's Essay on Johnson. Edited by WILLIAM SCHUYLER, Assistant Principal of the St. Louis High School.

Macaulay's Essay on Milton. Edited by C. W. FRENCH.

Macaulay's Essay on Warren Hastings. Edited by Mrs. M. J. FRICK, Los Angeles, Cal.

Macaulay's Lays of Ancient Rome, and other Poems. Edited by FRANKLIN T. BAKER, Teachers College, Columbia University.

Memorable Passages from the Bible (Authorized Version). Selected and edited by FRED NEWTON SCOTT, Professor of Rhetoric in the University of Michigan.

Milton's Comus, Lycidas, and other Poems. Edited by ANDREW J. GEORGE.

Milton's Paradise Lost, Books I and II. Edited by W. I. CRANE, Steele High School, Dayton, O.

Old English Ballads. Edited by WILLIAM D. ARMES, of the University of California.

Out of the Northland. Edited by EMILIE KIP BAKER.

Palgrave's Golden Treasury of Songs and Lyrics.

Plutarch's Lives of Cæsar, Brutus, and Antony. Edited by MARTHA BRIER, Teacher of English in the Polytechnic High School, Oakland, Cal.

Poe's Poems. Edited by CHARLES W. KENT, Linden Kent Memorial School, University of Virginia.

Poe's Prose Tales (Selections from).

Pope's Homer's Iliad. Edited by ALBERT SMYTH, Head Professor of English Language and Literature, Central High School, Philadelphia, Pa.

Pope's The Rape of the Lock. Edited by ELIZABETH M. KING, Louisiana Industrial Institute, Ruston, La.

Ruskin's Sesame and Lilies and The King of the Golden River. Edited by HERBERT E. BATES.

Scott's Ivanhoe. Edited by ALFRED M. HITCHCOCK.

Scott's Lady of the Lake. Edited by ELIZABETH A. PACKARD, Oakland, Cal.

Scott's Lay of the Last Minstrel. Edited by RALPH H. BOWLES.

Scott's Marmion. Edited by GEORGE B. AITON, State Inspector of High Schools for Minnesota.

Scott's Quentin Durward. Edited by ARTHUR LLEWELLYN ENO, Instructor in the University of Illinois.

Scott's The Talisman. Edited by FREDERICK TREUDLEY, State Normal College, Ohio University.

Shakespeare's As You Like It. Edited by CHARLES ROBERT GASTON.

Shakespeare's Hamlet. Edited by L. A. SHERMAN, Professor of English Literature in the University of Nebraska.

Shakespeare's Henry V. Edited by RALPH HARTT BOWLES, Phillips Exeter Academy, Exeter, N.H.

Shakespeare's Julius Cæsar. Edited by GEORGE W. HUFFORD and LOIS G. HUFFORD, High School, Indianapolis, Ind.

Shakespeare's Merchant of Venice. Edited by CHARLOTTE W. UNDERWOOD, Lewis Institute, Chicago, Ill.

Shakespeare's Macbeth. Edited by C. W. FRENCH.

Shakespeare's Twelfth Night. Edited by EDWARD P. MORTON, Assistant Professor of English in the University of Indiana.

Shelley and Keats (Selections from). Edited by S. C. NEWSOM.

Southern Poets (Selections from). Edited by W. L. WEBER, Professor of English Literature in Emory College, Oxford, Ga.

Spenser's Faerie Queene, Book I. Edited by GEORGE ARMSTRONG WAUCHOPE, Professor of English in the South Carolina College.

Stevenson's Treasure Island. Edited by H. A. VANCE, Professor of English in the University of Nashville.

Swift's Gulliver's Travels. Edited by CLIFTON JOHNSON.

Tennyson's Idylls of the King. Edited by W. T. VLYMEN, Principal of Eastern District High School, Brooklyn, N.Y.

Tennyson's Shorter Poems. Edited by CHARLES READ NUTTER, Instructor in English at Harvard University; sometime Master in English at Groton School.

Tennyson's The Princess. Edited by WILSON FARRAND, Newark Academy, Newark, N.J.

Thackeray's Henry Esmond. Edited by JOHN BELL HENNEMAN, University of the South, Sewanee, Tenn.

Washington's Farewell Address, and Webster's First Bunker Hill Oration. Edited by WILLIAM T. PECK, Classical High School, Providence, R.I.

John Woolman's Journal.

Wordsworth's Shorter Poems. Edited by EDWARD FULTON, Assistant Professor of Rhetoric in the University of Illinois.

THE MACMILLAN COMPANY

64-66 FIFTH AVENUE, NEW YORK